D0359542

DISCOVERY

JOHN K. TERRES
EDITOR

DISCOVERY

GREAT MOMENTS IN THE LIVES OF OUTSTANDING NATURALISTS

WITH WOOD ENGRAVINGS BY
THOMAS W. NASON

J. B. Lippincott Company
PHILADELPHIA
AND NEW YORK

PRINTED IN THE UNITED STATES OF AMERICA

LIBRARY OF CONGRESS CATALOG CARD NUMBER 61-8687

First Edition

"Each man's necessary path, though as obscure and apparently uneventful as that of a beetle in the grass, is the way to the deepest joys he is susceptible of. Though he converses only with moles and fungi, and disgraces his relatives, it is no matter, if he knows what is steel to his flint."

—HENRY DAVID THOREAU—

Books by John K. Terres

Discovery (*Editor*)

The Wonders I See

The Audubon Book
of True Nature Stories (*Editor*)

Songbirds in Your Garden

INTRODUCTION

I believe that all naturalists at some time in their lives have had one great adventure, and that the shock, ecstasy, beauty, wonder, tragedy, or intellectual illumination of that moment, hour, or day, they carry with them the rest of their lives. Professional naturalists are usually unobtrusive men who shun publicity. They labor quietly at their scientific specialities in the halls and archives of great museums, in the laboratories of universities, or in their own private studies. Some of them are professors who inspire their students to follow their fascinating trails of scientific inquiry that lead to the ends of the earth. At least once, perhaps several times a year, they travel to the faraway, still-wild places to collect birds, mammals, insects, plants, and other materials needed for their own researches, or to fill a need of the institution with which they are associated. Most of them keep notebooks or journals of their travels and collections, but few of them, unless he is that rare naturalist who is also a writer, set down the vivid details of possibly the one unforgettable experience of a lifetime. They do carry that moment in their minds, but too often it goes unshared and unknown to retire with them to their graves.

It was to keep alive some of these experiences that I wrote a letter to forty of the world's outstanding naturalists—to men in Africa, Asia, Australia, Great Britain, India, continental

Europe, Canada, the United States, and Central and South America. In the letter, from which I quote in part, I said:

> For some time I have believed that a book which would include some of the finest moments or hours in the lives of naturalists would make an excellent contribution to the literature of natural history. The publishers whom I represent in gathering material for the book believe in it just as I do. If you are interested, you may write of any experience you wish, but we would prefer that the emphasis shall not be too autobiographical, or your own life story, but one memorable experience about the discovery of a fascinating fact about nature. It might be as simple as the discovery of a new and possibly exciting insight into the behavior of a bird, mammal, or insect, or as grand as an experience that revealed to you an important biological principle at work. Of course, it could also have been one of many other things, including the thrill of discovering an animal new to science.

In response to that letter, all forty naturalists replied, and only four begged off because they were too busy or had schedules of travel that would keep them away for a long, long time. Many of them thought that the book was "an excellent idea" and exclaimed, "Why didn't someone think of this before!"

Within a few weeks after my first letters were written in December of 1959, manuscripts began to come in—from John Kieran, Olaus J. Murie, Arthur A. Allen, and Alexander Sprunt, Jr., in the United States, from Dr. David Lack and Dr. David Bannerman, world-renowned ornithologists in England, from Jean Delacour of France, one of the world's best-known aviculturists, from Colonel Richard Meinertzhagen, internationally known authority on eagles and other birds of prey.

When all the manuscripts were in, they included thirty-six accounts of magnificent spectacles of wildlife in Africa, the

Himalayas of western Asia, and the Canadian Arctic, an account of some of the last of the paradise parrots of Australia, of renegade wolves along the Mexican border, and thrilling adventures in pursuit of birds and other wildlife from rugged Funk Island off the coast of Newfoundland, to Oregon, California, the Gulf of Mexico, the tropical jungles of Central America, and the high Andes of South America. It is a splendid collection of experiences of men (and of one woman) whose names will be remembered for their contributions to the science, art, and literature of natural history.

JOHN K. TERRES

New York, N.Y.

Contents

I

II

V

PART ONE

CLARENCE COTTAM

Wildlife Wonders of Texas

Dr. Clarence Cottam, Director of Welder Wildlife Foundation, Sinton, Texas, was for twenty-five years a biologist of the U.S. Fish and Wildlife Service. During his government career, he became Chief of Wildlife Research, and later, Assistant to the Director. He was born January 1, 1899, at St. George, Utah, and attended Brigham Young University, where, after resigning from government service in 1954, he returned to become Dean of the College of Biology and Agriculture.

In 1955 he left the university on a leave of absence to become Director of Welder Wildlife Foundation. He has been President of the Wildlife Society of America and President of the Texas Ornithological Society. He is a Fellow of the American Ornithologists'

Union, and of the Texas Academy of Science, and has been honored with the Leopold Award in Wildlife, conferred on him by the Wildlife Society. Throughout his career, he has specialized in waterfowl research and waterfowl management.

WILDLIFE WONDERS OF TEXAS

EACH fact and facet of nature discovered and understood becomes a window through which man may discover the infinite. An ancient Persian poet said that if he had only two loaves of bread he should sell one and buy hyacinths for his soul. Humanity needs more hyacinths and understanding of life and its purposes. In this troubled world mankind needs the peace and serenity that can be found in nature.

Anyone who goes afield, and whose eyes, ears, and heart become at all attuned to God's great out-of-doors, cannot help but make thrilling, stimulating, and satisfying discoveries. These may or may not have been independently made by someone else or by many others.

Discoveries in nature may, of course, have immediate practical value, or, more likely, they may only warm the heart and give one a little clearer understanding and appreciation of how nature operates. These discoveries will likely convince him that nature shows perfection of law and order and, therefore, a purpose. Who can deny that a chance or studied observation of a habit or response of an animal or plant may not ultimately pay high dividends educationally, economically, and aesthetically? Emerson observed that "the beautiful is as useful as the useful."

Here at this 7,800-acre Welder Wildlife Foundation, formerly a small segment of a large cattle ranch 30 miles north of Corpus Christi, Texas, I have sensed the joy that comes from exploration, discovery, and the feeling of being myself a part of nature. Here where wildlife is abundant, we are daily thrilled with interesting and often unusual sights. Enormous flights of migrating anhingas, pelicans, hawks, roseate spoonbills, and wood ibises present a sight never to be forgotten. One day as my wife and I were rounding a bend in the river, we saw above us an exquisite aerial ballet of some twelve hundred rare wood ibises, now called wood storks. These large white birds with dark heads and black wing tips were gliding with the air currents, spiraling in graceful curves, all in amazing coordination, going up and down, around and over. It was breath-taking to be witnessing something many naturalists miss in a lifetime.

To completely unravel the intricate mysteries of bird migration would be unlocking the door to one of nature's most guarded secrets. What better illustrates this mystery than to know of the annual arrival of cliff swallows each spring at almost the same date to the famed San Juan Capistrano Mission in Southern California! Yet equally precise observations of unerring regularity of movements, migrations, and habits can be made of many kinds of birds.

At Welder we have trapped and banded distant migrant and wintering birds that nest in specific habitats from the Pacific to the Atlantic Oceans and in areas extending even far north of the Arctic Circle. For example, four kinds of thrushes wintering on the Welder Refuge were live-trapped from the same brush pile and thicket in the same week. Some of these same birds have been retaken in the same trap and on the same square foot of ground on which they were initially captured, one, two, and three years previously. What a thrill it is to trap a bird and find that it has traveled to the far parts of the continent that very year.

Several races of geese and other birds winter amicably together here in South Texas, yet their nesting ranges may be several thousand miles apart. When spring comes, nature instructs each to depart to its own section of the continent and there reproduce in its selected favored habitat. When fall arrives, the surviving bird again instinctively knows when and where to go, and generally it again unerringly returns to the precise habitat and area that it had previously chosen for its winter home. Once established, migratory birds usually return to the same nesting site, provided the environment remains attractive.

Some years ago when I served with the Fish and Wildlife Service, U.S. Department of the Interior, we attempted to determine details of flyway movements of ducks and their fidelity in holding to an established wintering ground. Four groups each consisting of some thirty-five or forty pintails were live-trapped in late January on Avery Island, in coastal Louisiana, and shipped to distant places immediately. They were liberated at Lake Merritt, California; Klamath Lake, Oregon; Cape Cod, Massachusetts; and the Potomac River at Washington, D.C. With few exceptions, all returns from these birds the next fall or in subsequent years came from their point of capture in Louisiana, or from some point en route to Louisiana despite the fact that in all probability none of these birds had ever before seen any of the four areas where they were liberated. This certainly gives convincing proof of their deep-seated instinct to cling to their ancestral flyways.

For each of three successive years, on the evening of May 8, many thousands of chimney swifts formed a great funnel and swirling cloud surrounding the lighted dome of our national Capitol in Washington, D.C. They circled this continuously from dusk until the lights were turned out at midnight. The swifts then disbanded and presumably went to roost.

Usually, but not always, they traveled counterclockwise. Their great numbers in such close proximity, obviously, made it imperative that they all fly in the same direction or collisions would have been inevitable. Apparently the concentrations of newly arrived swifts were attracted to the vicinity of the lighted dome by hordes of small gnats and other insects, in turn attracted by the bright lights of the dome of the Capitol. It seems probable that the spring arrivals of the swifts coincided with the emergence of large numbers of those small insects that are attracted to bright lights at night.

Similarly on the night of October 28, each year for three years, thousands of night-migrating chipping sparrows literally filled the city of Washington, D.C. The grounds and roof of our national Capitol were lighted, and thousands of these tiny sparrows swarmed over the lawns in a leisurely fashion, feeding on seeds and the insects that were attracted by the lights. Perhaps the bright lights temporarily stopped them in their instinctive night flight and also induced them to rest and feed. It was interesting to observe that regardless of weather, brightness, or other conditions, these birds made a mass migration on precisely the same date each year.

Egg laying and the period that young songbirds are in the nest is always a precarious time when losses inevitably are high. This mortality is nature's weeding-out process, and the success of a species, in large measure, is determined by the resistance and protection it develops against its innumerable enemies in the prevention of excessive losses of young. The efforts of a pair of nesting lark sparrows to protect their nest against the parasitic cowbird may illustrate the struggle that ensues. The cowbird does not incubate its own eggs, but lays them in the nests of other birds. The foster parents incubate the eggs, then feed and raise the young cowbirds. The cowbird egg usually hatches in slightly less time than that required for the eggs of the bird which it has parasitized. The aggressive young cowbirds have a higher survival rate than do the progeny of the rightful occupants of the nest.

For a week or more our lark sparrows were building a beautiful compact and secluded nest in our evergreen *Ligustrum* tree just outside my study window. The female laid her first egg between six and six-thirty on April 28, and she laid one egg on each of the two succeeding mornings. The lark sparrow does not normally start to incubate until the full clutch of four or five eggs is laid. By nine-thirty on the third morning (April 30) a female cowbird had found the nest. She promptly pecked a hole in one lark sparrow egg, picked it up in her bill, and flew to the sidewalk about 30 feet away where she dropped the egg, which broke on the pavement.

By this time the lark sparrow discovered her loss and, with frantic calls, took after the larger cowbird. To protect her two remaining eggs, the lark sparrow returned to her nest and sat on them for forty-five minutes. Then she left and fed for about one hour in almost constant view of her nest and returned again and sat on her eggs for fifteen minutes, then joined her mate. Her time on and off the nest was about equally divided until 1:05 P.M. At that time, while she was away, the cowbird flew to the *Ligustrum* tree and alighted beside the nest. The lark sparrow was apparently watching, as she chirped excitedly and flew back in haste to alight on her nest. The cowbird left. Throughout the afternoon the lark sparrow divided her time between nest watching and feeding. She was not on the nest during the night.

The next morning, May 1, the lark sparrow was on the nest at the break of day, but did not lay her egg until 7:40 A.M., well over an hour later than usual. By evening it was apparent she had started to incubate her three eggs. Several times the cowbird returned, but with the sparrow incubating so persistently, she had no opportunity to lay an egg in the lark sparrow's nest.

On May 12, or after a little more than eleven days of incubation, the three lark sparrow eggs were successfully hatched. Ten days later all three young left the nest.

Much yet remains to be discovered concerning the behavior and social patterns of birds, mammals, and other vertebrates. At our ranch home we have had opportunity to enjoy the rather close association of many creatures of the wild. What a thrill it was to have a big male wild turkey jump up to our window feeding tray and peck rather loudly on our window when his ration of food was exhausted. Some people are repelled at the idea of wild skunks or coyotes in close proximity to human habitation. The almost nightly chorus of coyotes, often only a few hundred yards from our home, adds immeasurably to our joy of living. Each evening we place food in front of our kitchen window. Usually from one to a dozen skunks compete for this handout. Not infrequently I find myself eating dinner within 5 to 20 feet of a half-dozen or more quarrelsome, but entertaining, skunks. Occasionally an opossum and more frequently a raccoon joins them. It was a thrill to reach out our kitchen window and have a raccoon take a chicken bone from my fingers on its third visit.

Skunks show an amazing degree of variation in color pattern, behavior, aggressiveness, and fear. Even though our boarders represent but a single species, they vary from predominantly white, or albinistic forms, to almost black, or melanistic. These variations and color patterns enable us to study individuals and to learn something of their responses and habits. Eyesight of these predominantly dusk and nighttime creatures, as it is with armadillos, is poor, yet their sense of smell is unusually keen. Their hearing is fair but decidedly less keenly developed than it is with deer, bobcats, or most birds. While skunks are fairly agile and move about rather rapidly, they are not fleet of foot and cannot rely on speed to protect them from danger. Their defense is largely in their scent glands, and in their expert marksmanship in directing their stinging musk fluid to the eyes of man or predators that try to molest them.

One evening our raccoon tried to drive a skunk away from its food. This was a grave mistake as the skunk fired at close range and hit the raccoon squarely in the right eye with his powerful, pungent, penetrating musk. The pain must have been agonizing, for the raccoon lost all interest in food and rolled in the grass and rubbed its eye, trying to wipe away the stinging fluid. In a few minutes it left on a run toward a pond a little more than a city block away, apparently to wash the fluid from its eye. The next night it did not return, but the second night it was back with its eye still bloodshot, and showing evidence of much lachrymal secretion. Since then it has been a less frequent visitor, and it has been decidedly more respectful of its neighbors.

Skunks are almost completely solitary in their foraging for insects and other foods. They seem to be more repelled than attracted by others of their own kind. On several occasions they objected less to sharing their suet, oatmeal, dog chow, table scraps, and chicken bones, with an opossum than with other skunks. When these odoriferous creatures feed in too close proximity, they soon develop a social hierarchy or dominance over each other that shifts considerably.

Our first boss of Skunktown was a large old male whose dominance was largely attained because of his large size. He could easily push the weaker members of the tribe away from a feeding tray. Skunks feeding together normally do a good deal of pushing. The skunks raise their large plumed tails at right angles to their bodies as they push each other from the rear or sideways from the hips. Occasionally they push from the shoulders. Such sparring rarely produces any odor—except by an occasional nervous individual. Obviously, skunks have developed great immunity against the musk which they or their kind produce.

When serious fighting ensues, which is most common between belligerent males during the mating season, fighting is savage and brutal, with an effort to kill. Sharp teeth and claws are then used. When such encounters develop, there is considerable emission of scent notwithstanding most published accounts to the contrary.

Our first dominant male lost his eminence in the hierarchy to an agile and relatively young, irritable female of perhaps half his weight. The female was the first to arrive at the feeding station and was enjoying her evening repast when the large male arrived. Both fed for a few minutes together. Then the two, in normal skunk fashion, tried to drive each other away by rear-end pushing. Because of her much smaller size the little female was no match for such maneuvering. In desperation, she whirled, grabbed the old male by his rear end, and bit with such force that he screamed in agony and ran at full speed to his den in the woodpile, nearly a city block away. Only occasionally would he return, and when he did, it was with great caution. If this female was within sight, he would move away hastily in the opposite direction, regardless of the attractiveness of the provided food supply.

As evidence that the vision of skunks is not keen, on several occasions in the woods I have stood motionless on a trail where a skunk was approaching. Invariably when it got within 10 to 15 feet of me, it sensed human or other animal odor, and its tail would flare up, ready for defensive action. Generally it would either retreat or leave at right angles to the direction it had come. Recently one skunk that met me on its path erected his tail in defense, yet he did not use his defensive liquid, but cautiously approached with his tail erected and smelled of my shoes and trouser legs. Finding me motionless, he went between my legs and soon continued his foraging for food within a few feet of where I stood.

Competition for food is always an important factor limiting populations of plants and animals. At Welder we have been making some studies of our abundant and interesting, although poisonous, cottonmouth moccasins and diamondback rattlesnakes. We want to know their habits and ecological requirements so they can be understood, managed, and appropriately restricted. Both of these related species are quite general in their food habits and, within limits, take whatever they can get most easily. Availability of food is a predisposing factor in their selection. Like all snakes, they swallow their prey whole, and their remarkably adapted anatomy and physiology enable them to ingest prey of almost unbelievable size and texture. Both can grow new fangs so that when they strike a bone of a prey animal or otherwise break off a fang, nature rather quickly provides them with a new one. Both feed commonly on rodents and birds, and occasionally on lizards.

The cottonmouth moccasin, which most generally lives in marshes or wet places, also feeds on fishes, salamanders, and other snakes. I was surprised to find a large 41-inch-long moccasin that had just ingested a 49-inch rat snake! The moccasin was much larger in diameter than its victim; therefore, the ingested rat snake was folded and compressed in the extended stomach of the belligerent moccasin. A 49-inch moccasin, when caught, had swallowed a diamondback rattler of only slightly smaller diameter and length than itself. Many water snakes are also captured and swallowed by the moccasin. Both the moccasin and rattlesnake commonly kill and consume animals of unbelievable size; yet, occasionally, they attempt to swallow prey too large for their digestive tracts.

While these two poisonous species of pit vipers feed on other snakes, they in turn are prey to many other predators. I have seen a 2-foot cottonmouth killed by a great blue heron, and small reptiles, poisonous or harmless, are the common fare of that ground cuckoo, the road runner. Likewise, a number of hawks commonly feed on whatever snakes of appropriate size they can capture.

One day I chanced to observe a death struggle between a giant indigo snake and a 43-inch-long diamondback rattler. The indigo, which was later captured alive, was 98¼ inches long and, incidentally, the longest snake yet recorded in Texas. Despite the great disparity in length there was not a great difference in diameter of the two species, and the wide head of the rattler probably exceeded that of the indigo.

When I chanced on these struggling reptiles, the indigo was wrapped around the rattler and was trying to crush it. It was biting and shaking the rattler just back of the head, obviously trying to break its neck. When the rattler was subdued and could not crawl away, the indigo proceeded to swallow it, head first.

The rattler's mouth opens wider than does the indigo, and even the decapitated head of one can open its mouth widely and bite with its large protruding fangs. A lack of knowledge of this fact has caused three of my friends—all biologists—to lose a finger or thumb; that is, they each were bitten by a decapitated head of a rattlesnake and the poisoned finger or thumb had to be amputated.

The indigo was obviously aware of the danger of the rattlesnake opening its mouth, and grabbed the rattler by the side of the head. It was able to clamp the two jaws of the rattler together with its own recurved teeth and swallow it head first. In 1½ hours, 31 inches of the rattlesnake was ingested. At that time we captured the indigo. It immediately regurgitated its prey, as we expected it would. The forward 16 inches of the rattler had already undergone considerable digestion; yet this rattler, although presumably dead, continued to writhe and to open its mouth, ready to bite. The dead rattler was found to have recently swallowed a large cotton rat.

In the fight between the two snakes the rattler had inflicted at least one vicious bite with its poison fangs into the back of the indigo. Noticeable swelling developed almost immediately. Yet in twenty-four hours this swelling was gone, and the indigo seemed to be perfectly normal and healthy, indicating, as we had suspected, that it has a high degree of immunity against the poison of the rattlesnake.

The few examples I have cited from my diary of day-to-day observations will illustrate, I hope, that nature is, itself, a great storybook, continuously open for all to read and learn from, to discover and enjoy.

JAMES P. CHAPIN

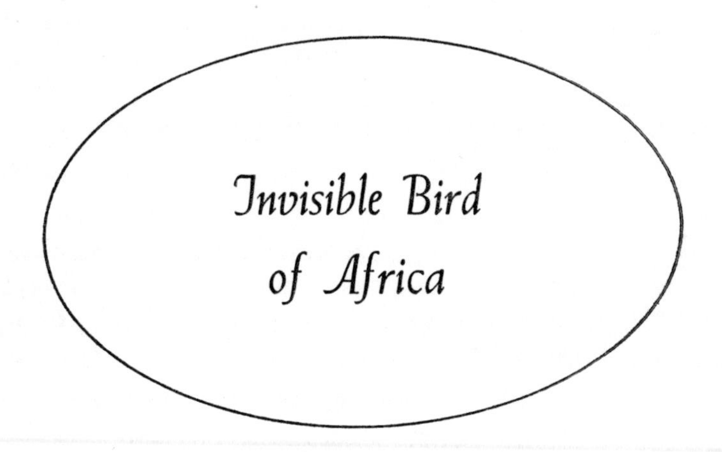

Dr. James Paul Chapin, Research Associate in African Ornithology, American Museum of Natural History, New York City, has been associated with the American Museum since 1905. Born in Manhattan July 9, 1899, Chapin soon moved with his family to Staten Island, where he grew up and made the acquaintance of William T. Davis, "the grand old naturalist of Staten Island." Before he was graduated in zoology from Columbia University in 1922, Chapin had spent six years in the Belgian Congo of Africa with explorer Herbert Lang. His many years of zoological research in Africa resulted in his four-volume work, The Birds of the Belgian Congo *(1932–1954). The first volume won for him the Daniel Giraud Elliott Medal, awarded him by the National*

Academy of Sciences for his distinguished African work, and the late King Albert of Belgium conferred on him the Chevalier de l'-Ordre de la Couronne *in recognition of his zoological researches in the Belgian Congo. Dr. Chapin is a past president of the Staten Island Institute of Arts and Sciences, the American Ornithologists' Union, and the Explorer's Club.*

INVISIBLE BIRD OF AFRICA

AMONG the most impressive and extensive forests on earth are those that occupy bands of very heavy rainfall within a few degrees of the equator, in South America, Africa, and other lands around the globe. The profusion of plant species composing them, and the diversity of animals inhabiting them, are unsurpassed elsewhere.

Many birds in such equatorial forests are all but invisible because they live in thick vegetation and make little noise that might betray their whereabouts. It was in this way that the Congo peacock managed to escape the eyes of professional ornithologists until 1936. But when a bird frequently produces a series of sirenlike noises in the open sky above a forest, during the warmer hours of the day, and manages to elude even the keen vision of African natives, it must certainly cause wonderment. These sounds are familiar to the forest-dwelling peoples all the way from southern Nigeria and the Gaboon coast eastward to the borders of Uganda; and a name is given to the bird in nearly every tribal language, usually imitating the sound it produces, such as *yelé-yelé*, *pemé-pemé*, or *vébek*. Yet rarely will one find a man who claims to have seen the bird or who can describe it with any degree of accuracy.

I may here admit that I myself was puzzled by these very distinctive noises for four years. It was early in 1910, at the little post of Medje, located on a hilltop in the great Ituri Forest of central Africa, that they first attracted my attention. I was here to track down and collect for the American Museum of Natural History any and every kind of bird I could find, yet this one baffled me, and it was only by sheer good luck that eventually I could begin to solve the riddle. All about Medje, except where felled by man, the great trees rose to heights of 120 feet and more. The series of bisyllabic notes, of a strangely nasal quality, for which we may as well use the word *pemé*, would last for fifteen to twenty-five seconds, gradually rising in pitch until toward the end they quickly dropped lower again, then ceased.

It was plain that they came from the open sky, high above the treetops, and that their peculiar quality, almost ventriloquial, did not furnish a very precise indication of direction. One might stare up until one's neck was stiff, but the bird responsible for the noise remained invisible, just as one's native companions always agreed it would. This creature could not be of any great size, and yet the noise often sounded as though it might carry for a quarter-mile or even double that distance. Frequently one heard it while walking in the forest, and there, of course, the search was hopeless, since the upper boughs of the great trees blocked off nearly all view of the sky.

After our first year in the Ituri Forest, Herbert Lang and I moved northward into the savannas of the Uele District, and there we never heard the weird *pemé-pemé* noises. Not until July, in 1913, did I come back into the heavy forest belt. Then at Pawa, where the strips of forest were still interrupted by sizable stretches of high grass, I at once began to hear the *pemé-pemé* noise again. It seemed to come from the air above the dark green strips of high trees, and its maker remained invisible.

Fortunately, by this time I had acquired an efficient helper, Nekuma by name, one of the sons of the head sorcerer and soothsayer of Okondo, an important chief of the Mangbetu tribe near Niangara. Nekuma had grown up with bow and arrow in hand, one of the small boys who would sit under some wild fig tree waiting for bulbuls, barbets, colies, and other birds to come to eat the small fruits of the tree. He was barely twenty now, and already a gifted observer of birds, with a large vocabulary for them in the Mangbetu tongue.

Nekuma told me at once that this invisible bird was called *ne-povwo* in his language, that he had never been able to see it, but that some people claimed it bore a good resemblance to a woodpecker, or *nangalibobo*. The woodpeckers of Africa do not have very loud voices, and I knew of none that was accustomed to fly high above the treetops, so that observation left me still wondering.

We continued on by foot to the post of Avakubi, deep in the Ituri Forest, where I was to spend much of the ensuing year repacking the numerous and varied collections Lang and I had been making, for transport on to Stanleyville and eventually by ship to New York. My time was to be largely occupied by supervising the work of three Azande carpenters who repaired our packing boxes and made other new ones. They told me that in their language our invisible bird was known as *nyêté*, the word that has always seemed to me the best imitation of its bisyllabic notes.

While at Avakubi, I found little time for roaming the woods, but I had taught Nekuma to use the shotgun, and nearly every day he was sent out in search of specimens needed for the museum. Whenever I was free, I accompanied him, and Nekuma, with keen eyesight and ears far better than mine, taught me a great deal about elusive forest birds. But we still could not divine the nature of the invisible *ne-povwo* which we had both heard so many times, at almost any hour between eight in the morning and late afternoon.

Eventually, in mid-April of 1914, I had caught up well with my work of packing. Lang was still off in the Medje country, and I decided to make a trip of a few days with Nekuma eastward on the road toward Irumu, at the eastern border of the forest. We did not get beyond the Ihuru, or Epulu, River, before word came from Lang that called me back to the post of Avakubi.

But at last, only a few miles from Avakubi, we finally gained our clue to the identity of the invisible bird. Nekuma and I together were walking along the new forest road, on which no wheel had ever turned, when from the crown of a great tree high above us came a loud, harsh, scolding sound, like *cutta, cutta*, repeated several times. I raised my field glass and by the greatest good fortune spotted the maker of this noise, perched on a bough. It was scarcely as big as a starling, mostly of grayish olive color, but with a tail that suggested nothing save an inverted fleur-de-lis, black at the tip.

This incredible tail left me no excuse for hesitation; I raised my twelve-bore gun, fired a load of very fine shot, and the bird came tumbling down with scarcely a feather injured. I noticed that a second bird, apparently of the same kind, quickly flew out of the same tree and off to my right. Then I picked up my specimen and examined its most unusual tail. The fleur-de-lis tip was not its only peculiarity. At each side there were three very narrow, stiff white feathers that reminded me of the similar tail quills worn by several species of snipe.

The *nyêté* had not yet entered our minds, but just at this juncture we began to hear one, high in the air, and in the direction toward which the second "fleur-de-lis bird" had taken off. Louder and louder grew the *pemé* notes, as they were repeated a dozen or more times. Then the tone fell off, the noise stopped, and that second "fleur-de-lis bird" came flying into a treetop, only to take off again silently before we could get a shot.

All this was quite sufficient to convince me, and Nekuma too, that now we had our invisible bird! It is with narrow outer tail quills that the snipe make their "winnowing" or "bleating" noises in flight. In my own boyhood how often had I watched the American woodcock at dusk come diving down from the sky, its wings half-opened, producing a still more musical twittering with its narrow outermost wing quills. There was just one narrow link missing in our chain of evidence. We had not actually seen our bird as it produced its nasal, tooting sounds.

From the woodpeckerlike feet, the blunt beak, and the general scheme of coloration, it was evident that my bird belonged among the honey-guide family, of which one justly famous species, in the more open grassy regions of Africa, regularly leads men by its incessant chatter to the hives of honeybees. Both Nekuma and I knew that bird well. Most of the dozen known species of honey guides are fond of honeycomb, so it was no surprise to find the stomach of this "fleur-de-lis" species well filled with beeswax and a few bits of insects.

Seven more months passed before I finally left the equatorial forest belt on my way back to England and New York. *Pemé-pemé* noises continued to come from the sky, but no more did I see of my honey guide with lyrate tail quills. World War I had erupted in the meantime, but luck stayed with me, and I was able to convoy our precious collections safely through the first German submarine blockade of the port of Liverpool, and then on to New York.

Back at the American Museum of Natural History, one of my first concerns was to learn the scientific name of my invisible bird. But that name, too, remained invisible for several years. No published description fitted my specimen, so in 1915 I described it as a bird new to science, a new genus and species, *Ceriocleptes xenurus*, or "the wax-thief with strange tail." Not until six years later did I find that in 1909 George L. Bates, who was later to become a warm friend of mine, had named the same species *Melignomon robustus*. His single specimen from the Cameroons, a female received from a native, had the whole tip of its tail so broken and frayed as to give no sign of the fleur-de-lis form. One year later Professor Anton Reichenow of Berlin had published a description of *Melichneutes sommerfeldi* from the Cameroons, based on a very young specimen of our bird with breast blackish and the tail quills not yet exhibiting the pronounced bifurcation they attain in adult life.

During all his years in the Cameroons, Bates never saw this bird alive, but before long he obtained a second female specimen in the Cameroons from natives. He did not connect his birds in any way with the *vébek* bird, so well known from its noise by all the Bulu tribesmen in his neighborhood. What I did not learn till still later was that Dr. Cuthbert Christy, while at Medje in 1914, also prepared the skin of a very young bird of this species for the British Museum, having received it, no doubt, from natives. In the Cameroons, too, Dr. Haberer collected a single specimen during this same period for a Berlin museum. Thus it was that between 1909 and 1915, six specimens had reached one or another great natural history museum.

Nearly incredible, however, is the fact that from 1915 to 1942 not a single specimen of this bird was received by any museum in the world, and my skin is still the only one in

America. During those years, George Bates and several American missionaries in the Cameroons continued to make collections of birds for museums in England and the United States. Several of these missionaries became friends of mine, and whenever opportunity offered, I would talk with them about the bird that now became known as the "lyre-tailed honey guide." They agreed that the nasal tootings were widely known to peoples of the forested Cameroons, but they were unable to have the noisemaker collected. I did all I could to publicize the lyretail. In my semipopular article of 1924 on honey guides, I described the form of its tail, attributing the noises to vibrations of its narrowed tail quills. I also suggested that its noisy flights might serve as signals to some mammalian or avian ally better able to extract honeycomb from hollows in trees. That might furnish a parallel to the guiding of men and ratels, badgerlike animals, to honey by the honey guide, *Indicator indicator*, in the more open countries of Africa.

George Bates was not impressed. As he saw it, I had "guessed" that the noise was made with the short outer rectrices, and "the attempt to picture the lives of these forest species of honey-guides leads us all to theorizing." I continued to write to anyone interested in birds in the Cameroons, the Gaboon, and the Congo. I even made three or four little phonograph recordings of my imitation of the *pemé* noises and sent them to my correspondents in Africa.

Not until April, 1942, did a native hunter finally shoot another female for Brother Joseph Hutsebaut at Barisi in the Uele District, which was forwarded to the Congo Museum in Belgium. Somewhat later Father Bernard Longo wrote me that in 1939 he had watched a bird high over the forest near Wamba making the noises I described, but he was not a collector of birds and could not identify it accurately.

Congo natives I had questioned, on many occasions. Some

of them assured me that the *pemé-pemé* bird often performed in the air not far from trees that were known to house colonies of bees. In later years one or two men told me that the bird with the lyrate tail would come with one or two other kinds of honey guides to eat bits of beeswax after men had robbed honey from a nest of wild bees. But none ever claimed that men, not even Pygmies, so wise in the ways of the forest, were ever shown where honey could be found by the strange nasal tooting with which all were familiar. In the forested Cameroons, Dr. A. I. Good told me, the *vébek* calls, as they were known there, were to be heard nowhere more frequently than well to the south, along the Gaboon border.

During the late 1940's I was hearing frequently from Mr. P.-C. Rougeot, who was studying birds and collecting them for a Paris museum in the coastal region of the Gaboon. In the latter half of 1948 I learned that his next post was to be Oyem, far to the north in the colony of Gaboon, near the Cameroons border. I suggested that, once there, he should listen and watch closely for the lyre-tailed honey guide.

All my highest hopes were soon realized. Before the end of the year Rougeot had heard the nasal tooting several times at a distance, usually in the middle of the day. The natives knew the noises well, attributing them to a bird they called *selem-ngomo*, which they regarded as invisible. The word *ngomo* in the Bulu language means woodpecker; *selem* is their imitation of one in the series of its double notes.

By mid-July of 1949, Rougeot had seen the bird several times during its noisy diving flight and noted its curious form, but no specimen was collected. In August a female was caught by a native in a trap baited with honeycomb, and in early September Rougeot and his friend J. Pouderoux were able to shoot a second female which came down and perched on a shrub near them. Rougeot has now watched the diving flights of the lyretail many times to his entire satisfaction. As a rule the bird will mount quickly in wide spirals high in the air, up to 150 or 200 yards, and then come diving down at an angle of 30 to 45 degrees from the horizontal, opening and shutting its wings and tail rhythmically. A speed of 60 to 70 miles per hour would seem to be attained, so that each spreading of the tail quills sets the narrow outer ones to vibrating. The bird's downward course may go into a tight spiral; sometimes it will be stopped midway, the bird becoming silent, only to start a second dive that usually ends in an upward swoop to alight on the bough of some tree.

The words *peintre* in French and *pantry* in English, pronounced in as nasal a tone as possible, are perhaps most useful to recall the double notes produced during the dive. As the bird accelerates, the tone rises; then as it slows down at the end, the tone drops very rapidly, and the noise stops abruptly.

The speed of the dive explains readily why the bird is so difficult to sight. If it is 600 feet away, the first "toots" will require a half-second to reach the watcher's ear. By the time he has focused on the starting point, the bird is perhaps 100 feet away in its downward course, and the more he keeps looking at the point where the noise seemed to begin, the less apt he is to perceive its maker. A certain ventriloquial quality of the sounds makes it still more difficult to know just where one's vision should be directed. One has a similar difficulty in sighting a small jet-powered plane.

Since 1952 my friend Rougeot has widened his acquaintance greatly with the lyretail in several different districts of the Gaboon. He feels that females as well as males probably make sonorous dives from on high, and he has noted that such tooting is often done in places where large hornbills are numerous. Can it be that the hornbills are accustomed to attack bee colonies? Some of my native informants have claimed that the lyretail performs near trees with colonies of wild bees, and when bee trees were chopped open by men, the lyretail sometimes came to eat any wax that was scattered about. Even chimpanzees have been said to pillage the sweet stores of bees, so that animals of many sorts, including squirrels or monkeys, might perhaps respond to the tooting of lyretails, if such is really the meaning of their noisy diving. It might, on the other hand, be only a sexual display. It seems unlikely that the birds form lasting pairs.

All honey guides lay their eggs in the nests of other birds, usually hole-nesters, and often in those of barbets and woodpeckers. It still seems likely that brown barbets of the genus *Gymnobucco* are the most frequent victims of the lyre-tailed honey guide, but of this we have no real proof.

In conclusion, I should like to point out again that, while my brief experience of 1914 convinced me that *Melichneutes*, our lyre-tailed honey guide was the maker of the series of nasal tooting sounds so well known across the whole forest belt from Southern Nigeria and the Gaboon coast to the Ituri, Semliki, and probably to the Mabira Forest in Uganda, there was one break in the chain of evidence. Neither Nekuma nor I had actually *seen* the bird make the noise. Despite all my efforts to stimulate interest in *Melichneutes robustus*, it required thirty-five years to forge that last single link in the final proof. One diligent and competent observer was required, and Pierre-Claude Rougeot proved to be that man.

ARTHUR A. ALLEN

The Day I Died in the Gulf of Mexico

Dr. Arthur Augustus Allen, Professor Emeritus of Ornithology, Cornell University, and Honorary Director, Laboratory of Ornithology, Ithaca, New York, was born in Buffalo, December 28, 1885. He was graduated from Cornell University in 1907 and received his Doctor of Philosophy degree there in 1909. He was first an instructor in zoology at the University, then assistant professor of ornithology, and, finally, full professor from 1924 to the time of his retirement in 1953. Early in his career he traveled on expeditions to South America, and he has led expeditions for the National Geographic Society to Mexico, Hudson Bay, Labrador, Panama, and Alaska. He is noted for his researches on ruffed grouse and the life histories of other birds; he was a pioneer in

American bird photography and the recording of bird songs. He was awarded the Outdoor Life Medal; the Burr Award of the National Geographic Society; is a fellow of the American Ornithologists' Union, and a past president of the Wildlife Society. He has written The Book of Bird Life, The Golden Plover, *and other books, and many scientific papers and popular articles on ornithology.*

THE DAY I DIED IN THE GULF OF MEXICO

IT was the last day of January in 1925. We were trying to sleep in a pup tent on a narrow strip of beach between the Gulf of Mexico and the extensive salt marsh known as the Caranchua on the Texas coast opposite the western end of Galveston Island. We were duck hunting. My hunting companion, Sam Lloyd, and I had elected to sleep ashore while our genial host, Dr. Fox, and Jim, his boatman, remained on the small cruiser in which we had come across the bay from the camp on Galveston Island. We had anchored the cruiser 100 feet from shore in about 4 feet of water—the whole bay at this point was rather shallow. Sam and I had come ashore in the dinghy. We brought with us a few sandwiches and a bottle of fresh water for breakfast, and planned to go back to camp on Galveston Island as soon as the morning flight of ducks was over.

We had not expected to fight mosquitoes in midwinter, but the temperature had risen to 90 degrees, and they were savage. We had no nets or repellents, so we crawled into the pup tent and covered our faces with the bandanas we always carried.

We almost suffocated. It was ten o'clock before Sam, unable to stand the heat any longer, crawled out of the tent and braved the mosquitoes.

"It's cooler out here," he called, "and the wind has driven away the mosquitoes." Just like that—the weather changed, and one of those unpredictable northers was upon us. In a few minutes we were shivering, and by morning the temperature had dropped to 20 degrees above zero. Everything was frozen, and there was a quarter-inch of ice over the entire marsh.

When it got light enough to see, we discovered that the anchors had held the cruiser securely, but the high wind had driven so much of the water out of Galveston Bay that the shoreline was now 100 yards below the boat, which was tipped on its side and well anchored on dry land.

We forgot about ducks for the moment. We were 20 miles from the nearest habitation, and the only way to get back to Houston was the way we had come, across Galveston Bay—the full length of Galveston Island to the bridge, and 50 miles inland to Houston. Dr. Fox, aboard the foundered cruiser, was a practicing physician, and he had to get back to his patients. After a breakfast of sandwiches and cold water, the four of us—Dr. Fox, Jim, the boatman, and Sam Lloyd and I—started dragging and pushing the heavy dinghy over mud and oyster shells to the water's edge. This would be Dr. Fox's only means of getting back to the mainland. We slaved for more than two hours before we had the little boat afloat.

But that was only the beginning. The wind still howled out of the northeast, blowing spray from the tops of the whitecaps and threatening to capsize the little boat. We learned later that for six hours Dr. Fox and Jim took turns rowing and bailing—heading into the wind lest they be swept out of the bay and into the open gulf. The bay was only eight miles wide at this point near the tip of Galveston Island, but it was nearly dark before they reached the lighthouse completely exhausted. What happened there was never completely explained to us.

Fortunately for Sam and for me, we did not realize what a time the oarsmen were having. We thought the wind would carry them directly across in no time at all; indeed, we half expected Jim to come back for us with another launch before dark. So we went happily about our duck hunting on the frozen marsh, rather unsuccessfully, since we had to break a hole in the ice for our decoys and the ducks gave this part of the marsh a rather wide berth.

Night came, but no launch came to our rescue. We built a fire to act as a signal so our rescuers would be sure to find us, ate the last of the sandwiches, drank most of the water, then went shivering to bed—lucky to have the pup tent to break the wind.

Morning came, the wind subsided, and we waited for the water to come back into the bay and float the cruiser. But apparently this is one thing that doesn't happen rapidly in Texas. There was no change in the shoreline by noon, nor by dark, and no sign of rescuers. Moreover the duck hunting was not very rewarding. That morning Sam got one mallard going over at about 100 yards, which we proceeded immediately to roast in the coals of our fire. We had eaten all the sandwiches the night before. When night came, while we were roasting a second duck and hugging the fire to keep warm, a spark ignited one of the side pockets of my hunting coat. This pocket held my shells, and, unnoticed, the spark burned through the khaki and the paper coating of a shell. Suddenly, when the sparks reached the powder, we had a mild explosion which scattered a dozen shells over the ground about us. No other damage was done, and we spent a third chilly night in the pup tent.

The next day the water began to edge back toward the

cruiser but ever so slowly. We managed to vary our diet, too. By watching the flocks of snow geese flying from their roosting grounds to their feeding area several miles away, and by a quick sneak, we got under their line of flight. They were pretty high for our ammunition, but Sam managed to bring one down. We lived high that day on roast goose—a trifle rare but good.

By nightfall the cruiser was almost afloat, and we began to talk about what we were going to eat when we got back to civilization. We didn't take time to worry about the key to the ignition, which Jim, the boatman, had in his pocket. To make sure of having something for breakfast, we shot a couple of coots ("pulldoos" they were called on the Gulf coast). The coots had returned with the rising water, though ducks were still unbelievably scarce. It was not quite so cold around the fire that evening—and the shivers were not quite so continuous in the pup tent. We passed the fourth night fairly comfortably, though we were getting a bit thirsty. We had drunk all of our water the first day.

The morning of the fifth day came, with roast coot for breakfast—and no water. The launch was afloat in 3 feet of water, which was well over the tops of our boots. Instead of trying to reach the cruiser, we decided to shoot more coots and hope for rescuers in the afternoon. Coots are not very good even when well cooked, but when merely warmed over—fire-burned on one side and raw on the other, with no salt except that in the sea water—it was just as well we were very hungry.

About three o'clock in the afternoon, a speck appeared in the distance. It was the first we had seen since the storm, and as the boat gradually took shape, we piled wood on the fire and began to send up smoke signals, lest our rescuer pass us by. It wasn't really necessary for the rescuing craft contained

Jim, our boatman. It wasn't long before we were safely ensconced in the cruiser, with all the water we could drink and some wonderful-tasting ham sandwiches. But we didn't realize our troubles were not yet over.

"You might be interested in this news item," remarked Jim with a wry smile. There it was, blazoned on the front page: "Big storm sweeps the Texas Coast. Two Cornell men carried out to sea and probably drowned, though the bodies have not yet been recovered. Dr. Fox and his boatman make the lighthouse on Galveston Point but Allen and Lloyd are blown into the Gulf."

The news item was an Associated Press dispatch and was carried in most of the newspapers all over the country. Sam Lloyd's mother was notified through a Cincinnati paper, but fortunately for my family, my wife, Elsa, and our children were vacationing in a Florida hamlet where they had no telephone and did not see the daily papers. Elsa knew nothing about my "demise" until later when she received a telegram from my sister telling her to disregard any report of my being drowned in the Gulf of Mexico.

As for my sister, she had such great faith in me, because of my previous adventures that when the editor of our hometown (Ithaca, New York) newspaper telephoned to tell her of the AP report and inquired for further news, she said: "Oh no! Please hold up that report. He's never done anything like that before. I know he must be all right."

Thus ended my reported death by drowning.

COLONEL R. MEINERTZHAGEN

In the Mountains of the Lammergeier

Colonel Richard Meinertzhagen, who lives in London, was born there on March 3, 1878. He received his formal education at Harrow and served in the British Army from 1899 to 1927. He has traveled widely over Africa, India, Afghanistan, Nepal, Sikkim, Persia, Iraq, Burma, Europe, Madeira, and the Canary Islands, and in North America, to Greenland, Arizona, and Texas. He has always had a keen interest in natural history, especially in birds and their parasites, and in plants. His honors include the Distinguished Service Order and Commander of the British Empire. He is an Honorary Member of the American Ornithologists' Union and has written seven books of which some are: Birds of Egypt, Birds of Arabia, *and* Kenya Diary.

The lammergeier, Gypaëtus barbatus, *of which Colonel Meinertzhagen writes, is one of the largest birds of prey in the world. In his book* Birds of Arabia *he reports that the expanse of its outstretched wings is well over 9 feet, its weight 11 to 12 pounds, its tail wedge-shaped. The northern lammergeier is the most impressive bird in the family of Old World Vultures and lives only in the most remote mountains from eastern Europe to China. Its legs are feathered almost down to the toes, and its food is the bones of animals, usually those that have been picked clean by other vultures.*—THE EDITOR.

IN THE MOUNTAINS OF THE LAMMERGEIER

I confine myself to recounting my experiences with that finest of Raptores, the lammergeier, or bearded vulture, *Gypaëtus*, the most impressive, regal, sinister, and portentous of birds. My many experiences with it have certainly given me more pleasure, more fear, more presentiment, and more searching of heart than my contact with any other creature, man included. No bird has caused me more discomfort, more anger, or given me such spiritual uplift and admiration for it than the lammergeier.

My first introduction to the bird was in the Himalayas, where the grandeur of its soaring flight impressed me. Every morning I watched some dozen birds soar from their roosting cliff with the rising sun, and every evening I watched them return to their cliff replete and satisfied. I hoped for a more intimate association with such magnificent creatures. Later, in 1913, when stationed in Quetta, Baluchistan, I found them common, and demeaning their grandeur by scavenging in barracks. I determined to get a closer contact with them in the rugged mountains of Baluchistan, and I was not disappointed.

I was one of a party of staff officers undertaking an exercise on Murdar Mountain near Quetta. I became separated from the rest of the party and found myself uncertain of my way back amid precipices, moraines, screes, and juniper scrub. I wanted to get home, and in working my way along the top of a precipice I was faced by a scree some 20 yards wide. I knew all about the treachery of screes when set in motion but my shortest way home was across this one. I decided to make the attempt. Treading delicately, I had not advanced more than a few steps when the scree commenced to crawl and then to move rapidly downhill, throwing me off balance. I found myself being carried rapidly downward amid the roar of rocks and approaching a vertical drop of several hundred feet. But an old gnarled juniper tree had survived on the scree, and on passing it I clutched desperately at the old stump, breathless, fully aware of my danger and with the cascade of rocks and boulders roaring past me. A hungry lammergeier had seen my predicament. Any animal in distress on a mountain slope is the lammergeier's opportunity. His trick is to strike his victim with his wings and accelerate his destruction by throwing him off balance. If he can hasten the end, he does so.

The great bird swerved toward me, passing so close that I could see his sinister scarlet eyes and the look of greedy anticipation on his satanic bearded face. Three times he passed me, the last time so close that I could have touched his wing tip with a stick; but I was protected by that friendly juniper, and by then the scree had ceased roaring in its downward rush. It took me some moments to recover my composure, after which I was able to make my way with great caution to solid ground. But that evil disappointed bird kept his eyes on me, hoping for my bones, until I left the mountain. I was elated by my victory and intensely interested in the fact that the bearded vulture should have the sense to recognize a prospective meal in one of his only enemies.

In July, 1914, I was again in the mountains of Baluchistan. The old world of lethargy and luxury was slowly realizing that a world war might be a possible end to an era of peace, though such a catastrophe seemed unreal and remote. On July 26, 1914, I was enjoying the solitude and silence of mountain desert. I strolled out from my cave in which I was camped to try and visualize what might happen if war broke out. I was soon convinced of the certainty of war and its bloody trail of misery and destruction. I wrote that evening in my diary:

> The finest view I ever had of a lammergeier occurred today. I came on him but a few feet away silhouetted against a gold-red sunset, magnificent against a horizon stretching for miles and miles into golden infinity. He was quite unconscious of my presence as he gazed into the sun. He sat on a rocky pinnacle, wings slightly outstretched and head turned upwards toward heaven. Was this the phoenix of the ancients, Pliny's bird of brilliant golden plumage around the neck, the throat adorned with a crest and the head with a tuft of feathers? Was this lammergeier conscious of his sacred relationship with the sun? The phoenix of the ancients presaged peace everywhere in the land. What I saw this evening seemed to foretell war, a long, bloody war. It was the finest, most beautiful and yet most terrible, the most romantic view of any bird I have seen at any time anywhere. As I left him undisturbed I walked slowly back to my cold cave, depressed and alarmed at the uncertainty of the future.

I have seen the lammergeier in many parts of the world: in the Drakensberg of South Africa, on Mount Kenya, in Arabia,

Palestine, Spain, and the Himalayas, but perhaps my most thrilling encounter took place on the top of Mount Sinai on my fiftieth birthday. I was staying as a guest with the hospitable monks of St. Katharine's Monastery at the base of the mountain. I expressed a desire to visit the chapel on top of the mountain and spend the night there. Every obstacle was put in my way, but eventually a monk and an ass were placed at my disposal and up I went. The monk and his ass left me before dark. A recent fall of snow enhanced the marvelous feeling of close contact with biblical days. It snowed all night; I slept on the stone altar in the chapel but spent most of the night walking about to keep warm. I wrote in my diary on March 3, 1928:

> I felt lonely and detached from the world, longing for the break of day. At last it came: first a faint blush of gray light in the east, rapidly flooding with gold. As I paced up and down in the snow, the mist-soft horizon slowly revealed itself, and I felt I was living in a wilderness of spirits, lost and abandoned in the ghost-robe of dawn which enshrouded the earth. And when the sun rose over the deserts of Arabia the mist began to clear, revealing a crystal-clear ruby blaze over the eastern skies, and I looked down on one of the most beautiful sights I have ever witnessed. To the east I could see the Gulf of Aqaba and on the west I could see parts of the Gulf of Suez. On this holy mountain I felt very near to God. I turned to look at the chapel. On the small wooden cross was perched a lammergeier, all hunched up in the cold, eyeing me curiously, but gloriously golden in the sunlight; and as I watched him but a few yards off, his great wings spread out and he sailed forth into the gorges of those barren mountains searching for his breakfast, as his kind have done since the days of Moses.

Soon after dawn my monk with his ass arrived, and reluctantly I left that sacred mountain, thrilled by what I regarded as a close contact with my God of Nature. My spiritual self was bubbling over with enthusiasm and success. I have never felt so close to God as when I stood on that mountain top where Moses stood nearly four thousand years ago.

WALTER P. TAYLOR

A Great Naturalist and the Long-tailed Tree Mouse

Dr. Walter Penn Taylor has been Visiting Lecturer in Conservation Education, Claremont Graduate School, Claremont, California, since 1954. He was born in Walworth County, Wisconsin, October 31, 1888, and attended college at Throop Polytechnic Institute, Pasadena; Stanford University; and the University of California, where he did work for his Doctor of Philosophy degree. He has been Curator of Mammals, Museum of Vertebrate Zoology, University of California; a senior biologist of the U.S. Biological Survey, later the Fish and Wildlife Service, U.S. Department of the Interior; Professor of Economic Zoology, University of Arizona; Professor of Wildlife Management, Texas Agricultural and Mechanical College; Professor of Zoology, Okla-

homa Agricultural and Mechanical College; and a visiting professor at other colleges and universities. He has traveled widely over the United States, in the islands of the Pacific, in the Far East, and in Europe. He is noted for his field researches on wild animals and in ecology; is a Fellow of the American Association for the Advancement of Science and a recipient of the Gold Medal of the U.S. Department of the Interior. He is coauthor of a volume, The Birds of the State of Washington *(1953), and editor,* The Deer of North America *(1956).*

A GREAT NATURALIST AND THE LONG-TAILED TREE MOUSE

> Something hidden, go and find it
> Go and look behind the ranges.
> Something lost behind the ranges
> Lost and waiting for you. Go!

To one obsessed with a desire to look behind the ranges, and to see what is really there, the life of a field naturalist, zoologist, and ecologist is pleasant, satisfying, and, in short, fun. In traveling about in most of the United States, Canada, the Pacific, parts of Asia, and the Near East, I have had an unusual opportunity to read, as best I could at first hand, a good many pages in the book of nature. Through the kindly indulgence and encouragement of my understanding parents, and the boundless vitality and unbelievable industry of my first science teacher, a great naturalist, the late Joseph Grinnell, I became inspired with a keen desire to become a biologist. The beautifully prepared specimens of birds and mammals, stored in those early days in plain wooden cabinets or even in cardboard suit boxes at the Grinnell residence on North Marengo Avenue in Pasadena, California, thrilled me. The vacation camping trips on which Grinnell took the boys in his classes were among the most pleasurable experiences of my life.

After these early experiences with Grinnell, there was never any serious question in my mind what my vocation would be. My own life history has exemplified a sort of progression in enthusiasms. I have been, at various times, passionately interested in birds, mammals, forest, grasslands, camping, travel, books, biological field work, religion, the humanities, civics, conservation, and even politics. Through all these—and this has given point and coordination and balance to a many-sided experience—I have been broadly concerned with the interrelationships between man and other living things, both plants and animals. More than that, I have been attracted by the manifestations of the great stream of matter and energy which flows restlessly through man, his living associates, and, in fact, through all of nature and the universe.

Perhaps a further word about my chief mentor, Dr. Joseph Grinnell, is called for. Among Grinnell's outstanding traits were keen curiosity, never satisfied, and almost irrepressible enthusiasm. To three of us boys—Joseph S. Dixon, Charles L. Camp, and myself—who had the good fortune to be in his classes at Throop Polytechnic Institute, Pasadena, California, these spelled lifelong inspiration. Grinnell's many years of service later as a professor at the University of California at Berkeley exercised a similar influence on many of his students there.

As all vertebrate zoologists will immediately recall, Grinnell (1877–1939) was one of the most eminent zoologists in North America. Born on an Indian reservation in Oklahoma, he early became absorbed in the study of nature, particularly of birds, mammals, and plants. His senses were as acute as an Indian's, his single-mindedness, energy, and powers of analysis, far superior to those of an Indian. As a field naturalist, teacher, and writer, his reputation is forever assured. One of his greatest contributions, of course, was his founding and building of the Museum of Vertebrate Zoology (sponsored by Miss Annie M. Alexander) at the University of California at Berkeley. This was never at any time a repository for dusty stuffed specimens. From its beginning and right up to the present, it has been one of the liveliest centers for the study of vertebrate taxonomy and ecology on the North American continent. Almost before there was a headquarters building, expeditions were dispatched to various parts of California, Alaska, and the West, and systematic and life history studies, especially of the birds and mammals, were enthusiastically pursued; a stream of meticulously prepared technical papers and books began to flow, and to this day is maintained by competent workers. Grinnell's personal bibliography totaled 554 titles. In fact, the "MVZ," as the Museum of Vertebrate Zoology is still familiarly called, became and remains one of the foremost dynamic working scientific organizations of its kind in the country.

Over the mantel of the living room of the Grinnell family home in Pasadena was the motto: "Blessed are they that hustle, for they shall have what they get." Joseph must have absorbed this sentiment from his earliest childhood, for a more persistently industrious and indefatigable worker it has never been my privilege to meet. Especially on zoological collecting trips did his activity reach its zenith. Up at daylight, Grinnell was ready to run the traps set for mammals the night before. Then breakfast, more field collecting, preparing specimens, writing notes, until well after nightfall, when more traps were set. In the cool of the evening, when dusk brought out the bats, attempts were made to intercept their erratic flights with special auxiliary shotgun loads. Sometimes, under cover of complete darkness, owls or other nocturnal animals were hunted. Grinnell paid no attention whatever to personal discomforts and never once let up on his passionate zeal for getting things done and finding out more about nature.

In any camp "grub list" with which Grinnell had anything to do, oatmeal mush for breakfast was sure to loom large. This was apparently because he himself was fond of it; furthermore, it was quickly prepared, economical, "stuck to one's ribs," and could be used for bait for small rodents. In the course of years of field work, I consumed such quantities of oatmeal mush that I have lost my relish for it.

Nevertheless, to those of us who were privileged to work with Grinnell and the MVZ during those early days, life, and especially biological field and museum work, was always exciting and alluring. The vertebrates of California, Alaska, and Nevada were all too little known. In consequence, as a result of a strong feeling on Grinnell's part that one ought to know the things near at hand before venturing too far afield, expeditions were organized to cover, so far as possible, our own hundred-million-acre state of California, first and foremost.

After participating in MVZ field trips to many parts of California from 1908 to 1912, I was assigned in 1913 to lead a field party to the north coast counties of California. There it was that I was put in the way of detection of a new subgenus (or group) of *Phenacomys*, a mouse new to science. The genus itself is made up of ordinarily inconspicuous little rodents belonging to the meadow-mouse family—variously referred to as lemming mice, a most objectionable misnomer, false lemming mice, very nearly as bad, or, by the scientists, just plain phenacomys (pronounced fen-*ak′*o′mis).

It is well-known that the members of the meadow-mouse

family are notably adaptable. They live from the mountains to the sea, and from open plains to the densest forests. While many spend most of their time on the surface of the ground, others are well-adapted for life underground.

In 1890 a new species of *Phenacomys* called *longicaudus* (lonj-i-caud'us), because of its unusually long tail, was described by Dr. W. P. True in the Proceedings of the United States National Museum. This was on the basis of a specimen taken at Marshfield, Coos County, Oregon. And so we learned about the long-tailed tree mouse, unmistakably a *Phenacomys*, but one whose habits notably differed from all of the others. For, of all the members of this great subfamily, *Phenacomys longicaudus* was unique in its choice of trees in which to live.

In 1901, eleven years after the publication of its original description by True, Dr. C. Hart Merriam of the United States Biological Survey, referred to *P. longicaudus* (the long-tailed tree mouse) as one of the rarest and least-known mammals of the world. That this was not too extreme a statement is shown by the fact that at the time only three specimens of the species ever had been collected—the type collected, as stated, at Marshfield, Coos County, Oregon; an aberrant specimen taken at Meadows, Lane County, in the same state; and one found dead on a road at Lierly's Ranch, near Mount Sanhedrin, Mendocino County, California. Our north coastal counties expedition was given special instructions to be on the lookout for the tree mouse. The three previously collected specimens all had been sent to eastern museums, as it happened, two to the United States National Museum, Washington, D.C., and one to the Academy of Natural Sciences of Philadelphia. Consequently, until the spring and summer of 1913 all that we at the MVZ knew about the animal was derived from second-hand accounts or based on the extremely limited printed material available. The new subgenus (or group) is based on this seemingly unique habit of the long-tailed tree mouse of living in trees, its cinnamon-reddish back, its long tail, and some tooth characters which are not easy to demonstrate except with special equipment.

While we were working in the vicinity of Mendocino City, California, our attention was first called to the red tree mouse by small boys. Having located the little animal, we endeavored, so far as possible, to solve some of the problems of its life and living. All the evidence seemed to indicate that it is wholly dependent on the trees in which it lives, for food, drink, and shelter. We found it feeding principally on the fleshy portions of fir needles and the cortical parts of fir shoots, leaving the resin ducts and stripped shoots to be incorporated into its nest structure.

The nests themselves were quite impressive. They were conspicuously spherical, slightly flattened on top. In diameter they varied from 8 inches up to 3 feet, truly enormous structures when it is remembered that their builder and occupant is a small mouse only about 7½ inches long, including its body and tail. In height above the ground the nests were from 4 feet to 100 feet. It is highly probable that the tree mouse ranges freely through the crowns of several trees in the vicinity of its nest. There is some evidence to show that the males live in nests separate from those of the females, for at least a part of the year, but the facts are inconclusive. The young, numbering from one to four in a litter, have been found in February and July. Nests found were built by the mice in the Sitka spruce, *Picea sitchensis*, the grand, or lowland, fir, *Abies grandis*, and the Douglas fir, *Pseudotsuga taxifolia.*

The tree mouse and the trees it dwells in are obviously quite closely interlocked, ecologically. They can scarcely be said to be interdependent, however, because the dependency is from mouse to tree and not the other way around. The whole of the tree mouse's individual and social economy may well be restricted to its tree habitat. So far as we could see, the animal had no pressing need to come to the ground for any purpose.

And so I present the long-tailed tree mouse, pioneer Californian and Oregonian, dweller for the most part unheard and unseen in the sheltering crowns of some of the most impressive trees in the northwestern United States, carrying on its daily life, its feeding, its constructions, its loves, births, marriages, and deaths, with almost no human being the wiser.

To the research worker in almost any branch of science, life can be one long and exciting experience of discovery, with some drudgery mixed in, of course, between periods of elation. After all, why should we trouble to do these things, investigate space, the stars, the world of the electron microscope, the life history of an obscure tree-dwelling mouse in the north coastal counties of California, and so on? Certainly not for profit, for national defense, or for empty honors. Chiefly, because these things are so, and we want to know about them—because of our curiosity concerning the fascinating world and the universe in which we live.

> Something hidden, go and find it
> Go and look behind the ranges.
> Something lost behind the ranges
> Lost and waiting for you. Go!

E. THOMAS GILLIARD

The Bony Treasure of Funk Island

E. Thomas Gilliard, Associate Curator of Birds, American Museum of Natural History, New York City, was born in York, Pennsylvania, November 23, 1912. He was educated in Baltimore, Maryland, at Deep Springs (Telluridae), California, and at the University of Santo Tomas, Philippine Islands. In 1932 he began working at the American Museum of Natural History as a volunteer; three years later he became a laboratory assistant in ornithology and in 1950 was appointed a curator. His first expedition was to the Gaspé Peninsula in 1934. Two years later he found a complete skeleton of the extinct great auk and some six thousand bones of this species in Newfoundland. He has made five expeditions to the interior of South America, one to the Philippines, and six to New Guinea. He has collected, for science, birds of paradise and bowerbirds, many which were new to the scientific world. Wagner College of Staten Island, New York, has honored him with a Doctor of Science degree. He has written popular articles in natural history and is the author of a book, Living Birds of the World.

THE BONY TREASURE OF FUNK ISLAND

IT was a hot summer afternoon some years ago in the laboratories of the American Museum of Natural History in New York City. As usual at this season, the Bird Department was an attraction for visiting ornithologists from many parts of the world. This seasonal influx had become heavy since our accession of magnificent collections of bird skins originally amassed by Lord Rothschild for his Tring Museum in England. His scientific specimens, together with our Museum material, some of it going back to John James Audubon, had, of recent years, made the American Museum and its bird collections a foundation piece for the scientific and popular bird literature of much of the world.

That afternoon on the fifth floor, I noted a stranger working under the west windows, a man with a weathered countenance. I soon learned that this was Harold S. Peters, a government field biologist of Atlanta, Georgia. He told me that he was doing research for a book on the birds of Newfoundland which was soon to be published by the Newfoundland government. We spoke briefly of the richness of the animal life there. Peters had traveled widely in Newfoundland gathering his data. As it happened, I had local knowledge of quite a few of the places he mentioned, and this clearly perplexed him. Turning quizzically toward me, he asked, "Ever hear of the Funks?"

The Funks indeed: three rocks among the thousands fringing the rugged shores of Newfoundland—three rocks some 30 miles off the northern coast, two awash and usually covered with breakers, the third with a headland rising less than 50 feet above the sea in the path of the Labrador current, with its wallowing, wooshing train of icebergs.

A surprisingly intuitive question, I thought, but before I could give my simple answer, exciting scenes of a youthful treasure hunt flashed across my memory. In retrospect, I saw two tireless youths in a small rowboat throwing caution to the devil as they approached a rocky islet through a breaking, frigid sea—an islet in the midst of an infamous ship graveyard. I saw them leap from the stern of the boat as it teetered on the top of a wave inches from a rock face, and I saw them cling to a ledge as the boat dropped away like an elevator. Next, I saw them scramble to the summit of the island, flushing kittiwakes, a kind of gull, from their cliff nests and driving a path through a crowded city of nesting sea birds that included murres and razor-billed auks. Finally, in memory, I saw them fall on their knees on an acre-sized plot of earth riddled with the nesting burrows of puffins. There the two youths picked up bones—bird bones. These they compared carefully with models they had carved from the wood of white pine nearly a year before, making exact replicas of certain bones of the great auk in the collection of the American Museum of Natural History.

Then I remembered how we two youths had shouted and begun a wild victory dance. With no handy goal posts to pull down, we fell in a flailing knot, trying, it seemed, to mash one another into the dirt of that bleak island. Certainly, I thought, no more incongruous sight had ever been seen at this tragic spot, the place where the great auk had been slaughtered into extinction.

For an instant I felt again the boundless enthusiasm of that exuberant victory dance. And then came flashes of the trials that had preceded it, which had served to make the adventure so sweet.

These I could have unfolded as if they had occurred the day before. Samuel Knox George, my partner and long time friend and boyhood neighbor from Maryland—then a Princeton student—and I, had already engaged in ornithological explorations in climbing to eagles' nests and in searching for rare birds. We were at a stage where we craved adventure, but we had no backers and little money.

Actually we had saved our money for most of a year and had accumulated a total of nearly three hundred dollars. With this, we planned to drive Sam's 1933 Ford from New York to North Sydney on Cape Breton Island, and from there to embark, by cheapest ticket, on the S.S. *Caribou,* the Newfoundland railroad ship that made a weekly connection with Nova Scotia. Then we would ride two days on the narrow-gauge railroad from Port aux Basques in southwestern Newfoundland to the northernmost part of the rail line, a spot called Gander Station. We had selected this place because it was geographically closest to Funk Island, but that island was still more than 100 miles off.

Today Gander is an internationally famous airport. When we arrived there, it consisted of a cluster of low houses and a wharf connected by narrow channels with semiprotected waterways through which one could travel in small boats to the hundreds of peninsulas and islets forming the broken coastline of northern Newfoundland.

Two pup tents and two packs of camping gear and warm clothes comprised our total outfit for this frugal expedition.

Also, we had one hundred dollars carefully tucked away for any skipper who would drop us off on Funk Island, preferably for a week, and then take us safely ashore again.

This was our plan. When I unfolded it to Dr. Frank M. Chapman, head of the Bird Department at the American Museum of Natural History, I was keenly disappointed to find him very much against it. Dr. Chapman believed the venture was too risky, and that it was ill financed. Then he almost cut the ground from under me when he said: "The whole plan seems designed to find the proverbial needle in the haystack. Even if you did manage to reach that low, storm-lashed island, there is very little likelihood that anything remains after all this time."

These objections caused Sam George and I deep thought. We again weighed the possibility of searching in other regions for remains of the great auk, but in the end we chose to tackle Funk Island in spite of Dr. Chapman's powerful arguments against it. We did this because our studies of the great auk, made before, and especially after consulting with Dr. Chapman, had indicated that Funk Island held our best chance of finding the bones of this extinct bird.

By the time we reached our decision there was very little we did not know about the great auk, also known as the garefowl, the penguin, the wobble, the Apponatz, and other less pronounceable names. The name penguin first belonged to the auk, we had learned, and was later transferred in error to the "penguins" of the southern oceans by sailors who failed to recognize any great difference between the flightless bird of the North Atlantic (which is a member of the gull stock) and the much more primitive flightless sea birds of the southern hemisphere (the sixteen species of birds we now call penguins).

Thirty inches in length, resembling a medium-sized penguin, the black and white great auk for ages was a source of food and arrow tips to men of the North Atlantic. Auk bones, we learned, had been found in stone huts constructed by primitive men some four thousand years ago in the Orkney Islands. And Stone Age men doubtless killed them along the coasts of Scandinavia, for there is evidence that auks began breeding along the shores of Norway, Sweden, and Denmark not long after the final retreat of the glaciers, perhaps nine thousand years ago. But even longer ago, before the retreat of the ice, the great auk lived in the Mediterranean Sea. This is believed because among the oldest finds are bones from the island of Gibraltar. There in a cave in a rock known as "Devil's Tower" bones of the great auk were found. And in this same cave, but in another stratum, were found fragments of a Neanderthal boy!

Other ancient bone finds show that the great auk was common ages ago along the coasts of the north and west Atlantic. The itinerant ancestors of the Norsemen, the Indians, the Greenland Eskimos, and many other peoples killed this goose-sized bird for food. Bones found as far south as northern Florida in a village kitchen midden, bones taken from Indian middens scattered widely along the coasts of New England, including sites on the islands of Martha's Vineyard and Nantucket in Massachusetts, and in many places along the coasts of Maine and New Brunswick, confirm that the flightless great auk ranged widely. At least it did so on occasion, during its swimming migrations.

Our studies indicated that the great auk apparently always nested on small offshore rocks protected from four-footed animal predators by broad moats of salt water, and it kept pretty much to the shallow cold waters of the continental shelves. This had been a species which numbered in the millions, and, as we studied it, we were incredulous at its rapid demise. Had not these same auks been systematically "cropped" by primitive man for thousands of years—men using spears, arrows, traps, wooden dugouts, hide-covered coracles, blinds of all sorts? Yes, but his toll of them seemed not to have affected the survival of the great auk.

By contrast, modern man, unscrupulously collecting auk feathers for pillows and mattresses, brought doom to the species in less than a century. How had he done it? We found that men had killed them with clubs like so many corralled sheep. Following the killings, they boiled the birds on fires fed by the carcasses of those great auks already stripped of their feathers. This sorry chapter ended as follows: according to the record, the last killed of the great auks were two specimens, said to be a pair, shot on Eldey Island (one of a number of reefs lying 15 to 25 miles off the southwestern tip of Iceland) on June 3, 1844. They were shot just ten years after the last one ever sighted off the European coast was seen at Waterford on the coast of Ireland. The last recorded appearance of the species was of a lone great auk seen at the Grand Banks, Newfoundland, in 1852. In earlier times great auks had nested on many of the North Atlantic Islands, including the Faroes, St. Kilda, the Orkney Islands, Lundy Island, and the Isle of Man. However, in recent times the only places where they appear to have bred was on Eldey Island and Funk Island.

Our studies indicated that Dr. Chapman was too pessimistic about the possible success of our venture. In fact, there were a number of indications that we would be looking for *anything but* the proverbial needle in the haystack, if we succeeded in reaching Funk Island. Our chief source of information was a report, yellowed with age, by F. A. Lucas, entitled "Explorations in Newfoundland and Labrador in 1877," made in connection with the cruise of the U.S. Fish Commission Schooner *Grampus*. Lucas had written, "The feather hunters probably went to Funk Island in the spring and resided there until the sea birds had finished breeding, systematically killing all the Great Auks they could; and this was kept up until, like the Rytina, the Great Auk had been slaughtered out of existence. The extermination took place about 1840, and at that date American ornithology was in its infancy, so that not a single specimen of the Great Auk was preserved out of all the millions that were, and there are in existence only two stuffed specimens of the Great Auk from America." On another page, he added, "That the feather hunters must have plied their trade with great vigor is shown by the millions of bones scattered over an area of many acres. . . ." These bones, the report continues ". . . are most numerous along the crest of the island [Funk], where the upturned sod reveals vast numbers of bones, interspersed here and there with patches of charcoal, showing where the kettles swung in which the birds were scalded."

And who was the man who had written this report? I found that Dr. Frederic A. Lucas was a former director of the American Museum of Natural History. However, when he wrote the report he was an assistant curator at the United States National Museum in Washington. So we went ahead with our plan despite Dr. Chapman's warning.

Funk Island had been discovered by the great French explorer Jacques Cartier on his first voyage to America in 1534. Cartier had visited the island where his men killed a boatload of great auks. These he recorded in his journals as the Great Apponatz, and after Cartier's visit other visits were made by men bent on plundering the auks for their guano, for food, and for feathers. However, only three naturalists had visited the island prior to our proposed visit: the Norwegian naturalist Peter Stuvitz in 1841, Professor J. W. Milne in 1873, and Dr. F. A. Lucas in 1887. None of these men were in time to see the living bird, although Stuvitz was only several years too late. All three had collected remains of the great auk.

Because virtually nothing had been saved of this bird, in 1887 Professor Spencer F. Baird detailed Dr. Lucas to accompany the U.S. Fish Commission Schooner *Grampus* on a voyage of exploration ". . . to northeastern Newfoundland and the Gulf of St. Lawrence, primarily to obtain, if possible, bones of the Great Auk. . . ." Of this mission Lucas wrote as follows: "From a scientific viewpoint it was extremely desirable to secure bones of the Great Auk, since up to 1887 there were but nine skeletons of that species preserved in museums, only one being in the United States, while the U.S. National Museum possessed but a single bone." Lucas added: "Even viewed commercially a collection of Auk bones would be of considerable value since the small number of existing specimens had caused them to bring a high price whenever brought to the market."

The *Grampus* expedition, which was able to land parties on Funk Island on June 22 and June 23, 1887, was successful in obtaining about ten nearly complete skeletons. One of these was sold to the Museum of Science and Arts, Edinburgh, for about six hundred dollars, and one each was traded for valuable scientific specimens to the American Museum of Natural History and to the Museum of Comparative Zoology in Cambridge, Massachusetts.

Thus our researches had shown that in 1936 some eighteen nearly complete skeletons were all that were known to science. Incidentally, we also found that seventy-nine birds and eighty-one auk eggs had been saved. Therefore Sam George and I thought there was a good chance that our three-hundred-dollar investment might be recoverable. In other words, our venture did have something of the flavor of a treasure hunt.

Like all young treasure hunters we were all too wont to

overlook the danger. We took very lightly the advice of earlier visitors to the island. It was perhaps this aspect that alarmed Dr. Chapman the most. For example, Lucas had written that Funk Island was a flattish granite rock rising 46 feet, half a mile long, a quarter-mile wide, and that it emerged from a seldom-visited sea filled with shoals. We were not alarmed by any of these things. We were at that age when nothing seems impossible, and we hardly gave a second thought to the somewhat staggering differences between Lucas's well-equipped and adequately staffed expedition and our plan.

In June, 1936, Sam George and I drove his Ford to North Sydney, Cape Breton Island, embarked on the S.S. *Caribou* to Newfoundland, and there managed to find a captain (Captain Coish of Fogo Island) to take us to the Funks (although his wife stood sobbing at his side as he made his decision!).

The accounts of our unusual success in finding many skeletal remains of the great auk were first published in a popular article in *Natural History Magazine* in September, 1937, and in a technical report in a 1937 issue of *The Auk*, official publication of the American Ornithologists' Union. In *The Auk* I had the pleasure of announcing our discovery on Funk Island of the fifth known New World breeding colony of the gannet, a bird which Cartier had found on Funk Island, but which was not seen there again until our visit. Indeed, Lucas had written, "The Auk, by the way, is not the only bird which has been extirpated on Funk Island, for the Gannet lives in name alone, although Cartier found it abundant."

We had some grim times, some close escapes, some hilarious adventures which will be with us all our lives. These occurred as we hiked along the bleak coasts of Newfoundland, sleeping in fields and shacks along the edge of a sea sprinkled with icebergs, trying to bargain with the Newfoundland cod fishermen we met. We lived mostly on fish and "canned terr," an awful concoction of razor-billed auk and assorted other sea birds that these fishing folk prepare like preserves at certain seasons of the year. Finally we found a fisherman with courage enough to risk a trip to the Funks—the shoals they all feared. These lay just over the horizon from where we were, or less than 50 miles from the nearest populated island.

To measure the dangers Lucas had warned us about, the following is pertinent: we were offering one hundred dollars for a two-day voyage to the Funks at a time and in a place where the local teachers boarded for *five dollars per month* in the very same homes of the seafolk who refused our one-hundred-dollar proposition!

When these facts became clear to us, we began to wonder if perhaps we were not a bit foolhardy. And we found ourselves listening wide-eyed to the tales of death on the rocks, and particularly to one about seven men who lost their minds and ran screaming into the sea from the cliffs of Funk Island when help finally reached them.

Sam George and I reached Funk Island on the sailing schooner *Trawler* under command of Captain Coish in the afternoon of July 20, 1936. After some two hours ashore during which time we worked like madmen, we had to leave because of the worsening conditions of the sea. That night we put further to sea to reach safe water, and the next day we worked back again through a fog to the island. Because we had failed to find skulls the day before, we made life miserable for the Captain. As a result, he let us go ashore for another hour of furious work. Thus, with incredible good luck, the sea had abated enough to permit our landings, and on the second day we found the skulls.

One nearly complete skeleton, three fairly complete skeletons, and some six thousand bones of the great auk was the booty we raked and dug up.

These were some of the thoughts that flashed across my memory as I stood that day on the fifth floor of the Whitney Wing in the American Museum of Natural History. "Oh yes," I answered Peters, "Sorry, my thoughts seem to have wandered a bit. About the Funks: Yes, I know them." And then I told him that with a friend, Sam George, I'd found auk remains and gannets there in 1936.

Peters snapped his head up, eyed me, and then said slowly, "I've just come from there. I thought I was the first naturalist to visit the island since Lucas." Clearly he was stunned at my story, and I was sorry. Our conversation quickly turned to the island: the gannets had increased to a massive breeding colony; the auk remains were still much in evidence; the narrow ledge by which we had landed on the northeast cliffs was still there, also the great concentration of puffins, murres, razor-billed auks, arctic terns, and kittiwakes.

At length I left Peters to work on his report, and as I did so the thought flashed across my mind that Funk Island had meant a lot more than the finding of gannets and extinct auks. It was probably the main turning point in my life. It served to open a glorious career of ornithological exploration which has led me into some of the least-known parts of the New and Old Worlds, including eight expeditions to the mountains of the Philippines, New Guinea, and New Britain, and five expeditions to South America, all in quest of unknown birds, all to areas then still blank on the ornithologist's map of the world—the map which thousands of naturalists since Linnaeus's time have been striving to complete.

I shall never forget returning to the American Museum with the auk remains. Sam and I put our prize, a nearly perfect skull, on a piece of jeweler's cotton, and bringing this, together with a liberal assortment of the bones, we knocked on Dr. Chapman's door. Chapman, one of America's greatest ornithological explorers, was then seventy years old, I should guess, but he still had the keen interests of the young explorer. He was a serious man, not given to idle talk, with extremely sharp ears and eyes. In his typically quizzical manner, he glanced at me as we entered and then at the tray I carried, fixing his gaze on the skull. After a full second, he stood up, smiled broadly and extended both his hands, one to each of us.

That, I believe, was the most important moment of my life.

That winter I accompanied Dr. Chapman to Barro Colorado Island in Gatun Lake, Panama Canal Zone. Then, in quick succession followed more expeditions, the first a mule-back trip over the Andes collecting birds, the second to the Lost World on the border of Venezuela and Brazil—to a mountain made famous that year by the discovery on its sides of the highest waterfall in the world, Angel Falls. Then on and on, for a quarter of a century now, leading a life of adventure and scientific exploration, to wilderness areas of the world, sometimes among people still living in the Stone Age, perhaps rarely to areas never trod upon by man, but always to areas which had remained, biologically, little known.

Sam George and I never recovered a dime of that three hundred dollars, but no one can deny that we had found great treasure on the tragic Funks.

JOHN KIERAN

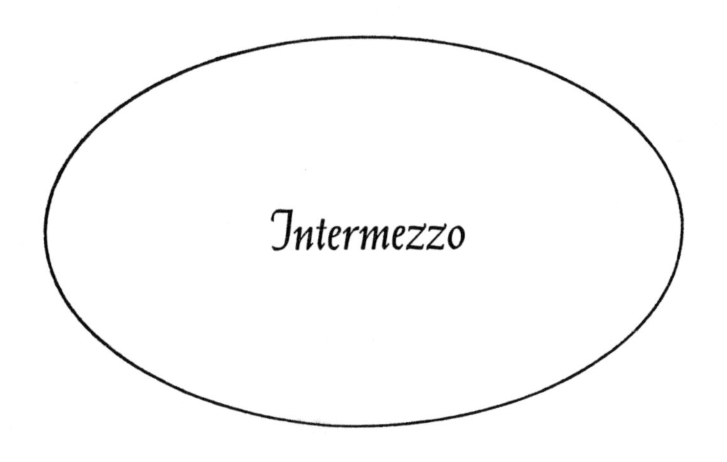

John (Francis) Kieran, writer of nature books, a former newspaper writer and erudite member of the radio panel of "Information Please," was born in New York City, August 2, 1892. When he was eleven, his father bought a farm in Dutchess County, New York, to serve as a "summer place," and it was there that John Kieran's deep interest in nature was first stimulated. In New York City, he attended Fordham University, where he was graduated with a Bachelor of Science degree, cum laude, *in 1912. After graduating he went back to the farm to raise chickens and apples, and taught six pupils in a tiny country school. In later years he found New York City essential to his writing, the country imperative to his happiness. In 1914 he became a member of the Linnean Society, New York City. From 1915 to 1943, he was on the sports staff of* The New York Times *(with time out to serve in the U.S. Army in France in World War I), and in 1943 and 1944, he was a col-*

umnist for the New York Sun. *He received a Doctor of Science degree from Clarkson in 1941, a Master of Arts degree from Wesleyan University in 1942. He is the author of seven books, the latest,* Natural History of New York City, *published in 1959.*

INTERMEZZO

To quote that eminent military expert, Kipling's Private Terence Mulvaney, "I was a corp'ril wanst." In the First World War I held the exalted rank of corporal in the Eleventh U.S. Engineers, a regiment that landed in France in early August, 1917, and was assigned to railroad construction and maintenance behind the British lines in the northeastern sector of France. I took with me to the wars all my old enthusiasm for birds, trees, and flowers, but I had no field glasses or field guides of any kind and I had to grope my way among the new sights and sounds that I encountered on this foreign field.

Before we settled down for seven months of railroad work on the Somme, we paused for a week of gas training and bayonet drill at a British camp near Calais, and it was just outside the picturesque little village of Audruiq that I first saw how

In Flanders fields the poppies blow.

There they were, bright red flecks in the ripening fields of wheat, rye, and barley, and over them flew the flashing black-and-white magpies, just as I had dreamed the scene would be from years of reading. When we were quartered in the railroad yard at Péronne, I found a whole brigade of white-nosed coots paddling about the marsh made by the Somme River where it circles the base of the ancient tower in which Charles the Bold of Burgundy once held prisoner the wily Louis XI of France. At least, that's the gospel according to Sir Walter Scott in *Quentin Durward*, and I grew up believing every word that Scott ever wrote.

In that same marsh I also saw, as the months went by, a few species of ducks that I could call by name—mallard, pintail, teal, shoveler, widgeon—and a variety of wading birds much resembling our own species in that group. Through the late autumn and winter and early spring I gradually picked up an acquaintance with many of the smaller upland birds—finches, thrushes, wagtails, titmice, and such—but though each first meeting was a thrill at the time, so many years have passed since those old days in France that memory is vague about particular birds now—with one exception!

In mid-May of 1918 the Germans and Allies were locked in a last stand of trench warfare all across the northern border of France from the English Channel to Switzerland. Our regiment was digging reserve trenches behind the British lines, and we were camped on a wooded ridge overlooking the city of Béthune on the La Bassée front. It was a delightful change for us. We had spent the previous month camped behind Arras in an open field that was an inviting target at all times and a quagmire most of the time. Now we were on high and dry ground, and the trees in their fresh spring greenery screened our tents from enemy observation by balloons or scout planes. Our strategic position was good, too. We were far enough from the front line so that the light stuff didn't come near us and far enough forward so that the heavy stuff went whistling over our heads to the main crossroads and the railroad yards behind us.

Beyond the limits of our peaceful little patch of woods the war went on as usual around us. Most of the days were fairly quiet, but, near or far, there was always some firing going on. At night the blacked-out landscape was intermittently illuminated by the flashes of the big guns on both sides. When the wind was favorable, we often heard the sharp chattering of machine guns somewhere up front and now and then the eerie flare of a Very light would hang for a few seconds over No-Man's-Land in the distance. All these things were routine matters, and we regularly went to sleep on them.

It was a combination of moonlight and Maytime in a Flanders wood that brought about the strange interlude in the ordinary schedule of events. It was a warm quiet night, and I had rolled up the sides of my tent for ventilation. Long after taps I found myself lying awake on my cot admiring the loveliness of the balmy night. The nearer tents and the aisles between the trees were dappled with moonlight that filtered down through the branches above. The grass around my tent was silvered with dew. What I saw around me would have served as a setting for Act II, scene 2, "Another part of the wood," in a production of *A Midsummer-Night's Dream.* While I was lying there, reveling in the absolute beauty of the scene, my expert ear caught an ominous sound somewhere aloft, and I knew immediately what had awakened me. It was the telltale double-hum of German bombers coming toward us from over the lines. I knew what that meant, and so did everybody else who heard it. We were about to be treated to a loud demonstration of spectacular pyrotechnics.

I have to explain that our camp was in no danger. We were a scattered and unimportant target not worth the attention of bombers bent on big business. But within a mile or two of us there was an airfield and a big ammunition dump, and a few miles to the rear there was a railhead and a number of coal pits that were being worked on a round-the-clock basis for the precious fuel. These had to be strenuously defended against bombing attacks. For that reason our neighborhood was studded with concealed searchlights and anti-aircraft batteries.

This, then, was the situation as, audible but invisible, the droning bombers came closer overhead and the beams of a dozen or more searchlights went up to sweep the sky in search of a target. For a minute or two there was only the criss-crossing of the searchlight beams. Then something glinted brightly far aloft in one of the beams and almost instantly all the anti-aircraft batteries in the area went into action. The din was terrific. So were the fireworks as hundreds of shells exploded high in the sky and streams of tracer bullets from machine guns shot like meteors through the night. The effect was temporary pandemonium. Suddenly, probably because they had lost their target, all the guns ceased firing at the same time. We were dropped almost instantaneously from an eye-filling, ear-splitting uproar to what seemed like utter silence in a moonlit glade.

Before I could even catch my breath, from somewhere in the fretwork of shadow and moonlight just outside my tent there came the lovely, liquid, melting, soaring song of a bird pouring out a matchless melody, and though I never before had heard it in my life, I knew it immediately. The nightingale! What else could it be but that immortal bird? What else but the voice that found a path

> Through the sad heart of Ruth when, sick for home,
> She stood in tears amid the alien corn;
> The same that oft-times hath
> Charm'd magic casements, opening on the foam
> Of perilous seas, in faery lands forlorn.

For perhaps thirty seconds I lay there listening in ecstasy—"Was it a vision or a waking dream?"—and then *crash! bang!* the searchlights had picked up a target again and the interrupted uproar was resumed. When quiet finally returned to our woods I listened in vain for another moonlight sonata from the hidden songster. In fact, never since that night have I heard again the lovely liquid notes of that incomparable voice. That one ethereal offering stands by itself in memory. That was over forty years ago, but the whole episode was so unforgettable that I sometimes think I can close my eyes and still hear the nightingale singing in the Maytime wood and the moonlight of those vanished years.

PART TWO

ALEC H. CHISHOLM

The Last of the Paradise Parrots

Alec H. Chisholm, who lives in Sidney, Australia, was born at Maryborough, Victoria, on March 28, 1890. He entered journalism in his youth; has edited daily and weekly newspapers, also Who's Who in Australia. *He has been honorary editor of the* Emu, *journal of the Royal Australasian Ornithologists' Union, and editor of the* Queensland Naturalist *and the* Victorian Naturalist.

Besides his editorial work, he has written sixteen books of natural history and biography. Some of them are, Mateship of Birds, Nature Fantasy in Australia, Birds and Green Places, *and* Bird Wonders of Australia. *He holds honors from many ornithological societies and was the first winner of the Australian Natural History Medallion, awarded annually on a vote of societies for work in the study and conservation of animals and plants. In recent years he has been Editor-in-Chief of the ten-volume* Australian Encyclopaedia. *For this, and for other work, he was awarded in 1958 the Order of the British Empire.*

THE LAST OF THE PARADISE PARROTS

MEMORIES cherished by naturalists, unlike most others, are based mainly on personal discoveries: uplifting impressions drawn direct from the pageant of earth and air and sea. They may or may not have general significance, but because of their personal impact, their refreshing and even inspiring value, they are no less worthy of remembrance than were (shall we say) Wordsworth's recollections of the host of daffodils which he saw "beside the lake, beneath the trees, fluttering and dancing in the breeze."

The various discoveries—and, with most naturalists, their variety is quite considerable—may be made either by resolute seeking or by happy chance. Especially, I think, does the element of chance enliven the experience of one whose devotion centers chiefly upon birds, creatures which are free in movement and apt to be delightfully capricious in behavior; but, of course, "special" searches in birdland may also be richly rewarding.

For my own part, I return without effort to boyhood and hear and see full many sounds and sights, mingling birds and flowers, that left indelible impressions. And then, passing along the years, I recall my first sight of the majestic lyrebird in full display; the fantasies created by bowerbirds frisking in their woodland "theaters"; my first hearing of the compelling voice of *Atrichornis*, the rare little rufous scrubbird, in a picturesque mountain jungle; my sheer delight upon seeing a host of grey swiftlets' nests attached to the roof of a dimly lit cave on a tropic island, and at having some of the unafraid small birds alight on my shoulders; my first sight of an elegant, long-toed lotus bird walking over leaves of water-lilies; and, selecting further at random, my first acquaintance with the dainty, purselike nest of the mistletoe bird and with the decorative nest and wistful song of the tiny white-throated warbler.

After glancing back over many years and over many hundreds of miles of eastern Australia—I hesitate to say that any particular one of my recollections remains foremost in mind. Indeed, I incline to think that, because of exceptional circumstances, pride of place in my winged memories should be given to the rediscovery of the lovely creature which is known, or was known, as the paradise parrot.

My initial interest in this bird, as gained vaguely in youthful days, was stimulated to some extent by a man who, no doubt, had never heard of the species, namely John Burroughs. More precisely, it was the reading of Burroughs' essays, with their insistence on the need for eager inquiry in ornithology, and the thrill of delight that is apt to follow, that served as a general stimulus, and so "touched a spot" when writings about the paradise parrot became available to me.

These notes were scanty, yet impressive. They stated that the bird, *Psephotus pulcherrimus*, was known variously as the beautiful, scarlet-shouldered, paradise, and ant-hill parrot; that it was restricted to subtropical areas, in Queensland and northeastern New South Wales, and that it always nested in hollows burrowed into the ground-built mounds of termites. Further, the notes revealed that the species had originally been discovered by John Gilbert (assistant to John Gould) on the Darling Downs in 1844, that it had afterward been subject to much attention by trappers, and that it had not been recorded in the wild, nor in any aviary in Australia or elsewhere, for many years.

As to the appeal of the bird, a writer of the nineteenth century described it as "one of the most lovely of the Psittacidae [parrot family] yet discovered"; another declared it to be "surely the most beautiful paroquet that exists"; and a third man, after stating that no one could see it "without desiring to possess so beautiful and graceful a bird," went on to say that "large sums are constantly being paid for handsome specimens" but they were always found to be very difficult to keep in captivity. With these and similar tributes of the same period in mind, an author of a later day (about 1916) expressed deep regret that the paradise parrot had, apparently, become extinct before any record of its life history had been made known.

Here was a sorry state of affairs. What could be done about it? I asked myself this question in a flush of youthful zeal; but, since I lived in the south of Australia, at least 1,000 miles from the relevant scene, the problem was quite beyond my scope.

As matters fell out, however—possibly through the intervention of some good fairy!—within a year or so I transferred to Queensland's capital city, Brisbane, and there I presently learned from my landlady, a widow who had formerly lived in a country area, that she cherished among her recollections a frequent sight of the ant-hill parrot. Surely, she said, that beautiful bird had not wholly vanished?

So my quest began, in the year 1917. Enlisting the aid of newspapers, in both the capital city and country areas, I sought for information about a parrot that nested in termitaria on the ground—a parrot 12 inches in length, slim in body, and having (in the male bird) brown on the back, emerald green on the breast, neck, and lower back, black on the crown, and bright scarlet beneath the tail, on the forehead, and in a distinguishing flash on each shoulder. From time to time, too, I searched for the bird during excursions and asked questions of many bushmen.

Throughout almost three years, the inquiry drew lots of responses, but, unhappily, all were retrospective: all referred to the parrot as it was known in other days. Eventually, in 1920, a promising report arrived; it came from a man living in a lonely part of coastal central Queensland, and it stated that a single bird answering the description of the "lost" parrot was contained in a cage in his locality.

Quite promptly, then, I and a botanical colleague, my companion of many excursions, traveled by rail almost 300 miles northward. Disembarking at a small station, we shouldered packs and cameras and walked 9 miles, under a hot sun, to my correspondent's home. He, poor fellow, was a cripple (a young timber-getter who had lost the use of his legs through sleeping in damp places), and his movements were much restricted.

"I haven't seen the bird," he said, excitedly, "but you'll see it all right. Go down to the creek, and you'll find a small boat for crossing; then follow the track for about half a mile until you reach a house."

That boat being very leaky, we removed our shoes and socks and rolled up our trousers—thereby providing myriads of sandflies with a feast whose effects remained with us for several days—and, having crossed the tidal stream, we found the house indicated. Its occupant, a woman, had not a word of English, but when my colleague produced a fragment of German, she nodded understandingly and led us around the house to see her bird. Was it a paradise parrot? No—it was another member of the group, a fairly common species usually known as the redwing, and one which could be seen, perhaps, in a dozen aviaries near our own homes!

"Heaven help us!" I exclaimed. "How are we going to break this news to our crippled friend? Maybe the best thing to do will be to get around and find some plants and birds of special interest, so that we can tell him we have been well compensated for the journey."

In truth, we did add materially to our knowledge during the next few hours, and so on returning to our host we were able, with some effort, to temper his bitter disappointment. He became reconciled, I think, when assured that each of us was able to say, regarding almost every bush excursion, "Whichever way I go, I am glad I came."

Several months later, yet another report concerning the missing parrot reached me, this time, in 1921, from a cattleman living in the Burnett River country, rather more than 200 miles northwest of Brisbane. Now there could be no doubt that the "lost" bird was rediscovered; for, in fact, the settler had photographed both a male and female at their nest in a termites' mound and had sent prints to prove his claim. The birds, he said, had not nested in springtime, as might have been expected, but had begun their excavating in late summer (probably to coincide with the seeding of certain grasses), and the female had settled down to her brooding in early autumn.

Taking care not to cause any disturbance, the photographer had erected a "hide" near the nest, and, while crouched in that small enclosure, from day to day, he had greatly enjoyed watching the graceful movements of the parrots and hearing the male, in particular, a musical and very animated song—a performance which caused both the slim body and the long tail to vibrate, and which seemed to suggest "a very intense personality beneath the beautiful exterior."

A few weeks later, however, ill news arrived. Despite close

brooding, extending over at least a month, something had gone amiss and the nest had been deserted. The entrance tunnel was then opened, and five white eggs were seen resting in a 15-inch-wide cavity, which was lined only with fragments of the honeycomblike substance of the termites' mound. Every one of the eggs was infertile. This, it seemed, was the result of in-breeding, brought about by the extreme rarity of the species.

"I am very sorry over the failure," my correspondent wrote. "I had hoped to photograph the young birds when they became fledglings, and then to see them prosper and help to re-populate the district; and I had hoped, too, that you would be able to come up and see them. Now, the two adults have departed, but if you can visit me in springtime it may be possible to find at least one pair of the birds."

The year now was 1922. As it drew toward a close, it provided, apparently, my last chance of seeing the long-sought paradise parrot, because I was due soon to transfer southward again. So, on a day in the height of Australia's springtime (late October), I alighted from a train at a township in the Burnett Valley, was there met by my host, and was driven, in a horse-drawn vehicle, from 6 P.M. to midnight before reaching his homestead.

What a strenuous search was that which we made on the following day! The season was dry and the weather hot, the country parched and generally uninviting, and in those conditions we wandered mile upon mile, looking and listening, but all without the desired result. True, we saw various things of interest, and indeed when I sat near a small waterhole for two hours in late afternoon, no fewer than nineteen species of birds came there to drink; but not a single paradise parrot was in the throng.

Because of the poor seasonal conditions, my host and his family were not prospering. Neverthless, they were sustained by what was, it seemed, a strong natural piety, and after dinner that evening they invited me to join them in prayer—an invitation of a quite unusual type in my experiences of bush households. The elder son led the gathering. He prayed for his country, his family, and his neighbors. Moreover, he invoked blessings on his visitor, and, in addition, he besought divine guidance in the quest for the paradise parrot.

The next day was to be my last in the district. I could not possibly stay longer. Consequently, we made an early start and covered a different area. Again, then, mile upon mile, hour upon hour, we spent in fruitless search among the termites' mounds and elsewhere. We were becoming weary.

"It's now lunchtime," my companion said. "I'll find a clear space and boil the billy." * "All right," I replied. "I'll wander down the track and collect a few sticks for the fire."

Within a minute or so I stopped suddenly. A "new" bird-note had caught my hearing. Only brief, it seemed to be parrotlike, but rather more dulcet. At any rate, it was a call that I had never heard before. Hastily dropping the sticks I had gathered, I ran toward a tall eucalypt from which the voice had seemed to come.

Presently the call sounded again, and at once I caught, through a screen of leaves, a glimpse of a bird. It was, almost certainly, a female paradise parrot. As I gazed earnestly, while trying to get a better view, a similar call came from another part of the tree. After a trifle of maneuvering, I saw the second bird.

"Oh," I gasped, "you little beauty!" For there, sitting nobly erect on a dry branch, and with the noonday sunshine playing on his brilliant plumage, was a male paradise parrot. There, indeed, in glowing life, was my "storybook" bird: a bird I had

* A billy is a tin with a swinging handle that serves as the Australian bushman's teapot, and sometimes as a cooking pot. The word is from the aboriginal *billa*, meaning "running water."

known only through some few paintings and museum specimens, and which I had been seeking for five years almost to the point of despair. At this moment, perhaps more than ever before, I shared the feeling expressed by the young John Keats when he wrote:

> Then felt I like some watcher of the skies
> When a new planet swims into his ken;
> Or like stout Cortez when with eagle eyes
> He star'd at the Pacific. . . .

I returned a short distance along the track, still keeping the tree in view, and called to my companion. He came running, and after he had looked for some minutes at the two birds, meanwhile rubbing his hands and uttering exclamations of pleasure—after that, I settled down to make the most of the opportunity.

Flying from the tree to some dry grass near at hand, the two birds began feeding on seeds. Thus engrossed, they allowed me to approach to within a short distance, and there, while admiring their elegant figures, the warm colors, and the erect carriage of the male in particular, I was able to realize fully why John Gould had given this bird the name "beautiful," why dealers of old had used the term "paradise," and why some early settlers had coined the name "soldier" parrot.

I was much engaged, too, by the birds' melodious calls—few in number but each one more musical than those of most other parrots—and especially by that "new" note that had led me to the pair. It was, as I recorded at the time, a sweet and somewhat plaintive exclamation which might be rendered *Queeeeek*. Years later, after finding in England the manuscript diaries kept by John Gilbert in Australia during 1844 and 1845,* I was to learn that he had gained a similar impression in

* The discovery and nature of these diaries are described by the author in *Strange New World* (Sydney, 2d ed., 1955).

his early meetings with this species. "Its pretty note," he wrote, "at once distinguishes it from all other parrots; it may be described as *tit-sweet*, with a rather plaintive modulation."

The birds' method of feeding was simple yet effective. Each one would seize a grass-stem near its base and run it through the bill until the seed was reached; and sometimes, when the plant was rather too thick for the bill to grasp, the bird would stand upon the stem and bend it down by weight. Occasionally, the pair flew together into trees, where they appeared to feed among the leaves. At no time, though, did they show any indication of going to a termites' mound.

My homage to these birds extended well into the afternoon —indeed, lunch had been waiting for almost three hours before I returned. Meanwhile, I had been toying with various puzzling questions concerning the paradise parrot.

Why, I wondered, had this "aristocratic" bird, once reasonably plentiful, become so excessively rare? Was its falling away due to the ravages of trappers, to climatic conditions, to the competition of stock, to the burning off of grassy areas, or to a combination of all these factors? In contrast, why did the bird's close relative, the red-backed parrot, continue to prosper? Could it be that the paradise parrot's unusual choice of nesting sites, close to the ground, rendered it more liable to attacks by predators than was the case with the tree-nesting red-back? And, additionally, was there some inherent physical weakness, and perhaps some quirk of "temperament," that had affected the species, so that it had reached a point where it was inbreeding itself out of existence?

Those questions have been asked again, many times, since that day. They remain unanswered. More than that, any efforts which may have been made to re-establish the vanishing parrot, perhaps through the medium of aviaries, have been rendered negative by sheer inability to find, in later years, any of the living birds.

One or two pairs were seen, in the general area of our discovery, during 1923 and 1924, and a similar report came from the northeast of New South Wales some three years later; but there have not since been any reports of the kind made. A recent textbook has placed against the bird's name, paradise parrot, the saddening word *Extinct*. In these circumstances, it is curious to reflect that our lost bird was once described, in England, as "a joy for ever."

Whether the species has, in fact, disappeared beyond recall cannot be said with assurance. Personally, I cherish the hope, and indeed the expectation, that in certain parts of Queensland's extensive and sparsely settled areas some pairs of the beautiful birds may yet be found.

It is, perhaps, a matter for pride to have seen, in a state of freedom, any bird that is believed now to have vanished from the face of the earth. But certainly, there would be much greater gratification in learning of that bird's recovery, and especially so in the case of such an exquisite creature as the paradise parrot.

ALEXANDER SPRUNT, JR.

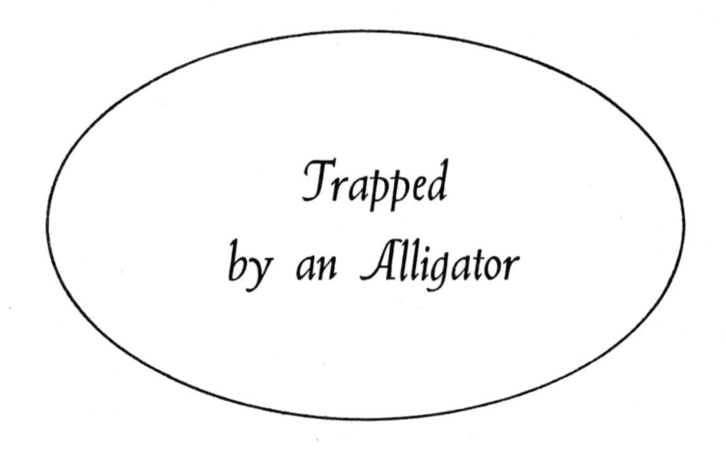

Alexander Sprunt, Jr., Staff Representative, National Audubon Society, was born in Rock Hill, South Carolina, on January 16, 1898. In 1901 his family moved to Charleston, where he grew up. He enrolled at Davidson College in North Carolina and in 1918 enlisted in the United States Navy during World War I. After the war he worked first for a bank, then a commercial business house, but soon abandoned the business world for a career in professional ornithology. Arthur T. Wayne, a famed ornithologist of South Carolina, became his mentor, and in 1924 Mr. Sprunt was appointed Curator of Ornithology at the Charleston Museum, a position for which he fitted himself by an intensive course in museum techniques at the Smithsonian Institution, Washington,

D.C., and at the American Museum of Natural History, New York City. In 1934 the National Audubon Society employed him in their sanctuary work, and he became Supervisor of Southern Sanctuaries. In 1954, Davidson College conferred on him an honorary degree of Doctor of Science. He is the author and coauthor of several books of ornithology and is a distinguished field ornithologist.

TRAPPED BY AN ALLIGATOR

AFTER many years of field work as a naturalist, I find that mental pictures of thrilling sights come to my mind as clearly as on a screen, most of them involving birds I have seen. Both beauty and drama have had a part in the scenes that come back, and certainly many of them were exciting.

Few of my experiences could be as memorable, ornithologically, as the rediscovery of the ivory-billed woodpecker in South Carolina in May, 1935, the first time it had been recorded in the state since the turn of the century; the unforgettable day I saw whooping cranes on the flats of the Aransas Refuge of Texas; the moment I stood on a wind-swept plateau above the Sespe Canyon in California, over which soared a magnificent California condor; my first glimpse of America's rarest and most unpredictable warbler, Bachman's warbler, in the South Carolina lowlands. All of these were combinations of excitement, beauty, and drama.

No other field experience, however, has ever had quite the impact on me than one I recall especially, though it was without beauty. Utterly unrelated to ornithology, it was, nonetheless, an experience so unusual that I had never heard of it happening to anyone, anywhere.

Many people appear to have a deeply rooted fear of alligators and consider them very dangerous, which, of course, they can be. Yet, well-authenticated reports of attacks of alligators on people are very uncommon, and such attacks are possibly quite rare.

At the time of my experience with one many years ago, I was on the staff of the Charleston, South Carolina, Museum. There had been a request from the Peabody Museum of Yale University, New Haven, Connecticut, for a specimen of alligator to include in their projected cypress swamp habitat group. Cooperation on the part of a local plantation owner resulted in the capture of an alligator on a baited trotline. In company with the noted naturalist-author Herbert Ravenel Sass and two others, I left Charleston and went to the plantation equipped to skin out the specimen and prepare it for shipment to New Haven. We hauled it up to the bank with the aid of two of the plantation Negroes, shot it, and laid it out on the side of the road, where the skinning took place. The 'gator was about 7 feet long.

Our work progressed, and we skinned the body out to the neck, cut the body away, and threw it aside in a ditch. We cleaned the bones of the legs of flesh and removed most of the fat, but the alligator's head was still attached to the body skin. It became necessary for us to then remove the soft parts of its mouth and neck muscles. Tying a length of rope about the alligator's upper jaw, we handed the end of the rope to one of the colored boys who raised the jaw to its widest stretch, keeping the rope taut so that I could work inside the alligator's mouth.

To keep the alligator's head steady, I placed my booted foot inside the alligator's mouth, on top of its lower jaw, or rather

I intended to. No sooner had my boot touched the alligator's teeth than the upper jaw slammed down on my foot like a steel trap, jerking the rope from the Negro's hands and clamping on my foot like a vise.

In amazement and some consternation, I fell backward on my hands, my legs outstretched, pulling as hard as I could. My companions stood motionless in stunned silence, staring at my predicament in disbelief. No amount of my efforts were sufficient to dislodge my foot. Finally, in response to my earnest entreaty, my companions aroused to activity. They cut two or three saplings to try to pry open the jaws of the alligator. It was useless. The jaws remained clamped shut, and the saplings crumbled into pieces. The two Negroes had run away in fright at the alligator that had apparently come back to life. Finally a stout oak branch was cut and sharply wedged. With this placed in the angle of the jaws and two of my companions bearing down as hard as they could, they at last forced the jaws open so that I could jerk my foot free.

Fortunately, the toe of my boot had been inserted squarely in the front of the alligator's mouth, and though the jaws had clamped on it tightly, the large teeth on each side of the alligator's jaws had not penetrated my foot. However, the alligator's teeth had made holes in both the top and sole of the boot, and the teeth had stopped just at the nail of my big toe, leaving only a bruise.

Reflex action of the alligator had been responsible for the whole affair. I had not cut its neck muscles, and the touch of my boot on its teeth set off its reaction. The surprise of it, the fact that the alligator was dead and that there were only its head and skin lying in front of me before I was trapped, made it as startling an experience as any of us had ever witnessed.

As we were finishing our skinning work, the two colored boys that had run away cautiously reappeared. They wanted the alligator's body as meat for their dogs. As they were carrying it away, I remarked that the incident had shown me that one could not trust an alligator even after it was dead. "E do' mo' dan dat, Cap'n," said one of them; "e mek a man know he cyan't trus' 'em *nex' week!*"

The finally prepared and lifelike specimen of that alligator is still in the Peabody Museum cypress swamp group at Yale University for any and all to see.

VICTOR H. CAHALANE

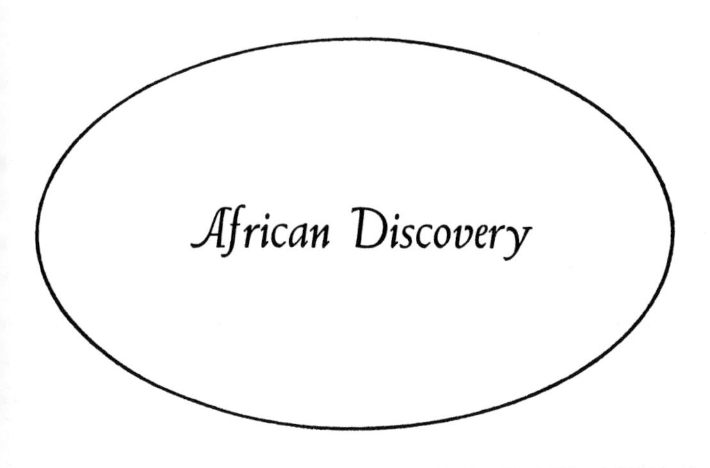

African Discovery

Victor Harrison Cahalane, Assistant Director of the New York tate Museum, Albany, New York, was born October 17, 1901, n Charlestown, New Hampshire, where he grew up. He attended he University of Massachusetts, Yale, and the University of Michgan. He has been a teacher of biology, a principal of a Vermont igh school, a deer investigator in Michigan, and Director of the Cranbrook Institute of Science, Bloomfield Hills, Michigan. From 934 to 1939 he was a biologist for the National Park Service, U.S. Department of the Interior, and Chief Biologist from 1939 until 955, when he accepted his present position with the New York tate Museum. He is the author of Mammals of North America *nd two other books; also articles and papers, many of which have ppeared in popular magazines and scientific journals in the United*

States and abroad. He is a past president of the Wildlife Societ and the National Parks Association, and he now lives at Delma New York.

AFRICAN DISCOVERY

It was a blistering afternoon a the end of October, and the plains of northern Kruger Par danced in the shimmering air. Towering cloud masses prom ised rain to end the seven-month dry season. Leafless thor trees and dead, brown grass gave the appearance of late fall i northern countries—but the heat was tropical. Because of th malarial hazard, most of the park had been closed to visitor for some weeks.

Four of us—three South African biologists and myself ("Yank")—had been counting game for hours. As we drove th narrow, dusty roads, we tallied about fifteen kinds of antelope from the great eland, as big as an ox, to the 12-inch-high steen bok. We had seen zebras, elephants, wart hogs, hyenas, jackal a leopard, and a bewildering variety of birds from the ostric downward in size. For the last twenty minutes we had bee driving through a host of impala antelopes. Their glistenin chestnut forms walked, ran, and leaped prodigiously in fron alongside, and behind us. The variety and number of anima were bewildering and almost overpowering.

"This is your first day in our game sanctuary," said one c my companions suddenly. "What do you think of it?"

"Don't speak!" I replied. "I'm afraid I'll wake up and fin myself back at my desk in Washington."

Like the majority of biologists, I had cherished a lifelong
mbition to see the magnificent animal life of eastern and south-
rn Africa. Anyone with a professional knowledge of mam-
nals knows that in Africa is the largest and most varied
ggregation of four-footed creatures left in all the world.
Modern man, in extending his rule over nature, has destroyed
ny possible rivals of the African fauna. Only there have vast
erds survived into the twentieth century—and these remnants
re shrinking rapidly.

More fortunate than most American biologists, I had had
wider-than-average experience in wildlife management for
he U.S. National Park Service. It had taken me to every
ational park from the Florida Everglades to Alaska's Mount
McKinley and on brief forays in Latin America. These field
rips, however, had been confined strictly to the New World.

Over the years I made contacts with persons who were con-
erned with national parks in Africa. They included French-
nen, Belgians, British colonials, and South Africans. Some
ppeared destined to remain signatures on letters. One of these
vas Dr. Rudolph Bigalke, Director of South Africa's National
Zoo and a member of the National Parks Board of that coun-
ry. I made other firsthand acquaintances with visitors who
ame to my office in Washington en route to see our parks and
vildlife refuges. Among these was the director of the National
Parks of South Africa, H. S. van Graan. As he was leaving, he
aid, "We need advice on our many problems in wildlife man-
gement. I wish you might come to our country and tell us
vhat to do." I echoed his wish!

Many months went by; then an official request came from
South Africa for the "loan" of my services. The National Park
Service agreed, a foundation made a grant to meet the cost of
ravel, and I was on my way.

As my B.O.A.C. flying-boat came into Vaaldam Airport

just before sundown, the level, yellow rays of light flashed on the numberless windows of Johannesburg's skyscrapers, and gilded the great mine dumps which ring the city. I was met by van Graan and his family and taken to Pretoria through the early darkness. The next day, Sunday, there were kaleido-scopic impressions of the capital city: jacaranda trees in full bloom, open house in the beautiful gardens of Government House, and "sundowners" at the home of a "checkbook farmer" friend of van Graan. As the light faded, native drums were throbbing faintly from far away across the parched golden-brown veldt.

Very early next morning, I was called for a hearty break-fast and my first meeting with a trio of scientists who were to introduce me to Kruger National Park. They were Dr. Bigalke ("Rudi"), my correspondent for more than a decade; Dr Nel ("Jeff"), biologist of the National Parks Board, and Dr Kettlitz ("Oom," meaning "Honorable," because of his white hair), ecologist for the Flora and Fauna Board of Transvaal Province. Together we made the 325-mile drive to Punda Maria ("Zebra Mare") at the northern end of the Park. We reached the camp—a few thatched huts—just before sundown. By the time we had eaten dinner, cooked by a native over an open fire, it was dark and we were more than ready for bed.

For me, The Day began when my companions wakened me at 5 A.M. It was warm and still when I joined my companions outside. Across the dense thorn thickets toward the Pafuri River, a thin mist hung between the palms, baobabs, and fever trees. As drowsiness left me, I became aware of animals mov-ing about through the shrubs. Looking down from the kopje (little hill), we appeared to be in a natural zoo. Nothing I had read prepared me for the variety of creatures that came into view in the next half-hour. Some I could name; others were identified for me by my friends. Graceful, satiny-sleek impala rams, with lyrate horns, moved about among their hornless wives and progeny. Majestic sable antelope bulls, black coats glistening, stalked along under their sweeping scimitar horns. Roan antelopes, larger but not as formidably armed as the sable, blended into the bush. Ashy-brown kudus, as tall as horses, nibbled browse with quiet dignity. Suddenly, two bulls locked their spiral horns together in a brief shoving match. Waterbucks, dressed in inappropriately shaggy, grizzled brown coats, trooped toward the river for a morning drink. They were soon followed by a mixed band of zebras and wildebeests (brindled gnus)—constant companions despite their apparent lack of anything in common. As they broke into a trot, they stampeded a family of wart hogs. Father, mother, and three piglets trotted rapidly away, their tails stiffly vertical and the terminal tufts flying, while Jeff and Oom Kettlitz laughed and shouted derisive remarks in Afrikaans. In the distance, faintly, came a roar followed by a series of coughing grunts. "Lion!" exclaimed Rudi. "He's hunting late."

After breakfast we climbed into our automobile and drove to the river. It was less than a mile, but I learned that the white man rarely walks far in the veldt. It would be particularly dangerous in the brushy areas with high grass and dense thickets of mopane and ilala palms. Although we were exempt from the rule forbidding park visitors from getting out of their cars except in the fenced campgrounds, we scientists would have been just as good to eat. Furthermore, even at 8 A.M. the African sun was already making it oppressively hot.

The wide strip of forest fringing the river was a botanist's wonderland. Even while repelled, I was intrigued by a tall tree with powdery yellow-green bark. This revolting apparition was the fever tree. Its preference for low, swampy ground led the earliest pioneers to apply the name, even before they knew the real cause of malaria. In an opening was a sausage tree, its wide crown festooned with many cylindrical fruits 10 to 18 inches long, like great gray sausages. Groups of ilala palms and the graceful wild date palm with leaves 10 feet long gave a tropical aspect. Towering over all were sycamore figs; high in their dark green canopies, black-faced vervet monkeys chattered and huge shaggy baboons screamed as they fed on the round, bluish fruits. An amazing variety of birds swarmed through the branches, attracted by the rotting pulp and a host of insects. The fruit that fell on the ground was eaten by antelopes, wart hogs, guinea fowls, and many other creatures.

Through an opening, looking out to a dry, stony ridge, I had my first glimpse of a tree that continued to fascinate me throughout my six months of travel in Africa. This was the baobab or cream-of-tartar tree, a monstrosity of the vegetable kingdom. Its misshapen, stubby limbs may reach a height of 50 to 60 feet. The *circumference* of the swollen, pink-barked trunk of old individuals may be even greater. The Bantus explain this unnatural appearance in one of their charming little legends: during the Creation, while God was busy elsewhere, the Devil planted the baobab—with its roots in the air!

Off toward the river wound several trails—hippo "highways." Stooping under the branches, we followed one of them to the bank. There in an expansive pool were several of the great beasts, only their backs, eyes, and nostrils visible. From the opposite shore, three hippos which had been sunbathing before we arrived, plunged into the water with surprising agility for creatures weighing 2 to 3 tons. Simultaneously, a half-dozen crocodiles slithered into the river and sank from sight.

Following the Pafuri, we came to the Limpopo River. It also was reduced to a series of large pools—its normal state at the end of the dry season. With a disgusted look on his face, Kettlitz exclaimed, "The Mighty Limpopo!" and spat into the water. Turning to me he said, "If you fall into one of our rivers, you probably won't drown—you'll smother to death in the dust." But high in the trees was driftwood left there during a past rainy season, when South African streams became raging torrents bearing the topsoil of the country to the Indian Ocean.

In shallow water a few feet from shore was a fish trap, skillfully woven of twigs by some native. Explaining that this was illegal, one of the biologists brought the trap ashore and destroyed it. Seeing another trap much farther out in the river, Jeff frowned and muttered, "It's too dangerous to wade; there may be crocodiles waiting out there on the bottom." Thus I learned another fact of life in Africa: these enormous carnivorous reptiles, armed with sixty-six conical teeth and an almost equally dangerous muscular tail, may be lurking in any river and even in small ponds. The caution with which thirsty antelopes approach the margin, sometimes taking an hour to cover the last 30 feet, demonstrates the terror which crocodiles inspire.

It was past ten o'clock when my companions exclaimed, "Time for tea!" We drove back to Punda Maria, where, at the ranger station, we had tea and crumpets with the British ex-Army colonel who watched over the game in the northern district of the park.

Refreshed, we started south on a trip through a wildlife wonderland that was to last five days and cover an air line distance of 200 miles. Throughout this first and most memorable day, the route was for me an almost continuous series of exciting incidents, a road into a new world!

Of the seventeen species and subspecies of antelopes inhabiting Kruger Park, we saw about fifteen. Blue wildebeests stared from the roadsides, then wheeled and charged away snorting, with their horselike black manes and tails flying.

There were small bands of high-shouldered tsessebes, their chocolate-brown coats shining like satin. Troops of waterbuck cows and almost-grown young, herded by imposing bulls, trotted across the plains. As they receded, the white ring was plainly outlined against the dark gray-brown of each rump. It was an American lady tourist who inquired of a park ranger, "What's the name of that antelope that looks like it had sat down on a newly painted toilet seat?"

Elands—the largest of all antelopes—are not abundant in Kruger Park, but we were lucky enough to see a band of a dozen or so. The cows and calves in their fawn coats were almost the shade of the tall dry grass. The huge bull, nearly 7 feet tall and weighing perhaps a ton, was bluish gray and thus more conspicuous. With his great dewlap and massive spiral horns, he was magnificent. Only the kudu, possibly, is more spectacular. The latter, while smaller, is more graceful, and the horns of the bull are proportionately much longer than the eland's.

It was the impalas, however, which gave us the greatest delight. Not because of stature—the ram is only 3 feet tall at the shoulder, and the ewe is even smaller. But impalas are beautifully proportioned and are neatly coated in short, glossy reddish-brown hair, and the long, slender horns of the male are gracefully lyrate. The impala is the most abundant antelope in the park, and, as if for our benefit, they flocked along our road by the thousands. It was this spectacle which led me to wonder if I was not dreaming and to fear that, if I were awakened, I would find myself back at my office desk. Even my South African friends—thoroughly familiar with Kruger Park—were impressed by the multitude.

Gradually the sandy road drew closer to Shingwedzie River whose life-giving water was the reason for the increasing swarm of wildlife. Near the paved ford, now completely dry two ragged native children were getting water. With their hands they dug through the sand and gravel. At a depth of about 30 inches, water flowed into the hole. Surprisingly, it was almost clear and quite cool. The youngsters filled their pots and started home.

Upriver, at a long pool where the water came to the surface, a huge troop of chacma baboons had congregated. Some were drinking while others sat reflectively on the sand among a scattered band of impalas—which seemed to pay no heed to the apes. Most of the baboons, however, were noisily inspecting a group of large trees. Some ran or jumped, screaming through the branches; others looked up from the ground. Great males barked as they swaggered among the smaller females, some of which had frightened-looking babies clinging to their backs. As the shadows lengthened, the apes were trying to decide on their sleeping quarters for the night. The question of safety from their most deadly enemy, the leopard, was paramount and this was causing a heated argument.

We came to a roadside warning sign in Afrikaans: "Olifante is gevaarlik! Pasop! Blei in u kar." Nel translated: "Elephants are dangerous! Keep your distance! Stay in your car." The words were hardly spoken when we rounded a bend and saw, crossing the road ahead, a herd of elephants.

We halted abruptly, and I was again advised: in the presence of elephants, keep your motor running and *never* approach closer than 200 feet. Inside this distance, an elephant is likely to charge. Even farther away a quick retreat may be essential at any moment. A stalled automobile offers about as much refuge from an infuriated or frightened elephant as a cardboard carton!

To my relief, these elephants were more than 200 feet away, and they continued to lumber ponderously but swiftly toward the river. Bulls with clean, long tusks moved like gigantic, silent tanks, their faces set in masks of sadness. Cows walked with more impatience, and beside or under some of them their calves trotted to keep up. Their trunks reached out, anticipating the delicious water, and great ears flapped forward and back.

After the last elephant had passed, we drove cautiously to an overlook to watch the herd at the open pool. Then, from the woods opposite and upriver, came a bachelors' club of five old bulls. They too were thirsty and eager for water, but they kept their dignity and moved like aldermen in a procession. Seeing the herd at the pool, and evidently sensing that the leader would resent any approach to his harem, the bachelors stopped. Then one of them began to dig through the sand for water. Kicking forward with his front feet, he threw out the sand and gravel in sprays. In a few minutes the hole was down to water. All five bulls then gathered in a circle, their heads in, and as water seeped into the depression, they took turns drinking. Apparently following some long established protocol, one by one, each elephant in turn sucked water into its trunk, curled it, and squirted the liquid into its open mouth.

For some time they relieved their thirst little by little, as the small water hole permitted. One elephant finally decided to take a shower and sprayed his back instead of his mouth. Whether this was considered a waste of water is uncertain, but the next bull shouldered the bather out of the circle. At once the two giants began a shoving match. With their sensitive trunks thrown up out of the way, they locked tusks and struggled. Hind legs were braced back and muscles strained while the thick gray-black hides stretched or folded in the most unexpected places. More than ever, the straining beasts looked like antediluvian monsters.

Finally, the smaller of the warriors began to lose ground. Breaking away suddenly, he ran. When he discovered that he was no longer being chased, he slowed to a quick shuffling walk and moved toward the forest. The shortest way to safety was blocked by a steep bank about 10 feet high. The outcast was unable to keep his footing on the slippery clay, and he skidded and fell back several times. At last, slowly and with tremendous effort, he inched his way up on "elbows and knees" while his conqueror trumpeted and swung his trunk menacingly—just to keep him on his way.

En route to Shingwedzie Rest Camp and supper, we passed several trees which had been pushed over by elephants. To knock down large, well-anchored trees, the elephant places his forehead against the trunk and rocks slowly with a fore-and-aft motion. Gradually, as the tree sways farther and farther, the elephant shoves harder and harder with each forward oscillation until the roots give way and the tree crashes to the ground. Sometimes the animal may take this means for venting a spite or "relieving" a toothache, but usually its objective is a meal of tender, fresh foliage or a couple of bushels of merula fruit. These acid-sweet, pale-yellow, plum-size fruits are refreshing not only to the elephant but to giraffes, antelopes, baboons, and mankind. If it becomes overripe, the fruit ferments and all partakers develop a delightful, exhilarated feeling.

Outside the camp gate, we saw several acres of mopane forest which had been devastated by elephants. The dense stand of scraggly trees about 30 feet high had been attacked repeatedly. Trees were uprooted and dismembered; every trunk and branch was splintered and broken. A tornado could have wrought no more destruction.

The camp consisted of about forty rondavels—round or square concrete-walled huts roofed with thatch—and several rectangular buildings for "amenities." Ranger Adendorf conducted us to a pair of rondavels, our sleeping quarters for the night, and we made ourselves at home.

As I started to write down my host of impressions, I was diverted by a flock of irridescent glossy starlings which searched for food near the doorway. Rudi identified for me some of the new and exotic-looking birds in the mopane trees: hornbills with large, curved beaks; lovely lilac-breasted rollers; weaverbirds which had hundreds of hanging nests in a tree nearby; and a gray lourie which harshly ordered, "Go-away, go-away," for an hour at a stretch. I thought of some other spectacular birds I had met that day for the first time: ostriches, sunbirds, hoopoes, and storks, vultures, and eagles of many species. Most were beautiful, some were grotesque (such as the enormous ground hornbill), and a few were ugly (like the hammerhead). I had seen birds that I had recognized easily —ducks and guinea fowl—and familiar species in entirely different plumages such as the several kinds of little kingfishers.

Darkness came before I had made more than a good start on my notes, but I was to have still another series of experiences. Unlike "paying visitors" to the park, who *must* stay within the fenced camps from sunset to sunrise, I was to have a tour by night. Raw, primitive Africa—the animals on the prowl!

Guided—and guarded—by Ranger Adendorf with his rifle, we drove slowly down the winding, sandy road through the soft, warm night. Our headlights made a tunnel of light, the sides shifting constantly as trees and shrubs cast flickering shadows ahead. At first, our ride was not very exciting. Cape hares, like small kangaroos, hopped away, their eyes reflecting red flashes as they glanced back toward the glare. A genet, looking like a cross between a weasel and a spotted cat, rushed across the road and took refuge under a fallen tree. A pair of huge porcupines, their foot-long quills erect, ran clumsily through the grass. In the bright light, the alternate bands of black and ivory rippled as the quills swayed and undulated under the exertions of the frightened animals. We were startled to glimpse apparently a thick-bodied serpent winding its way down the wheel track ahead. It turned out to be a family of mongooses, the half-dozen or more youngsters galloping along in close order, single file behind the parent. A tiny bush baby (thick-tailed lemur), only a few ounces in weight, put on an exhibition of its extraordinary leaping powers.

There were big-eyed night birds, also. Cape thick-knees, plovers whose swollen joints threaten to bend the wrong way but never do, trotted out of the road. Nightjars, startlingly like American nighthawks, flew up from the road at the last possible moment to avoid the car.

An elephant suddenly burst out of the trees, rushed across the roadway, and disappeared. It ran madly with its trunk thrown up, and it screamed in a wavering, high-pitched voice. That hysterical shriek bespoke the creature's terror; it also inspired terror. It was incongruous that such a huge, powerful animal could be frightened witless merely by the lights of an automobile.

As we paused to listen to the fading sounds of the elephant, we became conscious of other night noises. Small nameless creatures rustled in the dead grass. A leopard coughed, a short, harsh sound that it repeated several times. Some distance off, a long-drawn moan began far down the scale, then ran up to a high pitch and stopped. This was followed by insane cackles from several throats—hyenas around a lion's kill. Slow, heart-rending howls ending in yapping barks came repeatedly from jackals waiting for the leavings.

As I reflected on a variety and abundance of meat eaters, I was struck by the fact that here in Africa, for the first time in my experience, I was seeing something that approached the "balance of Nature." We had tallied thousands of antelopes that day, at the end of the most difficult period of the year for wildlife—the seven-month dry season. Yet we had not seen a single weak, emaciated, or crippled animal. Any ill or weakened creature would have been run down, killed, and devoured by the "sanitary brigade"—the ever-hungry and ever-searching carnivores. I thought of American parks, where mountain lions, wolves, and other predators have been practically eliminated and where underfed deer and antelopes may live for months before dying of starvation.

I had one final and momentous experience before returning to camp. As we rounded a sharp bend, our car headlights swung back to the road and onto—lions! Even my companions became excited as all four counted at once, "—three, four—seven—nine, ten! No, *eleven*!" Eleven great, tawny lions, sprawled haphazardly flat on their sides in the warm sand of the open road.

We stopped. Were the guidebooks right? Was it true that man's scent is obliterated by the fumes of gasoline and hot oil? Is it correct that lions will not attack an automobile? This was a test!

One by one the lions raised their heads. They rose slowly and reluctantly, stretched, and yawned. Moving stiffly to the roadside, they dropped sleepily into the grass. Most of them put their heads on their paws and apparently resumed their interrupted nap. This was my introduction to the King in the wild. Despite many subsequent meetings with much more wide-awake lions throughout the length of Africa, this moment remains most vivid in my memory.

It was almost midnight when we returned to our rondavels at Shingwedzie Camp. For all of us, it had been a long and tiring but highly satisfying day. As I thanked my friends, who had done so much to further my understanding and enjoyment, I assured them, "This has been my most memorable day. This has been a day of discovery—*my* discovery of Africa's wildlife!"

MARGARET M. NICE

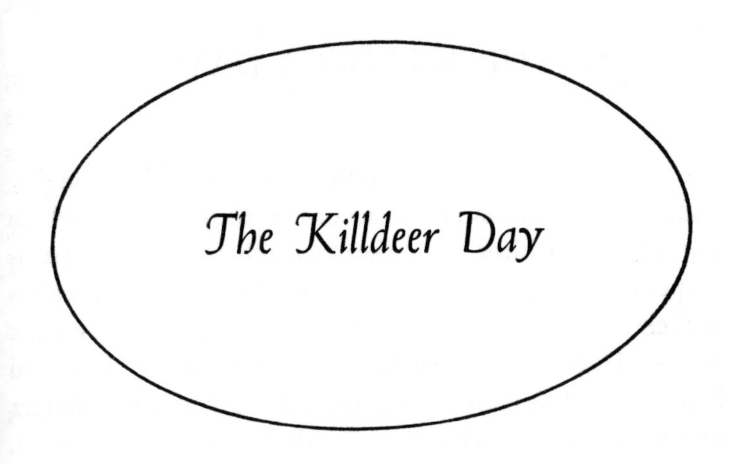

The Killdeer Day

Margaret Morse Nice (Mrs. L. B. Nice) of Chicago, Illinois, was born in Amherst, Massachusetts, December 6, 1883. She was graduated from Mount Holyoke College, worked for her Master's degree in biology at Clark University, Worcester, Massachusetts, and in 1909 married a fellow student at Clark who became a professor of physiology. She and her family have lived at Norman, Oklahoma, in Columbus, Ohio, and, since 1936, in Chicago. In Ohio, Mrs. Nice conducted an intensive six-year study of the life history of the song sparrow. Her researches were published in two volumes by the Linnean Society of New York City, and the work won for her the Brewster Medal of the American Ornithologists' Union, awarded for the best publication of the year on birds of the Western Hemisphere. She has been President of the Wilson Ornithological Society, President of the Chicago Ornithological

Society, and Associate Editor of The Wilson Bulletin *and of* Bird-Banding. *She has written 6 books, more than 230 ornithological articles, and some 2,800 reviews of ornithological books and papers.*

THE KILLDEER DAY

BABY birds can be roughly divided into two main classes according to the state in which they hatch. Songbirds, for example, hatch after short incubation periods, blind and nearly naked, unable to do much besides lift their heads and open their bills for food brought by their parents. These are altricial birds or "nest-sitters." Precocial chicks or "nest-quitters" on the other hand, hatch after longer incubation periods, well covered with down, their eyes open, and ready before many hours to follow their parents on land or water, and even, many of them, to find their own food.

I had watched the course of behavior development in various altricial birds—redstarts and serins in Austria under the guidance of Konrad Lorenz, the noted specialist in bird behavior—and a number of species of birds in America. Song sparrows, for instance, do little in their first week but eat and grow; then with their eyes open they start to stretch and preen, and three days later leave the nest, well covered with feathers but still unable to fly. They gradually acquire the skills needed for independent life and at the age of four weeks are on their own.

The opportunity to study the early behavior of precocial chicks, however, came through the Delta Waterfowl Research Station at Delta, Manitoba. There my daughter Constance and I watched many of those little birds hatch—ducklings, grebes, coots, spotted sandpipers, and others. We found much the same sequence of events in these precocial chicks as in the altricial ones, the most striking difference being that the precocial chicks passed through the early developmental stage in hours rather than days.

Now in our third season at Delta we were eager to see a baby killdeer hatch. There was a nest nearby containing two eggs, and this we visited daily. One morning it held a very new baby and an egg. Leaving the chick, we took the egg to the laboratory.

The egg was not pipped, but the baby killdeer within it was not idle. When I held it to my ear I heard a little squeak and gentle *tchipping* sounds. I put it in the incubator of our laboratory and examined it often. At one-fifteen I counted fifty-six *tchips* in a minute. Ten minutes later there was a little hole, and inside it the tip of a little bill was plainly visible. The peeps became louder. I took the egg out of the nest; the chick fell silent at the parents' alarm calls, but *yeeped* immediately afterwards. No more progress was made during the day or evening. I left it in the incubator with the fervent hope that the infant would sleep soundly.

When I woke the next morning about four o'clock, it seemed very early to start the day. Presently, however, I got up and reached the laboratory at four-thirty, just as the sun was rising. I rushed to the incubator and greatly to my relief found the killdeer egg still unhatched. It looked no different from the night before except that the bill was no longer to be seen. The chick inside *tchipped* and peeped mildly.

I turned to my other charges and was eagerly welcomed. There were six little coots a day to a week old, five Franklin's gulls one to four days old, a sora rail of ten days, a ruddy duckling of three days, and four very young grebes—pied-billed, eared, and western. I weighed all of these and was gratified to find that every one had gained since the morning of the preceeding day. All had to be fed, and by this time about an hour had passed. The egg looked about the same, and I wondered whether it would be a good idea to go out and visit a spotted sandpiper nest we had been observing.

But at five-forty, as I examined the egg once more, I quickly changed my mind. The baby killdeer was pushing the egg open, and twelve minutes later it hatched in my hand! Then began a wonderful day—an intensive watch of its every movement for the next seven hours.

It was rather a bedraggled little object, the down damp and close to the body. Its eyes were closed, but two minutes later they opened. The chick gave peeps, one at a time, fourteen in a minute; these had a killdeer quality. At nine minutes of age it sat up, as if ready to run, then took a brief nap. At eighteen minutes it called seventeen times in a minute; some of the notes sounded loud and unhappy, others soft and contented. The chick cuddled down in my left hand, and I sketched it with my right. At forty-three minutes of age it wagged its tail for the first time. Four minutes later it gave its first yawn. And at fifty-one minutes the young killdeer *bobbed* its head after the fashion of its kind. The next minute it sat up alert, picked at a spot on the shelf, and walked about on its tarsi. It lay down by a pied-billed grebe in the old pintail nest in a basin that held the youngest chicks. I could see that it had but one dark band across its breast in contrast to the two bands of the adult killdeer.

When one hour and three minutes old, the killdeer made an incomplete preening motion, reaching partway under its wing. And then it did something very strange—while it was sitting on its tarsi, its legs and feet went *pat-pat-pat!* Three minutes later the killdeer stood up on its feet for an instant, then snuggled down by the eared grebe. At one hour and twenty-five minutes it actually touched its side for an instant in preening. Five minutes later it walked on its feet with little nervous steps; another six minutes and it ran along 7 inches on its feet. It preened under its wing and fell over.

At two hours of age, our youngster was nearly dry and was looking more and more like a baby killdeer with dark lines around its forehead and neck and a dark line down the middle of its back. It pushed under the western grebe and rested a few minutes, pecked at tiny bits of frozen fish on the paper, took one up, and dropped it. It pecked at little spots on the shelf and at the end of the eared grebe's bill. Then, at two hours and six minutes of age, it picked up a bit of fish and *ate it!* Soon afterwards I was eating too—breakfast brought me by Constance. She took charge of feeding our menagerie and later brought me dinner.

The little killdeer grew more and more active—bobbing its head, wagging its tail, progressing sometimes on its tarsi, again on the feet, calling loud *dees* or whispering *sees* when resting by another baby bird or in my hand. In its fourth hour we offered it a small snail in the forceps; it tasted the snail but evidently did not like it, for the young killdeer scratched its face. It scratched "directly," like a chicken, not in the approved plover style, for members of this family drop one wing and bring the leg over it, like a robin, or like a dog that scratches its head with its hind leg over the front one.

The baby killdeer preened itself, stretched both legs back while lying on the shelf, then rose and stretched both legs up. Later it gave a leap and a cry as the western grebe took hold of its foot. We offered it a small leech, and this it swallowed. It accepted a mosquito but promptly scratched it out again from its bill. At five hours, it was running strongly on its feet. And at seven hours and forty minutes old, it dipped its bill into the water dish and drank. All in all, it was the most precocious little bird we had ever watched.

Now was the time to restore it to its family. When we arrived at the killdeer's nest from which we had taken the egg, we placed the youngster in the empty nest, where it crouched, while its parents shrieked and cavorted nearby. We hastily climbed to the roof of the lodge nearby and from there caught sight of the baby that had hatched the day before. Down we hurried and put our chick near its brother. We quickly retreated again to the roof, and from there we saw a parent brooding. Ten minutes later, both chicks came out from under the parent and started foraging; we noted that our chick was less venturesome than its elder brother. Soon the parent was back hovering the babies. We watched the parent bob twenty times in half a minute. With its disruptive plumage, it hardly looked like a bird.

Thus our lovely little chick forgot us—its foster parents and the strange associations of its earliest hours. For three weeks the family remained together, but at four weeks only one parent and one young bird were still on the nesting area.

The pattern of development had followed in general the usual course shown by the precocial chicks we had studied: attainment of locomotion on the tarsi, then on the feet; appearance of the different comfort movements; crouching when alarmed; exploratory pecking; and picking up of food and eating it. Three behavior patterns, however, were of particular interest, one peculiar to killdeer, and two characteristic of the family of plover. Further experience threw more light on these patterns.

A week later, we watched three other killdeer chicks from hatching for three, five, and six and a half hours. These birds were far less active than our first had been, spending most of their time napping. Yet they gave us information on two of the points in which we were especially interested. They first bobbed their heads at one hour and twenty minutes, one hour and twenty-nine minutes, and three hours and six minutes. One of them went *pat-pat-pat* on its tarsi at one hour and twenty-five minutes and later did the same three times during its fourth hour; another *pat-pat-patted* at two hours and forty-five minutes.

Bobbing the head is a striking characteristic of the killdeer, possibly indicative of the generally nervous, excitable nature of this species. The *pat-pat-patting* of the chicks before they were able to run would seem to be a foreshadowing of the characteristic gait of many plovers that habitually run in little spurts, then suddenly stop.

Finally it was of great interest to note that the first chick scratched its head from *under the wing*. The following year we kept a little killdeer from hatching to the age of seven weeks; it did not adopt the plover style of scratching *over the wing* until it was eight days old.

It had been a richly rewarding experience watching the development of our first killdeer from a comparatively helpless, odd-looking mite into a beautiful, fluffy, active little chick well able to find its own food and to adapt successfully to life in the wild with its family.

STANLEY P. YOUNG

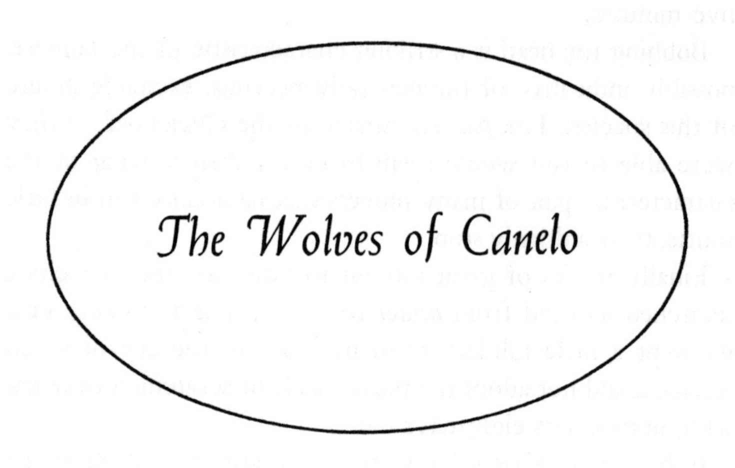

The Wolves of Canelo

Biologist Stanley P. Young has for his whole life been concerned with the study of wildlife. He was born in Astoria, Oregon, October 30, 1889, the youngest son of the late Honorable Benjamin Young, pioneer salmon packer on the lower Columbia River. An alumnus of the Universities of Oregon and Michigan, he entered the Bureau of Biological Survey, a predecessor agency of the Fish and Wildlife Service, in 1917 as a hunter of predatory animals, following brief association with the Forest Service. Through the years, he served as chief of various divisions, including wildlife refuges, game management, and predator control, and in 1939 he joined the Branch of Wildlife Research, compiling records and preparing manuscripts.

On his sixtieth birthday, Mr. Young retired after forty-two years with the government Service; the Department of the Interior has presented him with its highest honor, the Distinguished Serv-

ice Award for "outstanding contributions as administrator and mammalogist." He has, since retirement, been a collaborator writing monographs for the Fish and Wildlife Service.

Mr. Young is a member of the American Society of Mammalogists, the Explorers' Club of New York, the Outdoor Writers' Association of America, and the Cosmos Club in Washington, D.C. He is the author or coauthor of seven books, among them The Wolves of North America, The Puma, Mysterious American Cat, *and* The Clever Coyote. *He lives in Chevy Chase, Maryland.*

THE WOLVES OF CANELO

In 1918, I began work as a United States government hunter along the Arizona-Mexican boundary in the county of Santa Cruz. Here lived a goodly population of wolves that crossed the international border from Sonora, Mexico, into Arizona. One of the greatest economic losses these wolves were causing was in the killing of young Hereford bull calves, valued at close to one thousand dollars each the moment they were born. These calves were sold almost immediately after weaning, to purebred-cattle growers, or were raised until two years old when, of course, the price was much higher for them as breeding bulls.

In widely separated parts of the western ranges of the United States, a number of individual gray wolves have lived that were considered "renegades" because of individual peculiarities in their depredations on livestock and game. Each finally drew so much attention that it was singled out for elimination, as might be a human criminal. The stockmen knew these wolves either by sight, by peculiarities of their tracks, or by the characteristic manner in which each attacked, mutilated, or killed its prey.

Those in a position to know held the opinion that never did more intelligent wolves exist. During the long time they held forth on the open ranges, they became wise beyond the average gray wolf through their constant experience with the man-made devices employed for capturing them. At times, they seemed to be possessed of uncanny intelligence in avoiding steel traps and detecting various posioned baits, despite the variety of methods used in attempting to give the lethal drugs to them.

These wolves with marked individualities–generally scarred or with other defects received from the stockmen and trappers –earned such nicknames as "Old Lefty" because of a missing left leg, "Three Toes" because of toes lacking on front or rear feet, or "Big Foot" because of the size of the front-foot track it left along a travelway. Some of the wolves with defects appeared to become more serious killers because they were so handicapped.

After much study of them, directly or indirectly, I was later to discover that, in spite of what appeared to be almost superintelligence in avoiding capture, their final elimination was caused by a regularity of their habits which was the weak point in their armor and provided the main opportunity upon which the hunters of wolves capitalized.

The wolf has a runway or circuit, correctly referred to also as a hunting route, a travelway giving access to the territory of a given pair or family. It generally runs through more or less open country. It may consist in part of trails of game, cattle, or sheep, of old wood roads, or even highways in thinly settled areas; it may traverse dry washes and canyons and cross low watershed divides or swamps. In cold countries, frozen lakes may become part of a winter runway. Wolves have been known to use runways covering a circuit of considerably more than 100 miles.

The width of the run may be from a few feet, as where it coincides with a cow, horse, or game trail, to a mile or more where the animals are hunting. Along the runway one often finds that high points are used as vantages by them for observation. The wolves also use these sites for playing or resting.

On these runways, wolves have what are commonly referred to as "scent posts," or places where they come to urinate or defecate. These are on or near the bases of bunch grasses, on bushes, or on an old weathered animal carcass. These scent posts may be recognized by the scratches made on the ground near them by the wolf after it has relieved itself. This habit of having scent posts and of scratching near them is similar to that noted in dogs. The scratching by the wolf after defecating or urinating is possibly the vestige of a former habit of burying the dung or urine.

As wolves pass over their runways, they stop at these posts, invariably voiding urine, and often feces as well. As with the dog, the excreta contain much hair and bones which serve to indicate their food. Fnding these scent posts is of prime importance in trapping wolves, for it is at such points that traps should be set. If such posts cannot be found, then one can be readily established. When the travelway of the wolf has been definitely ascertained, scent made from the wolf's urine, and gall, to which is added the anal glands, mixed with 1 ounce of glycerine to every 3 ounces of the former, plus 1 grain of corrosive sublimate to keep it from spoiling, makes a powerful lure for a wolf. A scent post is established by dropping some of this on a few clusters of weeds, spears of grass, or stubble of low brush. The trap is then set at this point. Any number of such scent stations can thus be placed along a wolf travelway.

Time consumed in finding a natural wolf scent post is well

spent, for the success of a trap set depends upon its location. Wolves cannot be caught unless traps are set and concealed where the animals will step into them. If traps are placed where the animals are not accustomed to stop on their travelways, the chances are that they will pass them by on the run. Even if a wolf should detect the scent, the fact that it is in an unnatural place may arouse his suspicions and cause him to become shy and make a detour. Often the fresh tracks of shod horses along wolf runways are sufficient to cause the wolf to leave the trail for some distance. A lone wolf is much more cautious than a pack of wolves running together.

The shape of the wolf runway, or travelway, is generally an irregular circle, the diameter of which may be between 20 and 60 miles. Its extent depends on the amount of food available. In an area heavily stocked with game, cattle, or sheep, the runway is relatively small, but where food is scarce it is proportionately larger. Occasionally one finds what may be termed scouting courses, where wolves make short detours from the main runway. These eventually join the main runway again and are apparently deviations made in search of prey.

While traveling their runways, wolves move, usually in a counterclockwise direction, in a slow, regular trot, as they do in cross-country travel. They often run along sandy arroyos, washes, or soft dirt, possibly because these places are of less wear and tear on their footpads. In snow, where the going is difficult, wolves step in each other's tracks so exactly that it often is impossible to tell how many of the animals are traveling together.

In the early fall of 1917 I had an opportunity to thoroughly trace a well-established wolf runway. It was used at that time by two wolves—a male and a female, which can be distinguished by the size of their tracks; the female generally makes the smaller. Their starting point was approximately 20 miles south of Parker Canyon Post Office, Santa Cruz County,

Arizona. This point is about 14 miles south of the Mexican boundary in the state of Sonora. The wolves traveled northward and out of Mexico, a little west of Parker Canyon, crossing the San Rafael Valley to the foot of the Canelo (sometimes spelled Canela or Canille) Hills. At this point they swung into a deep canyon and headed for the crossing of the Canelo Hills known as Cherry Creek Pass. Going through this pass, they ran along the divide of the Canelo Hills, which bore a well-defined trail used by livestock and cowboys, until they reached the head of Turkey Creek. There they swung northward through the narrow valley of Turkey Creek, a distance of approximately 4 miles, turned west, again crossed the Canelo Hills, and headed toward the Patagonia Mountains. When about 12 miles west of the Canelo Hills, they turned south once again toward the Mexican boundary, which they crossed some 10 miles farther west than on the northward stretch. These wolves passed Cherry Creek Pass and the Divide with regularity every nine days. Their circuitous route totaled about 70 miles.

I noted in studying this particular pair of wolves that the male had a middle toe missing from his right front foot, obvious when he was traveling the runway over soft ground which definitely showed his track. And, too, it was this track that was always in evidence around many of the Hereford bull calves and other killings. Furthermore, it had been an animal much sought by trapping, and chasing it with dogs, and no one knows how many ounces of poison, such as strychnine and cyanide had been inserted into meat baits in attempting this wolf's riddance from the range.

Many weeks elapsed before I made a fortunate discovery while scouting the runway where it narrowed in going through Cherry Creek Pass some 6,000 feet in elevation. Here was also a deer and peccary trail not over 4 feet wide. It was flanked on each side for a distance of 60 or more feet by low pinyon trees and manzanita bushes. In all my coverage of this part of the runway, I had failed to notice a short detour by them which led some 30 feet at an oblique angle from the main runway to a flat limestome rock. This flat rock seemingly served as a bedding or resting spot at times for both wolves. It also provided a good vantage point for them to view the entire San Rafael Valley below. As no scent posts were in evidence, it seemed the height of folly to establish one for fear of arousing their suspicions. Instead, I carefully placed a "blind set" of two traps. Each was fully concealed at the point where the wolves, single file, stepped from the ground up onto the rock. Here seemed a two-way chance to capture them, for if the wolf missed in going up into the rock, chances were good it would step into the trap in taking the detour for a return to its main runway. My guessing was correct, but only partially so, for the female led, and she was the first one of the pair I caught.

The trap that she stepped into was anchored by 8 feet of quarter-inch linked chain, and a steel stake pin, made of gas pipe, which was 18 inches long and 1 inch in diameter, driven flush into the ground. As the trap closed on her foot, she apparently gave such a terrific lunge as to pull the stake pin out of the ground in her attempt to escape. To assist in determining what direction she took, I got two hounds, belonging to two cooperating stockmen who joined me, and put them on her trail. The dogs flushed her, approximately 200 yards from the place the trap caught her, where she had hidden and apparently had lain down in a small but heavily covered thicket. From this point, she scrambled nearly 500 feet to the top of the watershed, turned south into Cherry Creek, and finally came to the edge of the eastern side of San Rafael Valley, south of Canelo Hills Pass.

Following the trailing hounds, and mounted on horses, we three were led a chase through almost impossible country for about 5 miles, with the wolf well in advance. As the running wolf reached the edge of the valley, we were able, for the first time, to see her with the dogs not far behind. Every time the wolf leaped, the steel stake pin swung around and whacked her on the hind quarters. The chase continued well out on the valley floor, where we got an opportunity to take a shot at her with a .38-caliber Colt revolver.

To give some idea of the strength and endurance of this female, the weight of the trap, chain, and stake pin approximated nearly 7 pounds, and the chase had extended more than 6 miles. Yet, with all this encumbrance, the wolf was able to keep well ahead of the pursuing hounds while in the dense thickets before reaching the valley floor, and there was able to fight off the two hounds as they caught up with her. We all surmised that had we not come to the dogs' aid with the revolver, this wolf would have licked them and again made her escape.

After we had killed the female, seventeen days passed before I again saw the track of the male of this pair. From all indications he was seeking the female. It is well known that strong affection exists in a wolf family, and the tracking evidence along the runway and on the detour showed much bewilderment by the male and gave every indication that he was hunting his lost mate. The usual shyness of the male, noted heretofore, seemed to have disappeared.

Fresh scent that I prepared from the trapped female proved this wolf's undoing. Three days later, or twenty days after the female's capture, he stepped into a trap concealed at a scent post they had established where the detour turned off the main runway toward the loafing rock. I saved the pelts of these two wolves, and they are in the mammal collection of the United States National Museum in Washington, D.C., where they have been for more than forty years.

Long ago, I wrote that my regard, respect, and—yes, even affection—for the most intelligent of all North American predators, the wolf, had its beginning as I have narrated here.

Circumstances later made it possible for me to gain additional knowledge of this animal throughout most of its former and present North American range. During this field experience, I camped for long intervals in the habitat of this wild, predatory creature. Thus, I literally lived with it and meticulously studied its habits. The more I delved into its life history, the greater became my admiration for wolves, particularly for their ability to avoid those mechanical devices of man used for capturing and killing them. When one becomes acquainted with the complete life cycle of the wolf, coupled with its place in world-wide history, I am satisfied that it will appeal to students or anyone interested in natural history.

Hated, reviled and feared, hunted, trapped, and poisoned down through the centuries, always with a bounty on its head —to the extent of millions of dollars—as a symbol of the devil, and finally as the progenitor of the domestic dog, man's best friend, no other predator rivals the wolf in its profound effect exerted on human affairs.

May the wolf never cease to have a place in our North American fauna—a condition that, I am sure, can be made possible in view of the vast domain yet remaining in North America where it roams at will, and where its presence is not in conflict with human welfare. In other regions of scant human population, it may still be tolerated as a useful member of the wildlife community. To that end, I have through the years given every support.

Finally, it was the trapping of the wolves, around which this account is based, that changed my whole course of life. I gave up what might have been a more lucrative livelihood as a mining geologist, or as a professor of geology, for that of a naturalist with, at times, a near-starvation existence. But what happiness it has brought me in later life!

PAUL L. ERRINGTON

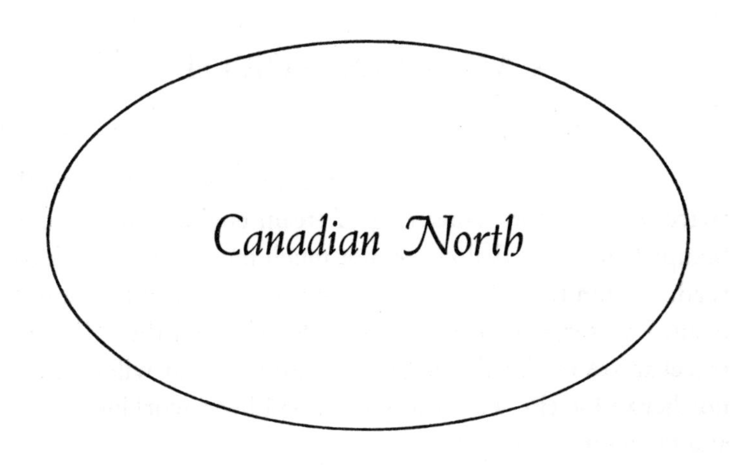

Dr. Paul L. Errington, Professor of Zoology at Iowa State University (formerly Iowa State College), was born June 14, 1902, on a farm near Bruce, South Dakota. He was graduated with the degree of Bachelor of Science at South Dakota State College and received his Doctor of Philosophy degree in zoology at the University of Wisconsin, where he was one of the first students in wildlife management of Professor Aldo Leopold, "father" of this science. He was a Guggenheim Fellow and Visiting Professor at Lund University, Sweden, in 1958 and 1959. His principal research has been with American fur bearers—mink, muskrats, and other marsh denizens; game birds, especially bobwhite quail; predatory animals and their effect on their prey; and studies of the rise and fall of animal populations. He has written three book-length technical bulletins published by Iowa State College and hundreds of

scientific and popular articles based on his researches. His book Of Men and Marshes *(The Macmillan Company, 1957) is the story of his love for American marshes and their wild inhabitants.*

CANADIAN NORTH

IT was the first of June, and the twice-a-week train—consisting of steam engine and caboose—bumped and rocked along on not much more than a corduroy road. Within the caboose, with my canoe and camping equipment, I was going to International Falls. From there I would travel across the border and on up into the great wilderness of northern Ontario. This was what I had been working toward and saving my money for.

My cash resources back then in the early nineteen twenties totaled about five hundred dollars—trap-line dollars, axework dollars, savings from hard, ten-hour-day labor with hoes, shovels, pitchforks, crowbars, wheelbarrows. I had a high school diploma, and I was also, at nineteen, something of a veteran hunter and trapper, having started hunting and trapping as a serious business at the beginning of my teens. The previous fall and winter had given me seven months of hunting and trapping in northern Minnesota's Big Bog country, northeastward from Upper Red Lake.

I wanted to be a naturalist, and a youngster who wanted to be a naturalist forty years ago had a very limited choice in ways of making a living. The sole professional opportunity that I could see for becoming a naturalist lay in a life at least partly dependent upon hunting and trapping.

Furthermore, I liked the freedom of a hunter and trapper's

life in the wild out-of-doors—the freedom that was still possible as of forty years ago. I wanted to hunt and trap and live off the land, to breathe clean air and to enjoy the beauties of frost and sundogs and landscapes having naturalness left in them. Without having any desire to be any sort of recluse—I liked solitude as long as I did not get too much of it—I could endure loneliness when needing to and took pride in being a wilderness man or, at any rate, in having a start on being a wilderness man.

Also, I can confess to a romanticism that gave me a liking for the physical dangers of a wilderness life. I would talk down the dangers to my worrying mother, but I knew that they existed. I knew the danger in a glancing axe blade but felt confident in retaining some control of the axe even when it glanced, and I liked to talk about it to people other than my mother. I liked to talk about the danger of going through thin or rotten ice, about the mishaps that could befall one out there all alone, about storms and hardships.

But I never did anything I considered really foolhardy—I just had a taste for chance-taking that might come close to the edge.

Firearms I treated with great respect.

En route to International Falls, I looked from the caboose windows at the settlers' clearings and the few small towns with frame and log buildings that we passed through. On snowshoes, I had gotten into some of this same country near the railroad the winter before, but my trapping headquarters had been many miles from any railroad and many miles from what could have been called much of an automobile road. It had been more in backwoods than in wilderness, but some of the spaces where nobody lived had been extensive. I had seen areas having no visible trace of people, conceivably areas in which no other white man had ever been. Although it had been no wilderness comparable to what I was heading for on past International Falls, the Big Bog had, I felt, given me in seven months an introduction to a North Woods type of wilderness, a minimum of apprenticeship for the Canadian North.

The winter before, Big Bog temperatures had gotten down below 40 degrees below zero, and snow had accumulated in depths up to 5 feet on the level. Northern Ontario surely could not beat that kind of winter very much. In the Big Bog, I had been accustomed to covering a trap line during the daylight hours and then, if I wanted to, prowling most of the night seeking an adventure with wolves. I felt that I had all of the durability that northern Ontario would require of me.

The lumbering industry dominated the economy of the area I rode through on the way to International Falls. Through the caboose windows, I looked at horses and teamsters, at sawmills, piles of cut lumber, loaded flatcars on sidings, storekeepers, people standing around station platforms. At International Falls were the largest piles of logs—spruce pulpwood—that I ever saw. Spread-out waters at the mouth of Rainy River were covered by rafts of logs.

The view was northern but not northern enough to suit me.

Soon after entering Canada at Fort Frances from International Falls, I came up against a dismaying reality. I could not attain the requisite legal status to obtain resident hunting and trapping licenses before winter began, and I did not have anywhere nearly sufficient money to pay nonresident fees and still buy a winter's provisions. If I were to winter in any remote wilderness, I would have to reach it and be established well before freeze-up in a snug camp, with plenty of provisions and game cached, plenty of wood cut, and a working familiarity with my hunting and trapping territory.

The Royal North West Mounted Police suggested that I

might work at a job somewhere until I qualified as a resident. Or, without any licenses, or with only a fishing license, I might look over the country, asking advice at Hudson's Bay Company and R.N.W.M.P. posts. The police advised me to take along enough to eat and watch out for dangerous waters.

The police were nice to me, and I left their office at Fort Frances feeling grateful and, at the same time, with certain underlying doubts. I had a disquieting feeling that my Big Bog experience might not be adequate preparation for what I was planning to do.

The area that interested me above all others was known as Patricia. I had read that this was as wild as any region of Canada and that it had lots of game and fur. From descriptions, I believed it the ideal objective for one of my tastes. The prospect of going to it was nothing less than enchanting. And, on the map, it looked more accessible than many other attractive blank spaces in the Canadian North.

I did not know exactly how to reach it but reasoned that I could follow main water courses and work along the side of James Bay. Nothing about this promised to be easy, but such a travel route might be possible.

For the first exploration trip, the best bet seemed to be to travel by train to Longlac, thence by canoe down the Kenogami River. The name Mammamattewa on the map might indicate a place worth heading for, as a preliminary try.

The view from the train illustrated what maps did not show. A vast wilderness burn—vast even in terms of Canadian vastness—was the landscape I watched for hours. Bare rock and charred tree trunks. There were more hours of a continuous succession of little lakes bounded by spruce-covered rocky hills. North of Lake Superior, almost every stream seemed to be a cascade half-choked with dead trees.

How did one travel by canoe in a place like that? Maybe one did not.

After unloading at Longlac and making camp near the railroad station for the coming night, I paddled over to a Hudson's Bay Company store that I could see on the other side of a lake. The waves were running 3 feet high but without whitecaps. Riding the troughs, I could manage the nearly empty canoe and still feel daring. The crossing gave me a workout and took out of me the stuffiness of the railroad travel.

In the morning, as I was rolling up the cruiser tent, the stationmaster came to ask if I wished to go with two Indians who were then starting for the town of Grant, which was about 40 miles to the northeast. I did wish to, and I got my light-travel outfit into the canoe just in time.

One of the Indians was a young man who spoke no English and paid no attention to me, but the older man was affable. As we paddled side by side, I asked the old Indian questions, and, when I ran out of questions, he did the talking. He said that he was seventy-five years old, that he had served in France during the war, and that he had lied about his age to get into the army.

His age was a joke to him. The recruiting people had not been particular about such things as long as a man could take care of himself. The old man could take care of himself. Despite a face about as wrinkled as even Indian faces get to be, he had strength and endurance left. At the beginning of a portage, I saw him heave onto his back and walk away with a pack the weight of which I estimated at 200 pounds.

He thought that I did pretty well, paddling alone, to keep up with them, paddling double. I was not overpaced in the actual paddling, but, when I had to make two trips to a portage—one carrying the canoe and another carrying the packsack, cruiser tent, and bedding—to the Indians' one trip, I had to work to catch up again when back on the water. When the Indians stopped for tea in the middle of the morning, I thought that I had better go on ahead of them and make up in advance some of the time lost on my two-trip portages. The old man told me to run the next two rapids and then portage around the third.

I ran one rapid, but, when I came to what I counted as the second rapid, it did not look right to me. I worked over toward the shore to be in a better position to get out of the current if I had to. The current helped—it took the canoe over to the shore and held it tight against the bank in a sparse willow thicket.

There I sat, looking at a rapid and thinking that the roar I was hearing must be from the rapid farther ahead that I was not to run. Still, I could see no inviting channel to run in the rapid directly ahead of me. I was sitting in the canoe trying to make up my mind where to run that rapid when the Indians came packing along the shore.

The old man asked me sharply what I was doing there. I replied that I was looking, got out, and started portaging.

In portaging around, I could see that there were no stopping places between the upper part and the roaring waters downstream. The Kenogami at that place was constricted into a long series of rapids, cascades, and falls, with great rocks and pouring water that no man could have expected to live through once he got into it.

The sight of it left me benumbed and with no immediate inclinations to be reflective in detail.

I remember another portage along the Kenogami. The trail of generations of portagers was worn hip-deep through the peaty accumulations of the forest floor, and in the places having firm mud in the trail were footprints of moose and wolves among the human tracks. In other places, the trail led over high rocks overlooking the white water of the river. Rocks and tree roots and fallen tree trunks had to be stepped over or gone around. Some of the rocky ledges over which the trail led were wet and slippery from the spray. I might have to steady myself by grabbing a limb or small tree trunk with one hand while hanging onto the canoe with the other hand.

Because of a slight leakiness, my 18-foot, canvas-covered canoe took up considerable water on that first day out, and, together with a carrying yoke hastily improvised from poles, it must have weighed substantially over 100 pounds. I weighed 140 and, on the longer portages, would be panting, and my legs would be wobbling, after the first quarter to half of a mile. It was, nevertheless, easier to keep panting and wobbling to the end of a long portage than to try to break up a carry with rests.

In one instance, after leaving the Kenogami to take a more cross-country route, I finished a portage having an estimated length of 2 miles, put down the canoe, and paddled across a narrow lake, only to find myself confronted by another long portage. My fatigue was so great from the portage just covered that I had a hard time getting the canoe back on my shoulders. When I got under way once more, I somehow staggered through this portage, too.

On the water again, however, I recovered quickly, but the Indians were so far ahead of me that I could no longer see them and had to do my own finding of portage trails. I had misgivings about this, for the trails were simply unmarked utility trails for northerners, never meant for tourists. I knew, broadly, the direction that the route had to take, sooner or later found what I had to find, and ultimately caught up with the Indians at another teatime.

My impression was that I portaged about 10 miles on that one day, but 10 miles was undoubtedly an overestimation. Such distances could be very easy to overestimate by a youngster carrying the loads that I had. But, even were my estimate to be halved, I still saw as much of portage trails from under a waterlogged canoe as I wanted to.

Along in the evening, while still a couple of hours short of Grant, we made camp, and I invited the Indians to share my cruiser tent with me, behind mosquito netting. This made a full cruiser tent, with two big Indians and me, but the mosquitoes of the darkness outside were becoming so savage that the old Indian admitted that he was glad to be inside.

We got along all right, and soon I was aware of daybreak.

Then, a splashing outside, and the old Indian made a low exclamation that I did not understand. He opened the mosquito netting and crawled out. There were three heavy, hanging reports, the sound of a body falling in water, some more splashing. I followed the young Indian out of the tent.

A yearling moose floated at the edge of the lake, about 50 feet away, and the old Indian was putting down a .38-.40 carbine. The Indians had needed dog food, and here it was. I built a fire while the Indians took a canoe to go out and do the butchering. Butchering under the circumstances was cutting off the hind legs, which had the meat concentrated in the most readily transportable form.

The morning mist cleared away from the woods and rocks and spruce-covered hills. The new day turned out to be still and hot. The Indians could not travel as fast with the moose meat as they had without it, and I had time to do some looking down through water at fishes lying deep below the surface. Water beetles traced endlessly back and forth. The sun grew hotter over the quiet water.

I would pick out targets for the bow of the canoe, and, with a quick stroke terminated by a flip of the paddle, would center the bow over a lily pad or run the bow between a pair of rush stems protruding out of the water. I would make little whirlpools with paddle strokes and watch the canoe glide as it left them behind.

All of us seemed to be getting somewhat lazy. The Indians had to stop for another tea before we reached Grant, toward the middle of the morning.

It took me until about the middle of June to acknowledge to myself that I did not have the means of doing in that year what I had come up into the wilderness to do—to live as a trapper. Meanwhile, I had seen a considerable portion of the Canadian North.

There had been more, much more, of the rock faces, burns, forests and wetlands, turbulent rivers, and names on maps that were names only of post offices. It was all the real North, and, at one pulpwood town where I stayed a night and most of a day, the people were so friendly that I was tempted to take a job there, but working at a lumber mill was still not what I had come up to do.

About then I acknowledged another reality: that I should do some more growing up before tackling, alone, a remote wilderness in the Canadian North.

I already had strength and toughness and stamina. I could endure hunger if I had to and could digest anything. I could sleep anywhere. When black-fly bites itched, I let them itch. I seemed able to keep my head in emergencies that progressed to the point of being recognizable emergencies.

Still, I needed more years. The idea did not please me, for I had long been touchy about my elders regarding me as just a kid and telling me that I needed years more than anything else.

I doubt if I would have admitted it out loud, but I had come to see that, in my case, there was no substitute for the years themselves in the process of growing up to be a man who could take care of himself wherever he went.

My mistaken judgment upstream from that rapid had been the one thing to bring me around to put it frankly to myself that the Canadian wilderness North was too dangerous for me at that stage of my development. I had probably been my closest to death right then, and, if I argued that the fault had not been mine, that I had gotten there through doing only what the Indian had told me to do, the unreassuring truth remained that I had not recognized a deadly danger. Veteran woodsman that I could consider myself to be, lack of years and the discretion of years could still betray me on a matter concerning which there could be no chance to try again and do better next time.

However gradually my attitude toward the romance of danger may have been changing in the process of my growing up, the experience of the rapid led to some sobering meditation. In that connection, among others, I was no longer disposed to maintain—as I frequently had earlier—that my life was mine, that, if I got killed, it would be nobody's business except my own.

Others did have some rights in me. I recalled my return after the winter in the Big Bog, when my Mother had exclaimed, "You are actually home!"—as if she had never expected to see me again. There had been the many nonrelatives who had put something in me, from small kindnesses to a great deal beyond anything their possible responsibilities toward me could have called for. For example, teachers, at the cost of inconvenience and extra work for themselves, had from time to time permitted me to stay out of school to trap and to make up my studies later—or to make up my studies in advance. They had actively encouraged me in my efforts to become a naturalist. They had talked with me in evenings. None of these people had made their personal investments in me so that I could waste my life dying in a rapid—or from starvation or in a tundra blizzard or in some other way before I was old enough to know better.

In my psychological metamorphosis at nineteen, I found myself coming up to another realization. Perhaps I should say that about this time, along with my developing views about the wrongness of taking unnecessary chances, I began to regard unnecessary chance-taking as professionally unbefitting. I was ashamed of the affair of the rapid. It had betrayed dubbishness of a sort that I could not excuse in myself—dubbishness that I should not have expected in an older, more mature man, even a man who had never seen a rapid before. Only a dub, I knew, took unnecessary chances in things that really counted.

The Canadian wilderness had neither an inimical nor a friendly aspect—only, out there in the vastnesses where no people lived, an impersonality and an unfeelingness that I often compared with interstellar space. If anything was there that could live, it lived; if it could not live, it did not.

Without my knowing the ecology of northern wildernesses as well as I would later, the impressions I had at nineteen as to enormous tracts being without much that a man could live on were, in the main, correct. A wilderness need not be full of game and fur merely because it is empty of people. The Canadian North could have its own kinds of emptiness in somewhat the same sense as the emptiness a mountain could have at timber line or higher. There could be expanses of not much more than water and rock, or of not much more than water, rock, bog, and forest, without much animal life except in special places.

In the special places, there might be trout, pike, moose, caribou, muskrats, grouse, squirrels, foxes, beavers, ducks, and hares living in abundance—though even the special places did not always have their abundances of animal life.

I knew where I would stand in that wilderness. I would live or die on the same terms as did the Indians, the wolves, the hares, the grouse, the chickadees, and the rest, living if I could and dying if I had to. I had better be using my head in what I did up there.

So I went back home to grow up some more.

In going back home, I was not giving up the Canadian North. I never did get to Patricia and never became a Canadian trapper, but I lived and traveled in or close to other Canadian wildernesses and northern wildernesses elsewhere—this after I had gained more understanding and expertness by first doing more living under conditions that allowed more leeway for the mistakes of inexperience.

The northern wilderness was beautiful, as the stars were beautiful. The northern wilderness offered no personal challenge to anyone except in so far as a person chose to make a challenge out of the fact that it was there. It was there, as were the stars, in magnificent impersonality.

In my scientific work, I saw more northern wilderness during my forties and fifties than during my teens and twenties, and some of it was in the Canadian North. I saw it traveling by auto, aircraft, and freight canoe as well as by paddling canoe and by foot trail.

I cannot say that all of this made me feel young again, for the travel had serious purposes, some of which I could not even have guessed in my earlier years; but, once in a while, I might have the feeling of almost being swept back into the years, of almost imagining myself a trapper again.

I might feel this way especially while comparing trapping tricks with an Indian in the Saskatchewan Delta or while eating a meal with some old-timer in a patrol cabin, away up somewhere beyond roads and railroads. When one old-timer told me of seeing seven otters in a single day on a canoe trip in my youthful dreamland of Patricia, I prickled all over at the thought of it.

Even in middle age, I dream of the District of Patricia where I have never been but I always know when I am there. There are the minor variations, but the essential patterns keep coming out so much the same way, in dreams that tend to recur about every year or so. I am young and jog along game trails by the hour without tiring, through the pine and spruce and white cedar, through the birch and aspen, over the rocks and around the edges of lakes. There is mist over the lily ponds where the moose feed; the rapids roar, and the water lies glassy in the quiet places; and neither mosquitoes nor flies bite, nor are any problems vexatious.

Or the full moon lights the snow and streaks it with shadows, while the wolves howl in the distance, and I feel like answering them and running on through the night, being a part of it all.

MYLES E. W. NORTH

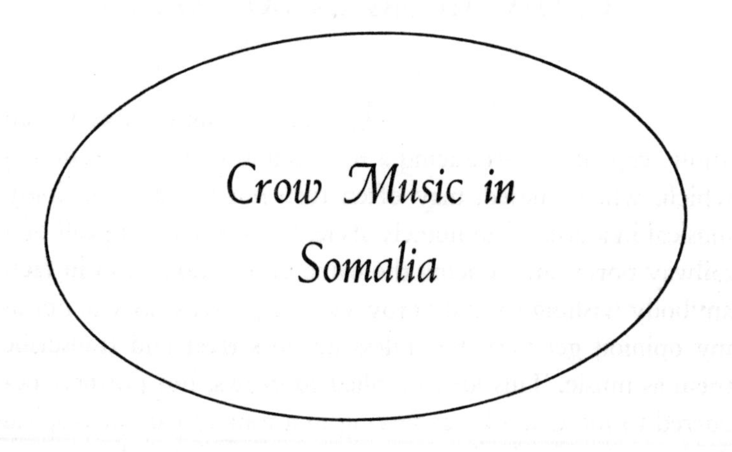

Myles E. W. North, Commissioner of Cooperative Development, Kenya, was born November 3, 1908, in Tokyo, Japan. He was educated in England and attended Corpus Christi College, Cambridge, from 1930 to 1934. He has been in Kenya since 1934, except during World War II, when he was with the British Military Administration of Italian Somaliland. Mr. North has been President of the Cambridge Bird Club, President of the East African Natural History Society, a member of the British Ornithologists' Union, and, in America, a member and Research Associate of the Laboratory of Ornithology, Cornell University, Ithaca, New York. He is the author of "Voices of African Birds,"

a 12-inch, long-playing record published by Cornell University, and is a coauthor, with Eric Simms, of Witherby's Sound-Guide to British Birds, *produced in England.*

CROW MUSIC IN SOMALIA

THE crow family is, as we all know, capable of producing a remarkable variety of sounds—which, when studied, may often turn out to be surprisingly musical in a crude and homely style, like the singsong call of a railway porter announcing the name of a station. And in fact, anybody wishing to study crow calls or porter calls will not in my opinion get very far unless he does treat and transcribe them as music. This idea (applied to crows, not porters) occurred to me when I was serving in a remote part of tropical Africa and was, of course, in no way original: I had a number of distinguished predecessors, one of whom I shall mention later. However, the idea, though unoriginal, enticed me into the most varied and interesting bit of research I have yet tackled and produced the pleasantest of consequences which I could never have foreseen, so it is not surprising that I regard crow music with favor.

Somalia—the scene of my idea—is a fine wild country in the eastern extremity of Africa. It was long an Italian colony but in 1960 proudly attained its independence. It was captured by Allied forces from the Italians early in World War II, as a result of which I, as a Civil Affairs Officer of the British military forces, was called upon to administer various districts of this country in a delightfully simple way. All I needed to ensure was that my Somalis kept the peace and obtained necessities in the shape of food and clothing.

To me, the best part of Somalia is the mountainous region of the northeast known locally as the Mijirtein and to the outside world as the Horn of Africa. Here I made many safaris, the nicest of which were when I visited the little coastal villages. Of these, the most attractive was Eil, on the east coast some 300 miles southward from Cape Guardafui.

Approaching Eil from the wide barren plateaus of the interior, you suddenly come upon the deep valley of the river Nogal. At this place it is no dry seasonal watercourse, but a clear-flowing stream—a rare and lovely thing in arid country such as this. Along one side of the valley there is a range of cliffs which terminates abruptly over the sea, overlooking Eil village, in a veritable gargoyle of a headland. In 1943 and 1944, these cliffs contained some fine breeding birds—including the great black Verreaux's eagle, *Aquila verreauxii*, which carried little dik-dik antelopes to its nest, and that rare bird the Somaliland pigeon, *Columba olivae*, whose nest site I found in a cave above the cliffs. I may be the only ornithologist to have experience of the breeding of this species.

Also, there nested and roosted on these cliffs the fan-tailed raven, *Rhinocorax rhipidurus*, whose shrill clear falsetto voice is a characteristic sound of the Horn of Africa. I had been interested previously in birdcalls for many years, transcribing them by the time-honored method of verbal imitation. Now this raven had a number of calls—a high, clear, and sustained *keh;* a *kair*, falling in pitch; a jangled *kerr* of excitement; and so forth—but any of these calls appeared liable to vary in pitch through as much as an octave; that is, *keh* might in deeper versions be *kah* or *koh*. It seemed obvious to me that when dealing with complexities of this sort, mere verbal imitations were inadequate, which impelled me to try music. Here I feel I was lucky to start with a simple voice like a crow's instead of getting bewildered by, say, a warbler's. I had with me a little wooden musical pipe called a descant recorder, an instrument of ancient lineage, by the way, much beloved of Pepys. Since this could produce a reasonably accurate chromatic scale, I wondered if I could locate the pitches of the ravens' calls on it?

One evening in July, 1944, I went to a place where plenty of ravens assembled and called prior to roosting. I sat down on a boulder to listen and experiment. The high, clear *keh* seemed a suitable start: what was its pitch? The recorder showed it to be B. Then I tried other calls until I had forgotten the pitch of this first one, after which I did another check on the *keh* and found, to my jubilation, that it was once again B. I made further tests with the various calls of this bird and found the results reasonably consistent. It was this experiment which started me off with music as a method of studying bird song.

I little realized, however, what I had got involved with! All sorts of technical problems at once cropped up, and it took five years of research before I could feel that I had attained a passably satisfactory solution. For instance, it seemed to me that orthodox staff notation, with its five-line staff and its key signatures, was unduly clumsy for field work, though it did at least show relative pitch by the position of the notes on the paper. Tonic sol-fa, on the other hand, appeared more suitable but did not show relative pitch like a staff did. Therefore, it seemed to me that a hybrid notation with the advantages of both systems should be worked out, and that this must be quick to operate and as foolproof as possible. Again, a matter which intrigued me was why, when I listened to a birdcall, this usually insisted upon presenting itself to my ear as if it were approximately in a musical key. Could the bird itself have a sense of key, or was it merely myself applying my own sense of key to what might well be purely fortuitous pitch intervals?

Eventually it transpired that this second solution was the right one, since I found that I "keyed" obviously fortuitous mechanical sounds, like the tinkle of a series of drops of water. I consider it advantageous to hear a birdcall in the coherent musical pattern that a key produces, since I find this so much easier to comprehend than a random unkeyed series of notes. And in order to tie any "keyed" transcript to the staff scale one merely requires to locate the apparent keynote by means of an instrument. This caused me to investigate likely instruments, and I rapidly collected an assortment of recorders, flageolets, bamboo pipes, ocarinas, swanee whistles, mouth organs, tuning forks, simple and chromatic pitch pipes, and in fact anything I could lay my hands on which might prove suitable for the purpose. Of these, the ideal instrument turned out to be the chromatic pitch pipe, which produces a full and most accurate chromatic scale by means of a mouth-organ reed with a sliding damper. This I have used ever since.

All sorts of other interesting problems arose in addition to the examples mentioned, and in my study I was lucky to have the advice and help of two excellent literary godfathers–Dr. James P. Chapin in America and Mr. W. B. Alexander in England. Eventually I worked what appeared to be a practical method and published the results in the *Ibis* for January, 1950. Then my American godfather Chapin stepped in and introduced me to sound recording, considering that my experience of bird song qualified me as a likely recruit.

In 1950 Mr. Walther Buchen of Chicago came out and met me in Kenya, where, after the war, I had returned to my substantive job of Administrative Officer. At Chapin's suggestion he handed over a tape recorder to me when he left, and it was with this that I had my first bash at making sound records of birds. The word *bash* is a fair description of my early efforts, since I must have made every mistake that any mortal could!

However, I learned by degrees, and then, once again through Chapin, I was introduced to Dr. Peter Paul Kellogg of Cornell University, America's leading exponent of bird recording, who, through further generosity from Buchen, chose for me the professional outfit which produced the material for my record, "Voices of African Birds." This was published by Cornell in 1957, and I have the honor of being a member of the Laboratory of Ornithology of Cornell University and am at present a research associate. I doubt whether any of these pleasant things would have happened to me unless I had sat down on that boulder and listened to the fan-tailed ravens at Eil in 1944, and it is appropriate that I was able to include this bird on my record.

In the back of my mind, I long had the impression that many years ago I might have read a book which treated crow calls by music in some striking way, but I got no further till I was at Cornell in 1959. I was discussing the subject with Kellogg, when he said: "Did you know that Ernest Thompson Seton was one of the pioneers?" When a boy, I was an avid reader and collector of the Seton books. When I returned home, I looked them up, and there, sure enough, in his *Wild Animals I Have Known*, is the moving story of that wise old crow called Silverspot who lived and led his flock near Toronto, Canada. In this story Seton has, with great effect, inserted simple musical renderings of Silverpot's many calls, which could, for instance, mean *all's well, come along*, or *danger*, or *great danger, a gun!*, and so on. Surely there can be no better example of the use of simple music as an aid to the understanding of a bird's call, and I like to feel that some recollection of this story may have returned to me when I first heard crow music in Somalia.

PART THREE

ALEXANDER F. SKUTCH

Dr. Alexander F. Skutch, professional ornithologist and botanist, and authority on tropical American birds, lives in a house he built for himself on El General, *a farm he bought in a forest in Costa Rica in 1940. Dr. Skutch was born in 1904 in Baltimore, Maryland, was educated in private schools, and attended Johns Hopkins University, from which he was graduated with a degree of Bachelor of Arts in 1925. He received the degree of Doctor of Philosophy there in botany three years later. He went to Panama on a fellowship for research in botany and while there became deeply interested in tropical birds. Visits to Honduras, Guatemala, and a long visit to Barro Colorado Island in the Canal Zone followed. He has traveled to three countries in South America, and the culmination of his studies of tropical American birds was the publication of two volumes of* Life Histories of Central American Birds, *a work that will probably encompass six volumes. In 1950, he was awarded the Brewster Medal of the American Ornithologists' Union for his studies of tropical American birds.*

THE ANT-THRUSH CHICKS

THE greatest forest on earth is the rain forest of tropical America. From southern Mexico it stretches, with minor interruptions, over 40 degrees of latitude to Bolivia and southern Brazil. In Mexico and Central America it occupies a rather narrow strip along the eastern side of the mountains; but in South America it extends from the eastern foothills of the Andes in Colombia, Ecuador, and Peru to the Guianas and the mouths of the Amazon, more than 2,000 miles away—a vast expanse of glorious greenery drained by the greatest of all river systems, the sea-like Amazon and its many broad tributaries.

The aspect of this immense forest varies endlessly with changes in soil, drainage, annual rainfall, and other environmental conditions to which, like any living thing, it is sensitive. Yet throughout its length and breadth it has certain common features and certain widespread inhabitants, which would tell a naturalist who suddenly found himself in its midst that he was in tropical America rather than in a forest of the Old World. The dominant trees tower up to great heights, usually exceeding 100 and sometimes reaching 200 feet. Orchids, aroids, bromeliads, trailing cacti, ferns, and other epiphytes grow profusely on their boughs, drawing their nourishment from the rain, decaying bark, and fallen leaves. Great lianas or "bush ropes," sometimes as thick as a man's waist, hang in graceful catenaries from the high boughs and often spread a smothering tapestry of leaves over the crowns of tall trees. There is a profusion of palms, some of which, tall and slender, thrust their rosettes of great feathery or fanlike fronds high into the forest canopy; while others, that often bristle with long, forbidding, black thorns, grow in clusters amid the undergrowth.

Seeking fruits and insects high in the trees, where they are difficult to see, roam a host of brilliant birds: green parrots, many-colored tanagers, glittering trogons, exquisite honey creepers, gemlike hummingbirds, toucans with huge and colorful bills, motmots with racket-shaped tails. In the dimly lighted undergrowth live birds of other kinds, whose subdued tints blend with the bark and the brown fallen leaves; even the long-billed hummingbirds which dwell in deep shade wear dull plumage to match their setting. Wherever in this vast sylvan realm man has not spread destruction, slender monkeys leap from bough to bough, and the more sedate howlers roar mightily at dawn. In the wilder parts lurk the tapir, the jaguar, the puma, and the ocelot; bands of peccaries roam in search of fallen fruits, betraying their presence by their heavy scent; small deer leap gracefully through the undergrowth, unimpeded by the vines that trip the human wanderer. Throughout this immense forested region, from Mexico to Paraguay and from Ecuador to the Amazon's mouths, many kinds of plants and animals range with little variation; while on the other hand every region, every mountain chain and major valley, has its own peculiar forms of life, found nowhere else.

In places where many columnar trunks lead the gaze far upward with their unbroken sweep, where shafts of sunlight illuminate the graceful foliage of fern and palm, the tropical forest exalts all but the dullest and least responsive of human spirits. Where fallen trees break its continuity, disorderly vines limit one's vision and impede his advance, and all seems tangled confusion, the woodland may appear gloomy and forbidding. Unless one has a special interest in it, this forest, of which each acre supports a greater variety of living things than is to be found in any other type of vegetation, and which is the headquarters of terrestrial life on this planet, may soon become monotonous and boring.

The forest resembles life itself in giving to everyone, as a rule, what he seeks and expects to find in it. If he comes prepared to meet violence and terror, he will doubtless encounter it, although neither so soon nor so dramatically as certain unscrupulous writers have led him to anticipate. If, already convinced that the forest is full of discomforts, he permits himself to be irritated by every mosquito bite, every drop of moisture, and every prick of thorn, he will be thoroughly miserable in half an hour. If he seeks beauty, the tropical forest offers it in vast profusion; if he thirsts for peace and tranquillity, it is here; if he craves adventure, he may also find it. If his chief desire is to uncover the secrets of nature, myriads await him, jealously guarded. The tropical forest rarely discloses its mysteries to the hasty or careless observer. The sea of foliage which is its roof is almost as difficult to explore as the ocean's depth, and offers as many baffling problems.

What I have chiefly sought in the tropical forest is its birds. Ever since, fresh from my studies at the university, I became aware of their immense variety, their beauty, and the dearth of information about their habits, the obscurity in which they live has been a challenge to me. Since they have so many enemies among the teeming woodland life, they must live under the cover of secrecy, hiding their nests well and approaching them with great circumspection. Nevertheless, a very large proportion of these nests, often as high as eight out of ten, are prematurely destroyed. After years of searching, one discovers a nest of one of the more elusive birds, only to have his hope of learning more about it cruelly extinguished when, perhaps only a day or two later, he finds it empty, plundered by a snake, weasel, coati-mundi, tayra, hawk, toucan, or some other of the inumerable enemies of breeding birds. More than once, frustrated and discouraged, I have exclaimed, "I'm finished with the birds of the tropical forest. Let me watch those of high altitudes or high latitudes, where nests are easier to find, where half or more of them escape predators and one can begin a study with some prospect of carrying it to a successful conclusion!" Yet the very elusiveness of some of these tropical birds incites one to persist stubbornly in his attempt to outwit them.

Prominent among these retiring feathered inhabitants of the tropical forests are the ant birds. Indeed, the warm and humid forest of tropical America has produced no family of birds more characteristic of itself, more closely dependent on the peculiar conditions of life which it offers. Of the approximately 250 species in this great family, not one has extended its range much beyond the Tropic of Cancer—not even as far as the valley of the lower Rio Grande in Texas, where so many tropical birds reach their northernmost limit. On the opposite side of the broad tropical belt, few reach beyond Capricorn; W. H. Hudson, the English naturalist, knew only one species in La Plata, and he had little to tell about it. Neither do the ant birds, like some other tropical families, have numerous representatives in high tropical mountains. Their headquarters are the vast forests of the Amazon basin and the Guianas, where they present a bewildering array. About forty species are known in Central America and Mexico, but not one lives in the West Indies. Although most of the ant birds are forest dwellers, some dwell in the densely tangled vegetation that springs up in openings in the humid woodland, including clearings that men have made and abandoned after taking off a crop or two. A few ant birds have invaded the thorny scrub of arid regions.

Ant birds are never brilliant; black and white, with many shades of brown, gray, and olive, are their predominant colors. Often rich tones of rufous and chestnut, or bold contrasting patterns, make them most attractive. On the heads of some are featherless areas that are bright blue in color. In size, they range from pygmy ant wrens that are among the smallest of all birds to the big bataras of Paraguay and tropical Argentina, as large as crows. Ornithologists solved the problem of providing English names for this vast assemblage of ant birds by calling them after more familiar birds which they superficially resemble. The smallest and slenderest of the foliage-gleaning species are known as ant wrens; the ant vireos are somewhat stouter, with thicker bills; the ant shrikes are still larger, with stout bills hooked at the tip; the ant thrushes vaguely resemble some of the true thrushes; the long-legged, short-tailed, roly-poly ant pittas reminded some ornithologist of the pittas of the Old World tropics. Thirty years ago, when I first became interested in ant birds, I learned that they had been minutely classified and their ranges had been mapped; but I could not find a moderately complete account of the life of a single one of the 250 species.

Of the ant thrushes, the most common and widespread in the northern parts of tropical America is the black-faced, known to scientists as *Formicarius analis*. Often, while sitting at my writing table, I hear its full, mellow whistles floating out of the forest 100 feet away. *Whoo who who* it calls, with an emphasized first note. Usually it whistles a triplet, but sometimes it gives as many as ten notes without a pause. Although I so often hear the ant thrush, I have never once, in many years, seen it on the open shady ground which separates my study from the woodland at the end of the garden. Many of the more tree-dwelling birds of the forest come into the trees around me, and some feast on bananas at my bird feeding shelf; but the birds of the ground and the lowest vegetation seldom venture beyond the closed woodland. Since the ant thrush never comes to me, to cultivate its acquaintance I must seek it in its own ambient.

To watch the shy ant thrush amid the undergrowth, in the dim light that has filtered through tier after tier of heavy foliage, is not easy. But sometimes, while I stand quietly, I have the good fortune to see the elusive creature emerge into a clearer space. With dainty, deliberate steps, the long-legged bird advances over the leaf-strewn ground with which its dark colors blend. Its upper plumage is deep olive-brown, relieved by a half-collar of chestnut on the back and sides of the neck. A black patch covers its face and throat. Behind each large, dark eye is a crescent of bluish white bare skin which imparts an appearance of keen-sighted alertness. The under plumage is dark gray and olive, brightening to tawny on the coverts that show conspicuously beneath the short, upturned tail, which tilts forward with each step as the bird advances. Meeting this unique bird for the first time, one would take it to be a small railbird rather than a passerine, related to the finches, warblers, and swallows. No other ant bird that I know walks as it does, advancing its feet alternately; even the terrestrial ant pittas hop over the ground with their feet together, like a sparrow or a thrush.

A solitary bird, the ant thrush usually forages alone. Walking gracefully over the forest floor, it flicks aside the fallen leaves with its short black bill. The insects, spiders, and other small creatures which it thus exposes are its chief nourishment. Sometimes, when a noisy crowd of small forest birds of many kinds have gathered around the deployed battalions of the army ants, intent on preying upon the obscure creatures which the hunting ants drive from their hiding places beneath the ground litter, an ant thrush hovers on the outskirts of the throng. No doubt it catches many a fugitive insect or spider that has escaped the ants and the birds that dash into the midst of the swarm. Sometimes it will vary its diet with a lizard or a small snake.

On a morning in May, as I wandered through the forest on the land that I had recently bought in southern Costa Rica, a whirr of wings and a sharp, metallic-clear *tleet tleet tleet* startled me. I looked around in time to see a swiftly flying ant thrush vanish amid the saplings and low palms. Its line of flight led from a slender, mossy, rotting trunk, about 12 feet high. In the side of the stub were two narrow gaps that began slightly above the level of my head. Piling some logs at the base of the decaying trunk, I stood upon them to investigate these holes. They gave access to a central hollow, into which I thrust the little mirror that I carried for such occasions. After my eyes had become adjusted to the obscurity, I vaguely discerned two eggs that seemed to lie far below. Later, when I returned with an electric bulb which I lowered into the cavity on the end of a cord attached to a flashlight, I saw that the eggs were white, finely and faintly stippled over the whole surface with some dark color. They lay, as at the bottom of a well, on a mat of fine, dark brown material, 2 feet below the smaller gap in the side of the stub. My first ant thrush's nest, found a dozen years after I first met the bird and began to seek its eggs!

I lost no time in setting my little wigwam of brown cloth in view of the opening in the trunk's side, for I was eager to discover all that I could about the domestic habits of these little-known birds. Through the following morning, watching from my blind, I learned that both parents took turns in covering the eggs, as in all the other ant birds that I had studied. They sat in the dark, damp cavity from an hour and a half to three hours at a stretch, each remaining until its mate arrived to relieve it. With a sudden whirr of wings, the incoming partner darted into the hollow before I could see it well. Once the departing ant thrush stood in the opening looking forth, its dark, rich colors beautifully illuminated by a sunbeam that found its way through the forest canopy. Here it sang a long series of full, mellow whistles; then it shot forth with strong, swift flight that carried it between the tree trunks to a point beyond my view.

A few days later, my light and mirror revealed a sight such as I never expected to see in an ant bird's nest. At the bottom of the narrow well lay two nestlings covered with long, dense, dark-gray down. Every other newly hatched ant bird that I had seen had been utterly naked, with no vestige of plumage; these nestlings were more completely clothed than most newborn passerine birds. They brought to mind the downy chicks of railbirds, just as their parents reminded me of adult rails. The two nestlings huddled into a single dark, downy mass; but sometimes, when one moved, I caught a fleeting glimpse of pink skin.

Since I could not reach these nestlings without making a larger opening in the side of the trunk, I restrained my desire to examine them more closely, but my concern for their welfare was in vain. As I approached the trunk three days later, a wide gap in its side made my heart sink. Some mammal had evidently torn it open to devour the tender occupants. Found after so long a search; lost so soon!

Seven more years passed before I discovered my second ant thrush's nest, in the forest near my home. A more unexpected situation could hardly be imagined. On a steep hillside stood a tall, dead chonta palm, propped up by thick, spiny roots that sprang from the base of the columnar trunk at a point above my head. Its top had broken off, and a 7-foot length of it stood nearly upright on the slope below, precariously upheld by a single loop of a dead frond of twining fern and swaying whenever it was touched. This length of palm trunk had been reduced by the decay of its softer inner tissues to a thin shell, with a hollow interior that occupied nearly all of its diameter of 6 inches. Into the bottom of this long, fragile, brown cylinder a pair of ant thrushes had carried many dead leaves, on which they fashioned a nest of fine leaf petioles. Inserting my light and mirror through a narrow gap near the bottom of the tube, I saw two white, speckled eggs. But the lowest opening through which the parent birds could pass was 5 feet above the ground and nearly as far above their eggs, so that in coming and going they were obliged to climb down and up this long pipe. Its open top afforded no protection from the heavy rains of May and June.

Sixteen days after I found the eggs, they hatched downy nestlings such as I had already seen. Rarely, when I lowered the lighted bulb above them, they held up gaping yellow mouths and made a buzzing sound. Usually they rested quiescent, huddled together in a dark, fluffy mass. Their most conspicuous feature was the enormous white flanges at the corners of their mouths, which doubtless showed the parents where to place the food that they carried into the dimly lighted cavity. The upper and lower flanges on each side did not fit together, and between them was a narrow gap. As I looked down from above, the nestlings seemed to stare up at me with great white eyes, each with a narrow horizontal pupil, the gap between the flanges. I wondered whether these seeming eyes would alarm animals that might come to injure the nestlings, as eyespots on butterflies and other insects sometimes hold hungry birds aloof. I rarely saw the nestlings' true eyes, dark and inconspicuous behind these bizarre projections.

Twelve days after the nestlings hatched, I found one lying dead beside its nest mate. The survivor remained three or four days longer, then vanished. Apart from its larger size, its aspect had changed surprisingly little since its birth. When I last peeped in at it, it appeared too downy, too undeveloped, to climb up 5 feet of vertical tube and venture into the perilous forest. And if it did leave spontaneously rather than in the mouth of some hungry animal, how did it go? Did it fly off or simply drop to the ground and hop away? As I watched the nestlings' slow development, I became eager for the answer to these questions. But without undertaking long, continuous watches which require a relay of observers, one rarely sees the departure of a young bird unless he already knows its normal period in the nest. Although they hatch without a trace of plumage, ant birds of other kinds are clothed in feathers and hop or flutter from their open nests amid the bushes when from nine to thirteen days old, depending on the species. I doubted that the ant-thrush chicks, which seemed to develop far more slowly, would be ready to venture forth from their dark nursery even at fifteen or sixteen days of age.

Four more years passed before I found my third ant thrush's nest. It was in the forest near the site of the second one; in the top of a standing trunk of a chonta palm that a falling tree had snapped off 12 feet above the ground. The central hollow was a tubular well 14 inches deep and 4 inches wide, just too long and narrow to permit me to touch the two eggs that lay in the bottom, exposed to the sky. By cutting a few inches from the top of the stub, I might have reached them without harming the nest; but I desisted, because such alterations reduce the chances of bringing forth the young alive. In due course the eggs hatched, and one nestling survived to leave the stub when eighteen or nineteen days old. Although I did not watch its departure, I now knew the age at which this occurred; and this was no small gain.

After another five years, I was walking in the forest near my home when a sudden whirr of wings close to my ears drew my attention to the slender, rotting stub beside which I was passing. There was a long, narrow gap in its side; and by standing on a stool and lowering a light into the hollow center, I could see the ant thrush's usual two white, dark-flecked eggs lying far below, beyond my reach as in the three earlier nests. They were exposed to the rain through another hole in the broken-off top of the stub. Only 100 yards from my house in Costa Rica, this latest nest was the most conveniently situated of all. Nearly thirty years had now sped by since I made the acquaintance of the ant thrush; sixteen had elapsed since I found the first nest. Would I at last succeed in disclosing details in the ant thrush's life that had long escaped me?

Twenty-four days later, I arose while the stars still shone and climbed the steep, grassy slope behind the house. When I paused to catch my breath at the brow of the hill, the sky was brightening above the high, wooded ridges beyond the river in the east. Among the trees below me, Gray's thrushes, scarlet-rumped black tanagers, buff-throated saltators, and other birds were already singing. Pushing through the wall of bushes and vines at the forest's edge, I returned to the darkness of night. As I descended beneath tall trees into a narrow dell, I scanned the ground in front of me in the beam of my flashlight. The bushmaster, the fer-de-lance, and other deadly snakes lurked in this woodland. Soon I picked out the form of the wigwam blind that I had set before the ant thrushes' nest. Carefully I took my seat in it, hung my field glasses around my neck, placed my notebook on my lap, and laid my breakfast within reach. I had come prepared to watch for many hours.

As the dawn light slowly seeped into the depth of the forest, the ant thrushes' slender stub, adorned with a variety of creeping air plants, took shape in front of me. In the weeks that had passed since its discovery, I had watched the two parents incubate their eggs and bring to the single nestling that hatched many billfuls of insects or other food, which was usually mangled by the parents beyond recognition. On the preceding day, I had found a number of white, gelatinous pellets stuck to the wall of the cavity near the doorway. These were the excreta of the young ant thrush, evidence that it could now climb up and take its meals through the opening, a yard above its nest. But when I peered in with light and mirror, it still rested on the bottom, a formless mass of dark, fluffy down, which except for greater size looked much the same as when it was a few days old. Beneath the down I could faintly distinguish what seemed to be wing quills. Even now, the chick's one prominent feature was its huge, staring white "eyes."

As I watched in the dim light, I reflected that in an hour or two it would be just eighteen days since I had first seen the nestling, so recently hatched that its down was still plastered against its pink skin.

Whoo who rang out close by me, while the light was still dim in the underwood. Looking around for a parent ant thrush approaching over the ground with the nestling's breakfast, I almost missed the event that I so greatly desired to behold. At that moment the chick flew out of the hollow trunk. Tracing a long, descending course, it alighted on the ground, where it called loudly *chip chip chip . . .* , as of late it had done whenever a parent fed it in the nest. As well as I could see in the dim light, it was a miniature of its parents, even to the black face and throat. The most conspicuous difference was the prominent white flange at each side of its mouth. Its olive back, and even more its chestnut hindneck, were shaded by the long, upstanding dark-gray natal down. Whenever I looked into the deep nest chamber from above, this abundant down had completely concealed the juvenal plumage that expanded beneath it, making the young ant thrush appear far more infantile than it actually was.

When I tried to catch the chick for closer examination, it managed to keep ahead of me by a combination of walking and hopping over the rough ground, while a parent followed us, calling sharply *tleet tleet*. When I gained on it, the young bird flew fairly well. Finally, it walked beneath a tangle of bushes, vines, and fallen boughs. I knew that further pursuit was futile. In my eagerness to study its plumage, I had already caused more disturbance than I care to do when a chick first ventures forth from its nest beset by many perils, and perhaps the greater hazards of its life amid the trees and bushes.

Elated by what I had seen, I folded up my blind. When I reached the open pasture at the forest's edge, the sun floated up above the high ridges in the east. My vigil had borne fruit far sooner than I had expected.

In July of the same year, there were again two eggs in the same hollow stub; and in the following year three sets were laid there, in April, June, and August. In all, there were ten eggs, and the parents reared eight chicks. At the age of sixteen days, one of these became alarmed when I looked in, rushed out past my light, mirror, and face, and promptly walked off through the undergrowth. Another chick left when only seventeen days old, and I did not see it go. Five left when eighteen days of age and one at nineteen days; and these six all took their departure in much the same manner, as I first discovered while watching from my blind. Each came forth at the parent's first visit to the nest in the dim light before sunrise. As the parent came walking over the ground and called, the chicks flew out to meet it. If the parent approached silently and flew up to the doorway before the young birds were aware of its presence, one of the young ones took the food. Then parent and chicks flew down to the ground in swift succession. Without delay, they walked off together, the youngsters traveling quite competently. Soon they were lost to view in the undergrowth; the young birds' loud *chip*'s became fainter, and then inaudible as the family advanced deeper into the forest.

This simple discovery, made after long seeking and waiting, then confirmed by repeated observations, pleased me almost as much as though I had unearthed facts that would shake the scientific world and perhaps change the course of biological thought. Unimportant as it may appear when viewed in isolation, it belongs to a class of discoveries which, taken together, are of the utmost importance. Although sometimes we may, by a stroke of good fortune, learn all the salient facts in an animal's life by means of a single series of consecutive observations, more often it is only by piecing together scraps of information gathered here and there, at long intervals, that we begin to understand how it lives. And from our knowledge of the patterns of life of many different creatures, our understanding of the great realm of living things is built.

JEAN DELACOUR

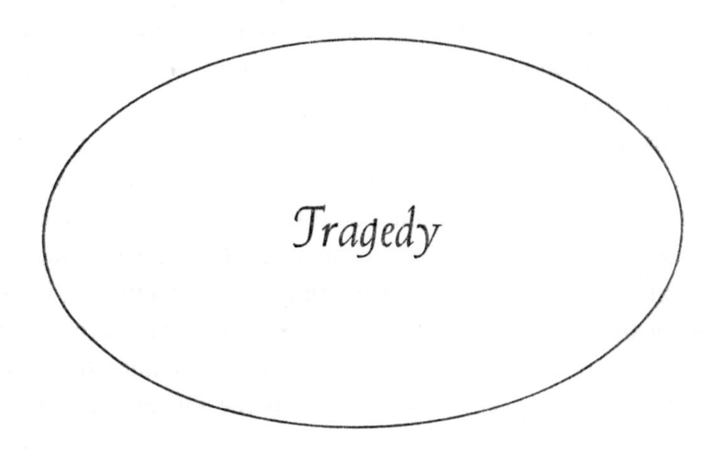

Jean Theodore Delacour, from 1952 to 1960 Director of the Los Angeles County Museum, California, was born September 26, 1890, in Paris, France. He is descended from an old and distinguished French family and was educated at the University of Lille and the Sorbonne. In two world wars he was a captain in the French Army and a liaison officer to the British Army. In his career as an aviculturist and ornithologist, he has led expeditions throughout the world, but particularly to Indochina and Madagascar. His collections numbered more than sixty thousand birds and twenty thousand mammals, and he has discovered and named hundreds of species and subspecies of birds new to science.

In his career as one of the world's most distinguished aviculturists, he has reared more than forty thousand birds and has brought to Europe many rare species never before known or kept in captivity. Among his professional honors, Dr. Delacour has been President of the Avicultural Society of America, Research Associate, American Museum of Natural History, and Technical Advisor for the New York Zoological Society. He has written many published volumes about birds, of which his latest is The Waterfowl of the World.

TRAGEDY

THE study of nature has always fascinated me. I was very young when, in France, I started to work with animals and plants, and to collect them. They have given a meaning to my life and afforded me tremendous satisfaction. Now that I am older, I still feel the same pleasure whenever I can observe and study new, rare, or interesting specimens, or find some new fact about them.

It was my luck to be able to explore and collect extensively in Indochina, the last large country where many new species and subspecies of birds could yet be discovered. Hundreds of novelties came my way through the years, and the most impressive of these gave me cause for wild excitement and some unforgettable moments. This was repeated, to a lesser degree, in Madagascar, and in the different parts of the world which it was my privilege to visit. To choose one of these many thrilling experiences as the most striking is beyond my power, but to decide what has been the most memorable event in my life as a naturalist, I must turn to a quite different set of circumstances.

Impressions received by us at an early age are no doubt the most keenly felt. The strongest which I ever perceived was not exhilarating, but on the contrary, tragically painful: the terrible emotion of beholding for the last time before total and inevitable destruction the many objects that I had accumulated for over ten years with the wild enthusiasm of youth, the result of all my efforts, and the aim of all my work. I was twenty-seven years old when it happened. Although such a disaster was to be repeated on an even larger scale, some twenty years later, the horror of the first experience has remained infinitely more vivid in my memory than subsequent horrors.

Circumstances had made it possible for me, at an early age, to acquire very important collections of birds and plants, and many valuable books. These were elaborately housed in one of my family's country estates at Villers-Bretonneux, in Picardy. As a child, I always had loved the country, its trees, its flowers, its animals. Villers was a paradise to me, although I now realize that the wide, rich plains of Picardy are not the most picturesque part of France. But there was a large park, extensive gardens, and farms full of horses, cattle, poultry, all purebred and immaculately kept. Above all, there were conservatories, greenhouses, and even a pheasantry. No one in the family was particularly interested in them. They were, in those days, an ordinary feature of country estates. The pheasantry contained pheasants, doves, and parakeets. I was soon given their control, and, at ten years of age, I acquired my first orchids and exotic birds.

At fifteen, I built a range of some hundred outdoor flight cages, a heated bird gallery, a waterfowl pond, and a score of enclosures for ostriches, rheas, emus, cranes, storks, and other large birds. All were built of steel, luxuriously equipped, and well planted; flowers and shrubs lined them, and each compartment was a little garden. More than two thousand birds, representing some five hundred species, lived there, many very rare. A number of them nested, some for the first time in captivity. Concurrently the greenhouses had been enlarged and filled with unusual and gorgeous tropical plants. To accomplish it all I had to be educated, and through the years I acquired degrees at the Universities of Lille and Paris.

My collections at Villers were probably the best private ones of their kind in the world in 1914. I had taken infinite care of them. I always thought they would remain there for the whole of my life and beyond, and continue to increase and improve. Then World War I came. German troops walked through Villers in 1914; little harm had been done, and it was soon again in allied hands. Ten miles only from the trenches (it was quite a safe distance in those days), things went on at Villers almost normally for the next three years. Despite the presence of thousands of soldiers and the near roar of guns, my plants grew and flowered, and birds nested much as usual. The house was the headquarters of high-ranking allied generals, and during my own leaves I met many of the great military chiefs in my own house.

All this changed in 1918. The last German offensive of the war brought the battle right into Villers. I was then stationed at Péronne, 20 miles to the east, as a liaison officer with the Fifth British Army, whose Commander, General Gough, was living in our château.

From Péronne, I saw the onrush and the break-through of the German Army, and I knew that, this time, Villers and all it meant to me would be destroyed. We were obliged to retreat west, and I went to Villers alone to see it for the last time. The town was already empty, its population of five thousand inhabitants having been evacuated early in the morning. All was still in perfect condition, the first shells just beginning to fall here and there. It was a beautiful, cool, sunny spring day. Everything still was in order in my park: the gardens had thousands of blooms, and the great trees were adorned with tender leaves. Small birds were singing in their aviaries, and larger birds were running on the lawns or swimming on the ponds. The conservatories were full of orchids and rare exotic plants, all things I had gathered through years of great effort. I spent one hour there, walking through those dear and familiar grounds. I left just when the heavy shelling started, blasting everything. I viewed again all my treasures: live birds and plants, cabinet specimens, library, great halls full of familiar art objects, family souvenirs. Then I left in despair.

Six months later, the war almost over, I returned to find unrecognizable piles of stones, crumbling walls, broken trees, and here and there, mangled remains of things I had loved.

Within a year, I established new collections at Clères, in Normandy, even larger and better. Clères provided even a better background for live collections. There is an historic Gothic castle there, an old ruin of the eleventh century, a river, a lake, forested hills, and magnificent trees. I had the gardens renovated promptly, the park fenced in, enclosures, aviaries, conservatories, and greenhouses built. After a year, the collections were better than ever, and they never ceased to improve and increase until 1939. It was a true garden of Eden, as the great French writer Colette has called it: "Paradis Terrestre," with mammals and birds roaming among the trees and flowers.

Twenty years after that first disaster of World War I, I was returning late one morning to camp on the ridge of a mountain in central Indochina. It was cold and wet, but I was happy as I had collected a few very rare birds. My head boy, who had traveled to Europe with me, greeted me with a smile: "There is a telegram from Clères for you, Sir." It had been sent by Frank Fooks, my superintendent, and it read: "DEEPLY

REGRET TO REPORT CHATEAU ENTIRELY DESTROYED BY FIRE. MANOR HOUSE AND PARK INTACT." I flew back in a hurry to find that, once more, most of my possessions, art objects, books, and files were reduced to ashes. But the birds and plants were still there, only to disappear the next year in the World War II invasion. By that time I was in America, tired of European struggles.

Despite these harsh experiences, I have not been discouraged. Clères has been rehabilitated, and, in America, I have been involved in more activities of a similar nature. I still delight in the same things I loved as a child. Notwithstanding frightful setbacks and losses, I have never regretted to have embarked on the career I have chosen. But I still crave for what I lost in 1918.

ROBERT P. ALLEN

The Whooping Crane's World

When Robert Porter Allen of Tavernier, Florida, retired June 30, 1960, as Research Director of the National Audubon Society, he was fifty-five years old and had served that organization for thirty years. Author of three of the Society's Research Reports— The Roseate Spoonbill, The Whooping Crane, *and* The Flamingos*—all the product of his National Audubon Society researches, Mr. Allen had become known to ornithologists over the world as an authority on the American wading birds. In recognition of his work, the American Ornithologists' Union awarded him the Brewster Medal in 1957. In 1958 his book,* On the Trail of Vanishing Birds, *published by McGraw-Hill Book Company, won for him the John Burroughs Medal, an award made each year by the John Burroughs Memorial Association for "a distinguished piece of contemporary nature writing."*

Mr. Allen was born in South Williamsport, Lycoming County, Pennsylvania, on April 24, 1905. At his home at Tavernier, where he has lived for more than twenty years, he is writing a book about the birds of the Caribbean.

THE WHOOPING CRANE'S WORLD

Aransas Wildlife Refuge, Austwell, Texas—

I knew that twenty-four of the big cranes had started north from Texas the previous April, as they and their kind had done for countless springs. They had responded to a rhythm and a pattern that had been old for long, long slumbering ages.

Now again, toward the end of the winter season there would be a shift in the prevailing wind direction, a new warmth in the damp Gulf Coast air. Since December, the big white whooping cranes on their wintering grounds at Aransas Wildlife Refuge had been solemnly demonstrating the strength of their marriage vows. For the union between these pairs is much more than an intense, temporary, sexual bond. It is a permanent mating, blindly and jealously guarded through innate structures that are firmly established in the character of the species. Even on the wintering grounds, where a relaxing of the strife of territorial defense is the general rule among other birds, there is seldom any letup in the fierce alertness with which the whooping crane pair resists the intrusion of others of its kind.

A neighboring pair that have, in their feeding, encroached a few yards beyond their own territory, will cause the next-door male and his mate to join voices in a shrill duet of violent protest. With bills pointed skyward they seem to stand on tiptoes in their desire to advertise their anger and disapproval. Even a young one of the previous summer, changing rapidly now from the russets and buffs of immaturity to a dirty, smudged sort of whiteness, raises his head with an air of surprising insolence for one of such tender age. But he only glares, for his voice is not yet very impressive, and it is seldom used.

If the invading pair fail to withdraw at the first series of warning notes, the male of our indignant family group struts about with anger in every wrathful line of his body. From my hiding place in my blind, 200 feet away, my binoculars reveal his baleful eyes in which is concentrated cold and furious suspicion. The iris, for all its yellow brilliance, is never warm. The Mexicans sometimes call the whooper the bird of the evil eye—*viejo del mal ojo*—and at close range one can understand why.

There is only a fractional lapse between the male's take-off crouch and that of his mate and offspring. Sometimes I have seen the young bird crook its extended neck just an instant before the male runs forward, wings spread and flapping. There is evidently some definite movement or posture or perhaps a shading of tone in the warning note of the adult male that releases the flight or chasing reaction. Perhaps it is a signal that is not discernible to me but that penetrates the releasing patterns of all three birds and results in a nearly simultaneous take-off.

All three run forward, heads lowered, necks outthrust, wings flapping rather heavily. Five or six running strides may be needed, and the business of getting each individual load of 16 or 18 pounds or more into the air impresses one as labored. Indeed, it seems probable that the wing manipulation of *Grus americana*, the whooping crane, is fairly primitive. Certainly the completely extended posture of the wings in flight, the stiff, "flicking" motion, and the narrow arc of the full beat are less efficient than the easy, graceful, effortless flight of other birds. The evident lack of wrist action suggests that this type of wing beat lies somewhere between the sailing or gliding flight of the earliest birds and the fully developed use of the principles of aerial dynamics exhibited in the flight of more modern species.

Following the lead of the male the trio swerves, banks, and heads straight for the pair that have invaded their territory. Twenty or thirty paces away they change stroke, still seeming to follow the imperceptible lead of the male, their legs thrust down and slightly forward. Then, as they make almost simultaneous contact with the ground, three pairs of wings are flapped in a slow backstroke that brakes the speed of actual grounding. Now the male of the family appears at his most male-ish. The mother and offspring stand stiffly in the background, alert to every movement in the formalized ethological drama before them, but merely a supporting claque, never active participants. The male again stands in the tiptoe posture and sounds his shrill challenge. Then he charges, half running, half flying, head and bill straight forward like a spear. The invading pair of whooping cranes, which have been standing perfectly still, their collective attitude one of guilty foreboding, retreat at once. Who wouldn't! Without apology or shame, they are up and off! The pursuing male is now in the air and bearing down on them. He gets on the tail of the nearest intruder and follows its swerving flight in much the manner of a gull or a tern harrying one of its kind.

The chase carries the two trespassers far into their own territory, even beyond it at times. When they attempt to land in what would seem to be an uncontested area, the relentless pursuer may charge a second time, his reaction still strong. Eventually he has chased the pair 2 miles or so, and, as if the rules of conduct have been satisfied, he returns to his waiting family. Their behavior seems to demonstrate a complete confidence in his ability, although it is more likely a simple lack of warlike male patterns in the female and the immature crane. Before the male has returned from his chase, they have lost interest and have been calmly poking about in the mud of a small temporary pond, looking for trapped crabs or killifishes. The master's return is modestly triumphant, his demeanor suitably arrogant but offhand. All in a day's work!

I suppose that in the solidarity, and the more or less permanent, year-around isolation of the family unit, one can find survival values. At least the evolution of behavior patterns intolerant of trespass by their own kind probably developed such values in the original, undisturbed population. At the present time, however, with the population greatly reduced, this aggressive defense of the wintering territories may actually limit the whooping crane's survival. In our current assortment of families—adult cranes with young; adult pairs without young; pairs that are not mated but are simply companions (perhaps second-winter birds and odd "pairs" of the same sex); and lone cranes—the chances of new breeding pairs being formed readily through close association of unmated birds on the wintering grounds appears to be more difficult. Sometimes this may even be impossible because of the defensive habits of males of established pairs.

For example, in 1947, an adult whooping crane arrived at Aransas Refuge from the [at that time] unknown northern breeding grounds with a young bird in tow, but without a mate. Throughout the winter this lone adult (I suspected it was a female) attempted unsuccessfully to establish a territory. Neighboring males were particularly vicious in driving off this whooping crane and its young one. Later this bird and its offspring joined company with two wandering whooping cranes that had no established territories. These two were probably subadults * in their second winter. The four were seen together on several occasions in later winter of 1948, wandering through the edges of various territories claimed by well-ordered pairs and whooping crane families. Eventually the attacks of the male birds in these territories separated this foursome, although I had hoped that from this situation, the "widowed" adult would find another mate. During the late winter and early spring the family of two was again alone and may have left for the northern breeding grounds by themselves.

Of course, since no observations had been made on the nesting grounds at that time, we did not know what possibilities existed there for renesting. Perhaps all pair formation, both the initial mating of three-year-olds and the remating of bereft adults such as the suspected female of our example, takes place at the nesting site. It seemed to be a difficult point to clear up.

There are periodic breaks in the defensive wall that normal groups throw around their winter territories. These relaxations result, perhaps, from a lowering of the physiological drive in typical male and family behavior. On occasion, especially toward the end of the winter season, a wandering pair or a single whooping crane will move slowly through a segment of a territory previously defended, and no challenge from the male and his mate will be forthcoming. The male seems aware of the intrusion, but he and his mate continue their preening or feeding without assuming any of the postures of aggressive defense.

Finally, with the arrival of spring, the southerly winds have set in for the season. Many other migrant birds have moved northward through Aransas Wildlife Refuge and have gone. Over the salt-flat grass the gull-billed terns search for insects, and on the edge of tidal ponds, brimful from recent rains, pairs

* A term used by ornithologists for birds that require more than one year to become mature.—The Editor.

of black-necked stilts stand demurely, side by side. On the chain of islands offshore the herons, egrets, cormorants, and gulls are already incubating their eggs. Willets flash their splendid wings, and their wild melodious cries fill the warm air. What hereditary vision now penetrates the consciousness of our white cranes? Poised on the outskirts of all this excitement, they give only slight evidence that they are on the brink of their long journey north. Once, three weeks before their departure, I saw a pair fly aloft to an unaccustomed altitude and soar in wide circles, moving gradually and with what seemed reluctance back to the slough below them where they had passed the winter months.

Suddenly the whoopers begin to disappear. For some weeks I had noted subtle marks of change. Pairs with young had begun to show annoyance at the presence of their offspring, each pair driving its gangling hopeful away with sudden jabs and threatening lunges. All of the whooping cranes flew about more, and they seemed more nervous. Less and less were they concerned about defending their winter territories.

Then, by two's and three's they were gone! Whatever it is that has been given them, it is strong enough to send them aloft into an appalling space of sky, to carry them on their widespread wings over thousands of miles of land, across networks of highways, across busy farms and cities, through leagues of foul industrial haze, and dangers unnumbered. It is quite as if they have flown upward and outward to another universe.

The summer passes. Then in autumn it is time for their return. Will they come back? How many of them? Will any young birds return with their parents? Every day I cover the ground at Aransas Refuge. Every acre is scanned and then scanned again. The daily effort becomes routine, it grows stale. You come to hate every mudhole in the road, despise the necessity for climbing out of the jeep at every lookout. You grow irritable, peevish. Another day goes by and then another. You come home at night worried and silent. Your supper is tasteless to you, and your family watches you furtively, but without comment. The children are sent quietly to another room so that they can laugh and talk and be normal. You, miserable wretch, must be alone and let your mind go dead, blank, empty. No one can help. No one can do anything. We can only wait.

Then, on a dull morning that is without hope or fear, you pull up at one of the lookout stations and there they are! The first pair of whooping cranes has come back! There is no russet-colored young with them, but your heart pounds. You had almost forgotten how serene, how magnificently dignified and aloof they are. Scarcely daring to breathe, you watch them. Their heads are up and they are watching you, but the distance is considerable and they are not alarmed. Slowly, elaborately, they pick their way along the rim of the pond, pausing to turn their fierce, searching gazes sharply in your direction.

They have returned. This year they would all return, all but one, one that was lost somewhere in that unknown breeding place and migration route of danger and uncertainty. After the long waking nightmare of the past weeks it seemed a miracle. But there they were, flesh and blood, satiny feathers and great, stiff wings.

Is it an accident that these tall birds have survived beyond the Pleistocene? Perhaps, but they are vital and alive, and now only Man has been able to change their world until it seems nearly untenable. If anything can save the whooping crane from the final indignity of extinction, it must be our doing, a belated balancing of the account for the low numbers to which our guns and drainage of their nesting marshes have brought them. There may still be time.

DAVID BANNERMAN

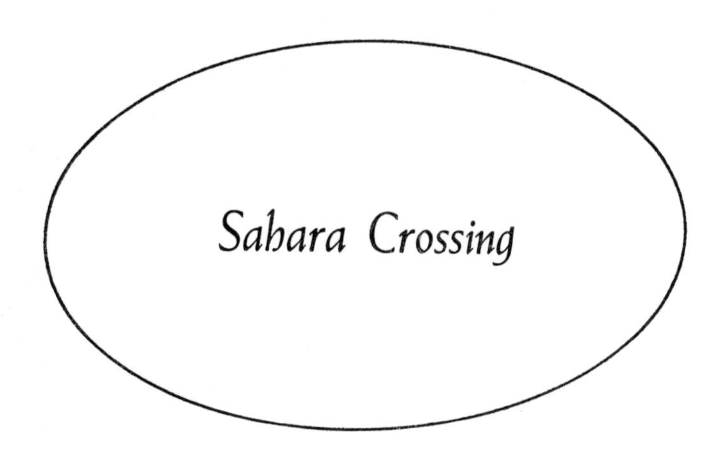

Sahara Crossing

Dr. David Armitage Bannerman, of ancient Scottish descent, has lived most of his life in London. He was born in Pendleton, Lancashire, on November 27, 1886, and now lives in Scotland, where he raises sheep and has a pedigreed herd of Galloway cattle. He was on the staff of the British Museum from 1911 to 1953 and served during World War I in France. During his service, he was awarded the Order of the British Empire, Order of St. John of Jerusalem, Mons Star, and French and British war medals. He also served in World War II and between wars made many expeditions in search of birds for the British Museum. He specialized in the birds of West Africa and was appointed by the British Secretary of State to write a history of the birds of all West African colonies, which involved twenty-two years of work. Between 1930 and 1951, his eight-volume work, The Birds of Tropical West Africa, *was published. He is also the author of* The Birds of the British Isles, *of which nine volumes of a twelve-volume work had been published by 1960, and several other books on the birds of West Africa and Cyprus. He is currently preparing* The Birds of the Canary Islands and Madeira.

SAHARA CROSSING

On the extreme northwest point of Africa, facing the Atlantic approaches to the Straits of Gibraltar, there is situated a lonely lighthouse on Cape Spartel, known to all mariners and many travelers on their voyages to and fro. South of the lighthouse lies what used to be neutral ground—a buffer between French Morocco of former days and the International Zone of Tangier. I shall have more to tell of this lighthouse and its immediate surroundings later in these pages.

We had come up from Colomb-Béchar by car, crossing the northern Sahara and taking a pass over the Great Atlas at its eastern end, thence making our way to Tetuán in the Spanish Zone. The whole trip was full delight for an ornithologist, particularly when shared with a wife of similar tastes, and as I think back over that journey, memories of "golden moments" come rapidly to mind.

We had started from Casablanca, and by way of Marrakesh had crossed the Atlas Range by the Tichka Pass to Ouarzazate, turning then eastward to Tinerhir and thence by an unfrequented track across the desert to Algeria.

We had reached a point on the *piste* to Goulmina and had pulled up at a picturesque river crossing to watch the flowing water in a normally dry nullah. The temperature was exceptionally low for the seventh of March, and we had put on the heater in the car. As we ate our picnic lunch, it began to snow. Snow in the northern Sahara is by no means unknown, but as the heavy flakes came down, we remembered the days when we had pictured the desert—for it was very arid desert where we were—a land bathed in everlasting sunshine with never a cloud in the sky!

We were facing south at the time, watching the falling snow, when to our astonishment, there arrived on the scene a big flight of storks, some hundreds in number, gyrating round and round, and, as is their habit when on migration, using the air currents so prevalent over desert country to aid them on their way. Whether they had become confused by the snowstorm, or had sighted the flowing river from above, we shall not know, but with their great wings outstretched and pinions extended, they glided to earth to alight close to the same river that had caused us to tarry on our way. It was an unforgettable sight—the outline of the Great Atlas Mountain chain stretching away behind us, the storks gliding down among the snowflakes, and the limitless desert to the south, all combined to print the scene indelibly on my mind.

We had journeyed far before we arrived in Tangier in the latter days of March and had thought that our ornithological cup was already full. Yet one more golden experience remained for us to chronicle. We had planned to spend the next day in the vicinity of the lighthouse at Cape Spartel, but before we were out of bed in the morning, we realized that something unusual was afoot, for we woke to the cries of bee eaters, one of the most beautiful and decorative of our European birds, passing overhead. Running to the window and gazing skyward, we were rewarded by a wonderful sight. The air was full of birds flying north. Among the flocks of bee eaters, whose cries had roused us so early, were innumerable dark objects which were flying very high. Using our binoculars, we saw they were black kites sailing over Tangier in the direction of Spain in countless numbers, each bird flying individually at spaced distance from his or her neighbor. A bedroom balcony is not the most advantageous place from which to observe migration and within an hour we were heading for the lighthouse on Cape Spartel and the high ground above it overlooking the international boundary, from which we knew we should have an uninterrupted view to the south. We soon discovered that an easterly gale was blowing of quite exceptional force, and the pine trees on the high ground above the town were bent by the force of the wind. We arrived above Cape Spartel in the nick of time to witness the most remarkable bird migration it has been my luck to see. Over the swaying pines the black kites were weaving their way almost at treetop level, some indeed, caught by the air currents, had difficulty in breasting the hill, and some even passed between the tree trunks in their efforts to top the ridge. Finding the wind intolerable at this elevation, we made our way down the winding path and eventually reached a little bay beyond the lighthouse where we hoped to find some shelter.

There a remarkable sight met our eyes, for the same idea had occurred to the birds! The sandy cove, and the scrub surrounding the bay, was covered with them—birds of all kinds—ranging in size from finches and redstarts to lesser kestrels and a Norfolk plover. Flying so close to the sand that their wing tips almost brushed the ground, an endless stream of swallows and martins came, never wavering as were many others, but pursuing a relentless course at ground level, till forced by the rising ground ahead to top the trees. At a higher level than the swallows were flocks of bee eaters bunched together and the never-ending stream of kites. A few large eagles then came into view, probably the short-toed or snake eagles, one of which, buffeted unmercifully by the wind, took refuge in a gully. Soon we were to have our greatest thrill of all when from over the sea came a stream of Montagu's harriers, magnificent in their slate-gray plumage, their black wings and pale wing tips making them conspicuous from afar. Seemingly exhausted, several came down on the sand, for they must surely have been off their course to come in from the sea. The small warblers were not in evidence. Had they been, they would have fared badly indeed. The bushes around the bay were full of woodchat shrikes—birds which before this day had been absent. Now the place seemed alive with them. Had they reached their journey's end?

From dawn till dusk the wind howled and the migration continued in full strength. The gray harriers, all males, continued to pass, their brown female consorts much less noticeable. We followed some with our binoculars past the lighthouse, but on the landward side, as if they feared to trust themselves to the exposed headland. We ourselves had difficulty standing against the wind. The swallows and martins never changed their courses. They must have been flying for hundreds of miles across the desert country which lay to the south. We watched them breast the hill and pass over the cliffs heading across the turbulent straits and hopefully making for Spain. A few parties of swifts were observed, but it was the black kites and the harriers which held our attention as they rose high in the air preparatory to making the crossing. Some were flying so high that they were almost beyond sight of the naked eye, each bird flying with purpose and seemingly unhurried.

The *levante* ceased in the night, and we awoke to a wonderful day, not a cloud in the sky, not a breath of wind. It was as if a miracle had happened—the sea was calm, the gale had lasted three days and had blown itself out. With the change in the weather, all migration ceased. Where yesterday kites, harriers, swallows, and kestrels, with hordes of smaller birds were battling for their lives—not a bird was to be seen. The migrants had passed on their way, and an almost deathly calm prevailed.

When two days later we boarded the little steamer which plies between Tangier and Gibraltar, the wind had risen once more, and sure enough, as we scanned the heavens, we saw the kites and the harriers again in the sky and listened again for the cries of the bee eaters which we already knew so well. High overhead they were passing as we tossed our way across the Straits—reminding us that spring in Europe was again on the way and that we too were returning home.

OLAUS J. MURIE

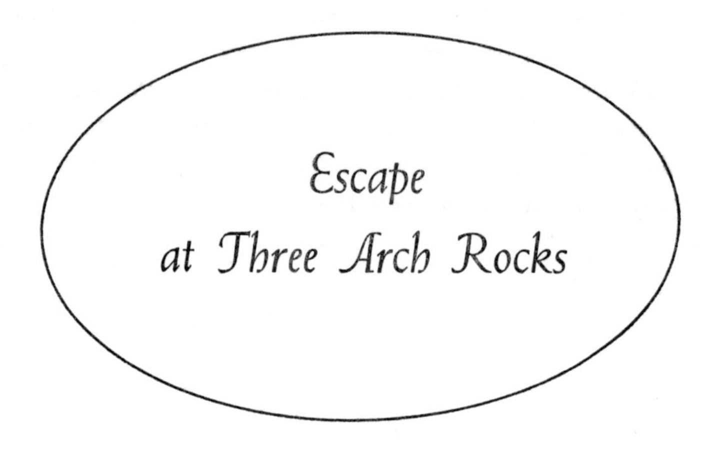

Olaus J. Murie, Director of the Wilderness Society, lives at Moose, Wyoming. He was born at Moorhead, Minnesota, March 1, 1889, and attended Pacific University at Forest Grove, Oregon, where he majored in zoology. He traveled on expeditions for the Carnegie Museum, Pittsburgh, Pennsylvania, to Labrador and Hudson Bay and later served in World War 1 as a balloon observer. In 1920 he was sent to Alaska by the U.S. Biological Survey to study Alaska-Yukon caribou. He retired from the U.S. Fish and Wildlife Service in 1949 to accept the directorship of the Wilderness Society, and in that year, Pacific University conferred on him an honorary degree of Doctor of Science. Dr. Murie is an author and artist who has illustrated his own books—The Elk of

North America; A Field Guide to Animal Tracks; The Alaska-Yukon Caribou, *and others. Among his honors are the Aldo Leopold Medal of the Wildlife Society and the Audubon Medal of the National Audubon Society, awarded him for "distinguished service to conservation."*

ESCAPE AT THREE ARCH ROCKS

"DON'T you want to go with me to inspect Three Arch Rocks?"

Since I was young, and eager for anything that promised adventure, my response was automatic. "Of course!"

L. Alva Lewis was in 1913 in charge of the federal refuges in Oregon, and I was working for William L. Finley, then State Game Warden and also one of the foremost lecturers on birds and a great conservationist. Lewis and I speedily made our arrangements, and on July 1, a motor launch took us out from the nearby coast town and helped us get ashore on Three Arch Rocks with our equipment and a small skiff. They would call for us again in a matter of five days.

Three Arch Rocks, comprising a group of three small rocky islets off the Oregon coast, rising several hundreds of feet into the air, all made up of cliffs and ledges where sea birds nested, is a federal bird refuge. Our camp was on a broad shelf well above high-tide mark on the outer of these three islets. We had sleeping bags, food and water, and all necessary equipment for photographing and banding the sea birds, which were there in thousands.

We didn't try to go anywhere that first day but fixed up our camp and explored around the camp island. Next morning early, with our light skiff, we eagerly set off for the second rock, with all our photographic and bird banding gear. There, on a low rocky shore was a colony of sea lions also. We hauled our boat well up and proceeded to photograph sea lions, murres, cormorants, and the clownish little puffins which had their burrows in the sod on the flat places.

Time has a way of flying when you are engrossed in interesting subjects. We had placed aluminum bands on the legs of many nestling birds, we had taken numerous photographs, and had climbed over most of the fascinating island, until it was way past noon. Then I noticed the weather. A west wind had sprung up, and there was already a heavy sea running.

"Hey, Lewis, we've got to get out of here right now; look at that water!"

My friend Lewis had some kind of hip ailment and used crutches. He got around very gamely but very slowly. We managed to get down to our boat and take off. This was in the lee of the island so was not very difficult. We pulled around and approached our campsite on the outer rock. I was dismayed to see that there, on the windward side, the water was already rough. Something had to be done right away if we were to do anything at all!

"I'll back you up to the rock on one of the incoming swells," I said; "then you get out on the rock as fast as you can and I will pull away as the swell comes down. Then I'll come in on a later swell and hop out with the painter * in my hand."

It was a tense moment, choosing the swell to ride in on, but I finally took a chance and came in to the rock. Lewis started to climb out, but because of his infirmity he was a little slow. He was halfway out, partly on the rock, partly in the boat, when to my consternation I realized that I was lingering too

* A rope, or "tether," usually at the bow, for tying a boat fast to a shore-point; also often used as a towline.—The Editor.

long. The ocean swell was about to fall away in the steep drop down the cliff, but I couldn't pull away, and as I waited for him to get out I knew it was too late.

The water dropped suddenly, the stern hung up on a rock, and the boat with all its contents was catapulted into the sea. The last I heard as I went down was a loud, earnest curse from the direction of the rock.

There must have been a strong undertow, for when I came to the surface I found myself, fortunately, far out from the dangerous cliff line. In the meantime the next wave had shoved Lewis safely up on the camp ledge.

All around me our equipment bobbed, still afloat. I fastened one of the life preservers to the boat, swam around and gathered cameras and tripods, and tied them to the straps of the life preserver. All the bird banding records for the day, written on cards, were floating about me, and I gathered these all into a pack and shoved them inside my shirt. Lewis's crutches and one oar I stored under a seat so they wouldn't float away. Then I climbed into the submerged boat, which let me down to about my waist in water, but saved me from continuous swimming. With one oar used as a paddle, I worked the boat still farther out from the dangerous landing place. I knew I couldn't make a landing with a boat full of water.

Up to this time my only feeling was one of chagrin at having let this thing happen, and I was very busy taking care of the equipment as well as I could, and getting away from the dangerous waters. I shouted something apologetic to Lewis, crouched there on the ledge, and then paddled out to sea, where the waves were now large, but at least were not breaking. I remember feeling a silly grin on my face as I looked up at my partner, and felt a deep gratitude that he had landed safely on the rock.

But a change came over me now. I had done all the things I could think of, and now I sat there, out in the growing storm, looking about me at a hostile sea and longingly surveying the rocks about which the waves were already lashing in white foam. For the first time a great fear swept over me. What could I do, out here with a half-sunken boat?

I decided to have a look at the lee side of the island, in the hope that there would be a little cove or a comparatively smooth shore line; any way to get my feet on solid rock somewhere. I laboriously paddled around, well out from the island, but found that the boat, under water, would not automatically stay upright. As each big wave came, I leaned against it and then leaned the other way as it passed by. Thus I managed to keep things right side up and came in sight of the lee side of the island. But considerable time must have elapsed. The storm had increased in vigor, and there was now "white water" all along the rocks on the lee side too. Now I really was scared, nearly panicky. I looked at the rough water all about me. I looked at the mainland, about a mile away, where huge breakers were pounding on the shore. There was not much choice, even if I could last long enough to get in where the breakers were. I began to shiver, not so much from the icy water I believe as from the emotions that were now welling up inside. I didn't know what to do.

Then suddenly a thought came to me. This bird reservation is known as Three Arch Rocks. That means that each rock has a tunnel through it, formed by the pounding of the waves over the centuries. Inside those arches or tunnels, the water would be going up and down as on the outside, but surely the interior of the island would not be receiving the full brunt of the storm and probably there would be no white water. At any rate it was something to do.

I required several acres of water surface on which to turn about, and it was hard to keep the boat going on any steady course because it was a foot or more below the surface, but I headed for the opening of the cavern in the middle rock. By some miracle I hit the opening squarely.

Here I came into a different world. A great avalanche of murres came flying out from the cavern at my approach, startled from their nesting ledges. Many of them hit the water before they gained the entrance, and I could see them swimming by me. How I envied them their abilities!

How I would have liked to take to the air at that moment, but I continued on into the archway, and sure enough, the water rose and fell along the cliffs, but in a serene and reasonable fashion. I looked around me and picked a ledge that the swells neared each time, and each time that I went up in the boat on one, I placed a piece of equipment up on the ledge, until all was safe. I planned to leap then, onto the ledge, holding the painter in my hand. However, I was not as dashing as I thought, for in the meantime I had become very stiff, and found myself ignobly crawling out onto the rocky shelf on my hands and knees!

But, I had the boat painter in my hand, and after watching the action of the water for a while, when the boat came up on one of the waves, I took a tight turn of the rope around a projecting rock and held on. As the water went down, the boat was tipped, and all the water poured out. When the next wave came in, it left the boat high and dry and on the level with me. Once more I had a buoyant empty craft with which to try to overcome our disaster.

On one of the trips of the boat on an upswell, I jumped in, gathered in all the equipment, and started out of the cave. "Now stop me!" I thought exultingly. I felt a confidence which was probably not entirely warranted by the situation, but getting into a dry boat encouraged me so that I felt I could tackle anything. I knew very well I could no longer land at our camp, but I got out both oars and headed for the most likely place on the lee side of our camp island. It was a furious scene, a turmoil of immense waves, dark clouds scudding before the wind, and night coming on. But, I had a manageable boat now and bent every ounce of strength to the oars, studied the shore line to get the behavior of the water lashing upon it, then pulled along on an incoming wave. With the painter in my hand I leaped out upon the shore. I was standing on solid rock, and on our camp island too! I drew the boat up as high as I could, with a little premonition that it would not escape high tide, but it was the best I could do single-handed.

A high rocky ridge separated me from the camp side of the island, and I started climbing. By relaying in short trips I finally arrived on top with all the gear. Now I remembered that the cliff leading down to the campsite was one which had been scaled before only once, by a famous ornithologist-mountaineer. But such was my enthusiasm and exultation at this time that in the dusky light, I brought down over that cliff crutches, cameras, and tripods, by relays!

But first of all I looked down toward our camp. I saw Lewis there, stooping over, working at something. I found out later that he was preparing match heads for setting off flashlights that night, to try to attract the attention of people on the mainland, even though the nearest settlement was around a bend of the coast, miles away. He had also been firing his pistol in a desperate effort to get attention, and I had not even heard the shots. I also learned that without his crutches he had managed to get to the top of the island to see where I had gone. At that particular time I must have been in the tunnel, for he saw no sign of me and assumed I had drowned.

Now suddenly there I was, yelling at him in a very hilarious voice and waving his crutches at him from the top of the ridge!

The smile on his face when he looked up and saw me was something I shall always remember!

EDWARD A. ARMSTRONG

Food Supply and Wren Behavior

The Reverend Edward Allworthy Armstrong of St. Mark's Vicarage, Cambridge, England, is a noted specialist in the study of bird behavior. In the preface to the first edition of his Bird Display and Behavior, *Oxford University Press, New York, 1942, he wrote: "An interesting observation of a bird's behavior should be no less carefully recorded and reverently preserved than the type specimen of a new subspecies. Lack of regard for this principle has long prevented the outdoor study of birds from being considered much more than the harmless hobby of men who preferred looking at birds to killing them."*

The Reverend Armstrong was born in Belfast on October 8, 1900. There he attended Queen's University, and later, Leeds Uni-

versity in studies for his Master's degree. His honors for work in ornithology are a gold medal from the British Ornithologists' Union and the John Burroughs Medal, awarded him in 1942 for his book Birds of the Grey Wind.

FOOD SUPPLY AND WREN BEHAVIOR:

ADAPTABILITY IN BEHAVIOR AS AN EVOLUTIONARY ASSET

If any of the few inhabitants of the beautiful island of Fetlar in the Shetland Isles had noticed a figure seated for hours on a rock by the sea, gazing at an overhanging bank, they would have wondered what he was doing. They might not have considered him very profitably employed had they known that he was watching a wren's nest. In fact this naturalist was following up clues which had already taken him to the fiords of Iceland, the mountains of North Africa, and other remote places where wrens lived.

From prehistoric times the wren has been regarded as a bird of mystery. Bronze Age men hunted and sacrificed it, and to this day a modified form of the ritual is celebrated immediately after Christmas in Ireland. Ornithologists have been puzzled by the bird, for it differs markedly in structure and behavior from other European species. Each male builds a number of nests, many of which are never occupied. Wrens sing practically throughout the year, and little mixed parties cluster together in winter dormitories. No other European bird shares these peculiarities.

Several years of studying wrens enabled me to check what was known concerning them and to realize how intriguing are their ways. The multiplicity of its nests was solved. The male, fluttering his drooped wings while singing softly and sweetly, invites a female to a nest and when she has been installed goes through the same procedure with another female, and, perhaps, yet another. He may mate with other females for the second brood. His persistent singing is his way of attracting successive females to his territory, which he defends throughout the year.

When a bird has been studied for a year or two, it is usually possible to set down on paper how it behaves without a great deal of qualification. Not so with wrens. I found that their behavior was quite variable. The male normally builds the nest, but occasionally the female may participate or do most of the work. The nest may be in the ground or 30 feet high in a tree; it may be hidden in a cavity or fixed in a bush. The male sings, but exceptional females may also sing. Often he gives little help with tending the nestlings, but occasionally, especially if his mate is killed, he feeds them with fanatical zeal. One male may be polygamous (or have several mates), while a neighbor is monogamous (single-mated) or remains unmated. A male which neglects his broods early in the season may be very attentive later. The male usually leads the fledged young to a sleeping nook, or dormitory, but the female may do so and even snuggle in with the family. Thus, although the roles of male and female are rather definitely distinct, as tends to be particularly true of birds with a multiple or temporary pair-bond, on occasion the male may act as a female or the female as a male.

The question forced itself upon me: When the wren establishes itself on moorland or the rugged coast of some northern island, are some of these adaptations accentuated and others suppressed? Do the bird's surroundings influence the character of its pair-bond, the amount of song, and so forth? So I found myself on that sea-washed crag in Shetland seeking the answer. There and at other nests I discovered that in these relatively austere surroundings the wren's behavior differs in a number of ways from that of wrens in English and continental woodlands and gardens. The males tend to be monogamous instead of polygamous, to build fewer nests, to breed later, to have fewer second broods, to sing less, and to help more with the nestlings.

What is the explanation of these very considerable differences? If my view is correct, food supply is crucial. Where food is plentiful, the wrens tend to be polygamous, where it is scarce, they tend to be monogamous. One wren can rear a brood in favorable surroundings, but two are needed to rear approximately the same number of young in bleak areas. Monogamy is adaptive in such regions and polygamy is not.

Thus it seems that the nature and availability of the food supply may determine whether wrens are polygamous or monogamous, build many nests or few, are single-brooded or double-brooded, sing much or little. Foraging has a bearing on the whole integrated pattern of their breeding behavior. This suggests that the food supply of other species of birds may be highly important in determining their way of life, and that the nature of a bird's other activities should be interpreted in relation to its feeding behavior. This principle—the fundamental importance of feeding behavior—may be found to be of great value as a guiding principle in interpreting the evolutionary development of birds. A slight modification in feeding behavior may start adaptations in the integration of the whole pattern of behavior, eventually resulting in such divergence that a new species emerges. The exploitation of new sources of food may lead to extensions of range and the isolation of populations in which evolution is relatively rapid.

Reflection on these Shetland wrens busy feeding their

young suggested another consideration concerning evolutionary development. Since increasing specialization may facilitate the formation of new species as birds become highly adapted to exploit a particular niche in an environment, it follows that successive refinements in adaptation are apt to render a bird ill-adapted should the environment change rather quickly. Specialized adaptation may also hinder it from invading new habitats. However, if a species can retain adaptability so that individuals or groups are able to cope with a wide range of situations, this characteristic is likely to enable it to be very successful in extending its distribution. The wren's achievement in spreading from North America across Bering Strait when the ice relaxed its grip, and establishing itself as far westward as Iceland and St. Kilda, and as far south as Burma and North Africa, appears to be due to two principal characteristics—its ability to forage for food in nooks and crannies into which no other bird can penetrate, and its adaptability. A latent capacity to revert to adaptations not primarily suited to the immediate environment may be as important in evolutionary development as the ability to initiate novel adaptations.

My vigil at the Shetland wren's nest not only suggested theories as to how evolution operates but aroused my interest in a curious type of behavior which, until I defined it as "transference activity," had not been given a name. I noticed that after feeding the nestlings the female wren picked up droppings from the ground that had fallen from the nest. When there were no droppings to pick up, she would carry off a small pebble instead. Dippers, too, will carry off substitutes for the fecal sacs of their young. Falcons, disturbed from their nests by a man, may attack and kill harmless passing birds. Exasperated birds will even attack inanimate objects such as tufts of grass, sticks, or tree stumps. A thwarted chimpanzee will assault an inoffensive companion, and an angry man may kick a piece of furniture. This "transference activity" by the wren thus drew my attention to a wide range of similar or related activities. Exploration of their nature should lead to a better understanding of the springs of behavior, both in animals and in human beings.

Thus, sitting by a nest observing the birds go out and in may lead one's thoughts far afield. This stimulation to follow out the implications of what one sees must be counted among the greatest delights of bird watching.

T. DONALD CARTER

When T. Donald Carter of Boonton, New Jersey, retired in the summer of 1960, he had spent more than forty years on the staff of the American Museum of Natural History in New York City. During his last thirty years of service, he was Assistant Curator of Mammals there, doing scientific research and traveling on twenty-seven expeditions for the Museum to collect animals from all the continents of the world except Australia. He made six collecting trips to Africa and has written numerous scientific papers and articles for popular magazines based on his experiences with animals around the world. Early in his career he worked for the New York Zoological Society and traveled on expeditions to Central and South America to collect live birds and mammals. He wrote the text for the book Hoofed Mammals of the World *and was one of the authors of* Mammals of the Pacific World. *He was born in Boonton on January 28, 1893. In retirement at his home*

in the wooded hills outside that town, he raises wild waterfowl as a hobby.

According to Mr. Carter, the mountain nyala should not be confused with the nyala of Zululand, Nyasaland, and the Kruger National Park. The mountain nyala of Ethiopia is a much larger animal, nearer the greater kudu in size. The bull mountain nyala in the exhibit of the American Museum stood 55½ inches tall at the shoulders; the male greater kudu in an adjoining case was 61 inches. The difference in their heights is, in part, accounted for by the greater development of the hump on the greater kudu's shoulders.

Mr. Carter says that Ethiopians do not differentiate in the names of the mountain nyala and the greater kudu; they are both known as "Argazin" in the Amharic language. The horns of the mountain nyala and the nyala are similar in general shape, but those of the mountain nyala are heavier and longer, reaching more than 40 inches in some of the larger bulls. In general color the mountain nyala is grayish-brown with white markings. These markings consist of a chevron between the eyes, patches on the throat and lower neck, three or four indistinct vertical stripes on the sides, and a longitudinal series of spots on the sides and flanks —hence this antelope's first English name was the spotted kudu. The cows do not have horns. Though they are of a color similar to that of the males, their white markings are less distinct.

THE MOUNTAIN NYALA

THE great highlands of Ethiopia are a naturalist's paradise. The invigorating climate, the superb scenery, and above all the unique plant and animal life make an expedition into these mountains an unforgettable experience. Many of its local mammals and birds live nowhere else in the world. The blue-winged goose, the Abyssinian ibex, the Abyssinian wolf, and the mountain nyala are good examples.

My interest in the mountain nyala was first stimulated in 1925 when Captain Harold A. White presented the American Museum of Natural History of New York City with its first specimen, the skull and horns of a bull he had shot a year or two previously.

It was shortly after this that the Museum was deciding on what mammals should be included in the twenty-eight groups to be installed in the new Akeley African Hall. It was a foregone conclusion that an animal as rare and as interesting as the mountain nyala should be included.

Although it was first described by a scientist in 1910, to my knowledge no live mountain nyala has ever reached America. The only specimens to reach any European zoological park were a pair exhibited in the Berlin Zoo shortly before the outbreak of World War II. Even in its limited home range in Ethiopia, it is doubtful whether more than a few hundred exist there today.

Three good friends of the American Museum of Natural History, Gertrude Sanford and the brothers Morris and Sydney Legendre, volunteered to finance the building of this Museum group and also to head an expedition to collect the animals and the needed plants and other materials that are built into an exhibit intended to show the animal in its home. I was fortunate in being invited to go along as the Museum's representative.

The expedition sailed from New York on December 1, 1928. On December 24, we reached Djibouti, the capital and seaport of French Somaliland. It was a three-day train ride to Addis Ababa, the capital of Ethiopia, for in those days the train did not run at night.

The process of getting the expedition's equipment through

customs and preparing for the trip into the interior took three weeks. Good mules to ride were our first purchases, for they were the only means of transportation in the city. The only automobiles in Addis Ababa were those owned by the Ras, and there were no automobile roads outside of the town.

Supplies, including fifty-four mules and three horses, had to be purchased, mostly in the native markets. Twenty boys had to be hired, a mule boy for every four pack mules, a cook, a cook's helper, an interpreter, personal boys, and a head man. Dignitaries had to be visited and in return visited us. We were granted an audience with Ras Tafari * and a few days later were graciously invited to dinner at the palace. This was an elaborate feast of fourteen courses with a table service of gold and a bowl of goldfish as a centerpiece.

Two days before our departure Gertrude Sanford received a mule as a present from the Ras. It was a beautiful animal, with a perfect gait. Its bridle, the velvet saddle blanket, and part of the saddle were embroidered with bright colors and gold thread. About the mule's neck was a collar made of silver cylinders which tinkled merrily.

Sixty miles south of Addis Ababa is Lake Zwai, the most northern of a series of large lakes that extend toward the south for about 175 miles. Although the lakes are separated by short distances, the water in some is alkaline, while in others it is fresh. Many hot springs are along their shores.

Just to the east of these lakes the land rises steeply to form the Arusi Plateau. Much of this plateau is a great grass-covered plain which reaches an altitude of 8,000 feet. Along its western sector the plateau rises to greater heights and forms the Chillalo or Sagatu and the Geder Mountain Ranges, between which flow the headwaters of Webbe Shibeli River. Several

* Ras Tafari (*ras* meaning "marshal") was the previous name of Haile Selassie before he became Emperor.—The Editor.

of these mountain peaks rise to more than 13,000 feet, and from about 8,000 to 9,000 feet upward the slopes are covered with forest. In the higher altitudes this forest becomes dense stands of bamboo. Above the bamboo the country opens up, and the slopes and summits are clothed with a giant heath, *Ericinella manni*, some of it 6 or 7 feet high. Many of the ridges have eroded away to form steep cliffs.

This unique and spectacular country extends in a north-south direction for about 100 miles and east-west for about 75 miles. It is here and only here that the mountain nyala makes its home.

Six days after leaving Addis Ababa we camped on the eastern shore of Lake Zwai. We were informed by natives that the nearest place we could find mountain nyalas was on Ansha Mountain about three days away. We made camp at the edge of a forest at the mountain's base. Early the next morning we set out on muleback to search for nyalas on the upper slopes. We each took a separate game trail up through the forest and later through the dense bamboo jungle. Upon emerging from this darkened tangle I faced a new world. There before me and stretching 3,000 feet upward to the mountain's very summit was a vast expanse of heath, miles of it as far as the eye could see. High above, near the mountain top, were some cliffs with great masses of fallen rocks at their bases. Later I was to learn that what appeared to be a smooth expanse of heath was in reality a series of washes and gullies, whose scattered stones and boulders made very difficult traveling.

I left the boy with the mules at the bamboo edge, and went on alone. The boy wore a white toga, which I felt was not conducive to stalking a nyala. I climbed nearly to the summit and saw very little sign but enough to know that nyalas were there. Throughout the day, although I did not see nyalas, I was not disappointed. I had experienced a most invigorating day in the home of the mountain nyala amid some of the most picturesque mountain scenery it had ever been my privilege to enjoy.

Upon my return to camp I learned that one of our party had had a fleeting glimpse of a nyala at the edge of the bamboos.

We spent three more days on Ansha Mountain with little results, then decided to try elsewhere. We visited Chief Pasha Tasama, and he assured us that we would find greater numbers of nyalas on Kaka Mountain, two days' travel to the south.

Kaka Mountain was even more impressive than Ansha. Again we made our base camp at the edge of the forest at the mountain's foot. The next day we moved three of the tents and pitched them beside a spring of ice-cold water on the heath. This was to be our home for the next three weeks.

From the signs about camp, nyalas were plentiful, and that very afternoon I was to experience one of my greatest thrills. I had been out all morning and was returning toward camp, following up a draw which had kept me hidden for some distance. The draw became more shallow, and as my head arose above the bank, a movement toward my left attracted my attention. There, feeding on the heath about 150 yards away, were three nyalas—a large bull, a cow, and a young bull with horns about 8 inches long. It was a beautiful sight in an enthralling setting. The lighting was perfect with the sun behind my back. In front of me and beyond the antelopes were the heath-covered slopes of the mountain reaching to the three distinct peaks. For fully five minutes I watched the animals quietly browsing. First one and then another would nervously look up, with their ears thrust forward, then return to their feeding. A tricky mountain breeze must have carried my scent to them, for at the same moment, three heads shot up and all gazed in my direction. Suddenly they wheeled and ran, the cow leading, followed by the young bull, the old bull bringing up the rear.

After that first day I saw many more mountain nyalas, but it is these three, in their majestic yet typical setting, that stand out most clearly in my memory.

For three weeks we lived among the mountain nyalas on Kaka Mountain. We discovered that they seemed to prefer to spend the nights and the heat of the day in the bamboos and the forest below, coming out to browse on the heath and graze on the patches of grass upon the mountainside during the early morning and evening. They were wary animals, and if at all disturbed they would quietly slip into the forest. We also discovered that it was almost impossible for us to hide our early-morning approach up the mountainside. We decided upon a plan to outwit them.

On Kaka Mountain there were a number of peaks, three of which gave commanding views of the slopes below. We each chose one of these peaks and had our cots and blankets placed there. There we spent the night to await the morning and the nyalas as they came up the mountain to feed. It was cold, and ice formed in the buckets every night. Almost every morning there was a dense fog covering the mountaintop until it was quickly dispersed by the rising sun. From our high place, using binoculars, we could now watch the unsuspecting animals below.

The older bulls seemed to prefer the higher reaches, and many of them appeared to live alone. We did see small groups consisting of a bull with two or three cows, two or three bulls together, and as many as nine cows in one herd. We saw a few cows in the more open forest where it joined the plain, but we found no evidence of very young calves. We also discovered that not all the nyalas went down to the forest for the night, for on several occasions, in the early morning, a bull leaped up from where he had bedded down in a thick clump of heath. In fact, nyalas could be found on the upper slopes at any time of the day. In all, we estimated we watched about forty nyalas during our stay on Kaka Mountain.

Other than man the mountain nyala has few enemies. Leopards live commonly throughout their range, and even inhabit the higher mountaintops. These big cats undoubtedly take their toll, especially of the younger animals. The altitude is too high for lions.

In March of 1958 I again had the opportunity to visit Ethiopia. Since my previous visit, thirty years before, the country had undergone many changes. It had experienced the Italian invasion and Addis Ababa had become a modern city.

Newell and Bettina Ward and I had just completed a safari in Kenya. Our Ethiopian Air Lines plane put down at the airport in Addis Ababa, where taxis were waiting to take us to the comfortable Ras Hotel. In the foyer, a surprise awaited me. On a calendar advertising the Ethiopian Air Lines was pictured the mountain nyala group exhibited in the American Museum of Natural History in New York City, the group I had assisted in collecting in Ethiopia thirty years before!

A tour of the city showed us modern office buildings, modern stores, many new schools, and wide, paved streets. Automobiles were everywhere. The railroad station, where we had spent long days arguing with the customs, was the same, also some of the native markets, but everything else showed progress. Again we received an invitation to call on Emperor Haile Selassie, but unfortunately the invitation was for the day that we had to leave for home.

Our stay in Ethiopia was limited to three days. Robert Proctor of the American Embassy volunteered his services and the use of his car. I immediately asked him if it were possible for us to take a trip to the Arusi Plateau. He said that it would be impossible to reach the plateau but there was a good road that skirted the western shore of Lake Zwai and that the trip and return could easily be made in one day.

The road to Lake Zwai proved excellent, much of it black-top. Rivers, such as the Awash, which years before we were forced to ford on the backs of mules, were now spanned by iron bridges. Instead of the caravans of camels and mules laden with coffee, hides, and grain for the markets of Addis Ababa, we passed great, heavily laden trucks, many of them with the same produce.

We turned off the main highway onto a sandy road which was in reality a series of cattle paths. Soon we came to the shores of the lake. This proved to be the watering place for the cattle and goats of the local people. Over a hundred head were on the shore and out in the lake, some of them standing with only their heads and upper backs above the water. Across the lake and in the far distance rose the high mountains of the Arusi Plateau. I could not distinguish any of the peaks, and the natives could not give us any names. As it was still early, we continued south until we reached Lake Shala. Mt. Kaka is about 40 miles due east of this lake, and though I saw a mountain which was in the right position for it and seemed to have a familiar outline, I could not be sure. Nevertheless it brought back pleasant memories.

To my inquiries about the present status of the mountain nyala I received conflicting replies. The general opinion was that they were still found in their old haunts but in reduced numbers. They are now classified as royal game, which gives them some of their much-needed protection. Undoubtedly the animal owes its existence at the present day to the inaccessibility of its habitat and also to the fact that the country it lives in is unfit for the grazing of domestic stock. Should the mountains be exploited, should minerals be found there, or should the great heath fields be destroyed, the mountain nyala would be doomed, and the world would lose one of its most beautiful and most interesting large animals. Let us hope that none of these things come to pass and that future generations will still know the mountain nyala whose stately bearing is so in keeping with the scenic beauty of its wild mountain home.

PART FOUR

DON ECKLEBERRY

Search for the Rare Ivorybill

Don Richard Eckleberry, artist for the Audubon Bird Guides *by Richard H. Pough, published by Doubleday & Company, New York City, has illustrated fourteen bird books and painted most of the birds of the continental United States. More recently he began painting the tropical birds of Mexico and Central and South America, and his tropical researches in the field resulted in his color illustrations of birds for the two-volume* Life Histories of Central American Birds *by Alexander F. Skutch and the color plates for James Bond's* Birds of the West Indies. *His most recent trip to Argentina with the jointly sponsored American Museum–Buenos Aires Ornithological Expedition was his eighth tropical venture.*

Born in Sebring, Ohio, in 1921, he says that he cannot remember a time when he did not draw, which seemed quite natural, as three of his uncles were artists. Beginning with an early interest in entomology, at thirteen he first began drawing birds. During World War II, he worked part time as a warden for the National Audubon Society in Louisiana, Florida, and elsewhere, and the other part of his working time doing art and editorial work for Audubon Magazine *in New York City. He is now a free-lance artist and lives at Babylon, Long Island, New York.*

SEARCH FOR THE RARE IVORYBILL

My arrival on the Singer Tract in Louisiana in 1944 was the end of a chain of events. These began twelve years earlier in the offices of the Louisiana Department of Conservation when, on an April day in 1932, a dead bird arrived, shipped from the northeastern part of the state. It was a big woodpecker, larger than a crow, strikingly patterned black and white, with a long scarlet crest and a prodigious ivory-white beak. The Conservation Department pronounced it a male ivory-billed woodpecker, *Campephilus principalis*, possibly the rarest bird in North America. None had been seen since 1926, and museum men were ready to dust off their specimens and put them on that shelf of extinct species already crowded with birds eloquent in their glassy-eyed reproach at our misuse of a continent.

When rediscovery of ivory-billed woodpeckers in Louisiana came, and with it some hope of saving them, the National Audubon Society made an immediate investigation of the area and found that there were at least six living birds in the Singer Tract, perhaps more. In this largest remaining southern hardwood forest of 80,000 acres, it was well-nigh impossible to make an exact census.

Effort for protection of the ivorybills began, and the Louisiana State Conservation Department had wardens on the Singer Tract. They forbade the collecting of any more birds; however, in order to make their rarity and value appreciated by the American public, a newspaper story had put an estimated value of one thousand dollars on an ivorybill skin. Forthwith a young fellow appeared with one of the big woodpeckers dangling from his hand, to collect the one thousand dollars. Wardens in the Singer Tract thereafter kept stricter vigil.

When a few ivorybills were also discovered in a similar wilderness along the lower Santee River in South Carolina, things seemed to be looking up. By 1937 the National Audubon Society had established a research fellowship at Cornell University which began with an extensive search throughout the South for more birds. This was to be followed by a careful study of the Louisiana group to try to find the key to an intelligent program to save the species.

James T. Tanner, a graduate student at Cornell University, was granted the research fellowship. He traveled thousands of miles on this assignment to the wildest, most inaccessible places where the ivory-billed woodpeckers had been rumored to be, or might persist. In many a small village and on many a backwoods farm, Tanner might have been seen showing photographs of the ivorybill to old-timers, logging men, game wardens, native guides, and hunters, but no more birds were found. In fact, the South Carolina birds had vanished, but from his travels and conversations, Tanner believed there could still be a few, perhaps as many as two dozen, lurking in the murky recesses of such habitats as Florida's Big Cypress Swamp.

Tanner settled down to his study of the Louisiana birds. His findings indicate that the ivorybill is, among birds, something of a gourmet, dining almost exclusively on certain wood-boring grubs which infest the inner bark next to the sapwood. Nature gave this largest of our woodpeckers (second in size, incidentally, only to the similar imperial woodpecker of Mexico) the very specialized job of keeping these particular insect larvae in check. Sometimes epidemics of these wood-boring insects kill large stands of trees.

After two or three years a dead cypress tree loses its bark and with it the insect food supply of the ivorybill. This means that the lordly ivorybill must depend on a regular supply of dying trees. Even in mature or virgin forest with its more or less regular death rate, even in these flood-plain forests where tree growth is especially rapid, the ivorybill needs plenty of range to satisfy its appetite. Perhaps the species was nomadic, and when natural catastrophes such as storm, fire, or drought killed many trees, the ivorybills would move into such places until the food ran out and they were forced to look for food elsewhere. This theory would explain the sudden appearances of ivorybills in new areas and its equally sudden disappearances from old haunts. It may be the reason why mated pairs have the habit of moving about together throughout the year except during the nesting season when females are tied down with their families.

However that may be, we know that the ivorybills retreated from their original range, which was principally the river-bottom forests from Texas to North Carolina and up the Mississippi Valley to Indiana. As the South was lumbered, and the wilderness melted away, the remaining isolated patches were so far separated that the remaining birds were restricted to them. Unless such areas met their exacting requirements, they disappeared. The Singer Tract evidently suited them.

Since 1926 the owners had leased the tract to the state of

Louisiana as a game refuge, but this lease did not prevent commercial exploitation. Logging rights were sold in 1937 while Tanner was still busy in the Tract with his research. The National Audubon Society worked rapidly with federal and state officials hoping that the area might be purchased and set aside as a park or refuge not only for the rare woodpeckers, but as a sample of primeval southern hardwood forest with its teeming wildlife intact, as a permanent living exhibit for the American people.

When the United States entered World War II, lumbering in this country was greatly accelerated. The last known home of the ivorybills was coming down around their heads. A final effort to save them got under way. John H. Baker, President of the National Audubon Society, went directly to President Franklin Delano Roosevelt, whose interest in such matters had always been great. The President expressed his interest in writing to the Secretary of the Interior. Baker followed through with the Secretary, with the Director of the U.S. Fish and Wildlife Service, and with the Director of the National Park Service. He spoke with the Acting Chief of the U.S. Forest Service, who stated that in the light of his knowledge of the inventory of southern hardwood timber, he did not think it necessary to cut all of the Singer Tract. The head of the War Production Board stated that he saw no reason why the board should not rule that the cutting of some of the timber on this tract might not well be excluded from the war production program.

Baker then went to the Governor of Louisiana and his Conservation Commissioner. It was decided that the state of Louisiana would spend $200,000 in the purchase of as much of the area as this sum would buy and set up an inviolate wildlife refuge. At the instance of the governor, a meeting was arranged at the offices of the lumber company in Chicago and was attended by the Chairman of the Board and President of the company, the Conservation Commissioner representing the state of Louisiana, the Chief of the Division of Wildlife Refuges of the U.S. Fish and Wildlife Service and his counsel, and Mr. Baker. The Wildlife Service was prepared to lease, with options to buy, a buffer area of cutover land.

Just prior to this meeting, the governors of four states sent a joint letter of appeal to the lumber company and the owners. In spite of all this demonstrated interest, the officials of the lumber company took the position that they were unwilling to discuss any form of cooperation in setting up a wildlife refuge which would involve any limitation whatever on their plan to complete cutting of timber in accordance with their contract rights.

With negotiations still stalemated at the end of 1943, Richard H. Pough, who was then, like myself, on the staff of the National Audubon Society, went down to the Singer Tract to see how the ivorybills were making out. After six weeks of careful investigation, Pough sent disastrous news: "I have been able to locate only a single female and feel reasonably sure that no other birds are here." Knowing Dick, I knew that "reasonably sure" meant "sure." With this report I was wild to be off to Louisiana, not just to see a living ivorybill, but to sketch and paint as an historic record the only one known to be alive.

Dick Pough told me that the best way to find the bird was to have Jesse Laird, a local man who was keeping tabs on it as best he could, show me the roost tree. As soon as I had established myself in a farmhouse within the tract, I visited Jesse and got the further bad news that during the three months since Dick had returned to New York, the lumbermen had been cutting in the immediate area and that the roost tree was down. Moreover, the Mississippi River had flooded, backing up the Tensas River, which meandered through the tract, and inundating most of the bottom lands. Temporarily at least, lumbering operations were going on in another section, but the water and the litter left by the lumbermen made it difficult to get through the woods. On the brighter side, Jesse said he had seen the bird a few weeks before in the vicinity of an old roosting tree he thought it might be using again, and that we might go in the next afternoon to see if that was the case. In the meantime, he said, he would arrange for a boat to take me up the Tensas to Greenlea Bend early in the morning in case the bird had moved over there. When Jesse left, I morosely turned to unpacking the art supplies I was beginning to doubt I would have any opportunity to use.

That evening Mr. Henry, my host, and I were on the back porch watching the deer come out of the forest one by one at the far end of the clearing, their white-lined ears twitching and now and then a tail flashing up like a white flag of surrender to apprehension.

I shall call him Mr. Henry though that was not his name and though he probably would see no reason for the disguise. My host ran the place, but, as it turned out, I saw very little of him during those two weeks, which was probably just as well, as a little of Mr. Henry went a long way with me. I suppose he was busy overseeing the tenant farms, or perhaps he spent most of his time in Tallulah.

"Never get tired watchin' them deer, though they eat up the grass somethin' fierce," he drawled. Then, swinging his solid bulk around to face the kitchen, he bellowed, "Liza, when we gonna eat? You gettin' lazier ever' day. You been catfishin' ag'in?"

"No suh, Mistah Henry, suh, I ain't," Liza answered.

"I just *bet* she ain't," he said, turning to me.

"We is 'most ready, Mistah Henry," said Liza, unperturbed.

"Well I'm hungry," he grumbled. "That ol' Liza can sure cook, too, I *got* to say."

When, shortly, we sat down to table, Liza served a large platter of lambfries and sweet potatoes, a bowl of greens, and a dish piled high with steaming hot biscuits. Mr. Henry was clearly right about Liza's cooking.

The next morning a fellow appeared with an outboard motor; we hitched it to a soggy old boat and went upriver. The day was mellow and smelled of spring, though in early April the bare trees were only hazed with the rusts and yellow greens of preleaf flowers. Some had clumps of mistletoe in their crowns like herons' nests; others wore manes of polypody ferns up their trunks and along their larger branches. Willows displayed chrome-yellow catkins, and gray rags of moss hung from the cypresses.

The river narrowed as we passed Alligator Bayou. Above the whine of the motor the only bird song I could hear was the thin little trill of the parula warbler, though cardinals flashed past and an anhinga flew vulture-high in circles. Around each bend the soft-shelled turtles sunning themselves on drowned branches would scramble back to the opaque safety of the brown water.

Here and there we cut the motor to listen; on higher ground we got out and walked. I was sure I would recognize the short, toy-trumpet call of the ivorybill if I heard it. I caught my breath once when we saw a large bird flying back through the trees, but it was only what my companion called a "Lord God," or pileated woodpecker, of which there are plenty there. We went up to Baker's Ditch, Andrew's Bend, and Greenlea Bend, but nowhere was there any sign of an ivorybill. So we returned.

It rained early in the afternoon, but by the time Jesse picked me up and we drove to John's Bayou, where we left the car and started walking in, the sun was sending long shadows on the puddles and over the sodden leaves. Pushing branches aside, tripping over snarls of greenbrier, and grasping at dangling grapevines for support brought sudden little showers. Saw palmettos wiped their broad surfaces against us. The trunks of the remaining trees were black with wet. As we moved in to lower ground our boots stirred cream mud into coffee water. We made our way around the great brush piles of lopped-off treetops and dismembered prostrate trunks. I believe these logs were ash, which Jesse said the lumber company cut while they were in to get the sweet gum, but which they planned to haul out only if the price later made it worthwhile.

Jesse signaled to be on the alert as we sloshed on, our rhythmic splashes sounding louder and louder in the already quieting woods. After about a mile of this, he stopped and pointed to a hole about 60 feet up in a half-dead ash.

We sat on a large log with our boots dangling in water to wait for the ivorybill. It was 6:15 P.M., and the sun was slipping down fast. A number of birds were still busy with their vespers. A prothonotary warbler sang with great persistence, nearly drowning out the more distant and melancholic notes of a titmouse. Woodpeckers were tattooing. A Carolina wren's rich and syncopated voice ricocheted around us. Towhee, myrtle warbler, downy woodpecker—I sorted them by ear and mentally pushed them aside. I looked at my watch. It was 6:25. I turned questioningly to Jesse, who shrugged his shoulders.

The cool shadows were creeping up the gilded trunk of the roost tree. The small birds became quiet, but a red-bellied woodpecker called nearby and beat out some overtime on a resonant stub. Barred owls had a round of hooting as their hunting time approached. It was in the midst of their hooting that I heard it, a somewhat nuthatchlike note but distinctive, and I turned again to Jesse, jerking my thumb in the direction of the sound. Jesse cocked an ear and paused some time until the note came again, followed by a loud double rap; then he smiled and nodded.

6:33. Only the owls called now, except for five toots from the ivorybill, no closer. I pulled out my notebook and wrote down the sound as "*henk!* or *hank!*, an abrupt falsetto note." More loud double knocks, two or three of these, a long pause, and repeated. I was about convinced she had a roost tree elsewhere. The mosquitoes were getting worse. 6:46. Then I saw her!

She came trumpeting in to the roost, her big wings cleaving the air in strong, direct flight, and she alighted with one magnificent upward swoop. Looking about wildly with her hysterical pale eyes, tossing her head from side to side, her black crest erect to the point of leaning forward, she hitched up the tree at a gallop, trumpeting all the way. Near the top she became suddenly quiet and began preening herself. With a few disordered feathers properly and vigorously rearranged, she gave her distinctive double rap, the second blow following so closely the first that it was almost like an echo—an astonishingly loud, hollow, drumlike *Bam-am!* Then she hitched down the tree and sidled around to the roost hole, looked in, looked around, hitched down beneath the entrance, double-rapped, and went in.

At 7:20, after I had finished all my notes and we were about to leave, she popped out and raced up the trunk to its broken top where, bathed in rich orange light of the setting sun, she alternately preened and jerked her head about in a peculiar angular way, quite unlike the motions of any other woodpecker I knew. I was tremendously impressed by the majestic and wild personality of this bird, its vigor, its almost frantic aliveness. She flew off after five minutes and in another five returned, calling once and going in to roost at 7:30 on the dot. By the time we regained the road it was quite dark.

During the following two weeks it rained a good deal, which prevented my painting outside as much as I wanted to. But when the weather looked favorable, I'd take my paper, brushes, paint, pencils, note pad, and binoculars and tramp back into the roost area early in the morning when the wild turkeys were gobbling, or late in the afternoon. I gave up trying to follow the bird through the ground litter. She would go a quarter or half a mile in one flight, and by the time I would struggle up to her she would be off to other feeding places. So with a few exceptions my observations were made at the roost tree, "putting her to bed" or waiting for her to get up. I sometimes got lost coming out after dark and would have to sit in the blackness waiting for the moon to rise and give me my bearings. Once I nearly bumped into a black bear which, as startled as I was, splashed and crashed off through the brush.

One day on my way in I investigated some desultory hammering expecting to find a pileated woodpecker, but it was the ivorybill working on a broken stub not 15 feet above the ground. I watched her for a good ten minutes. I hope I am not dispelling belief in what I have said about the regal qualities of this bird to add that there was something comical about it too. That big pale bill sometimes looked almost like an ice cream cone jammed into her black mouth, and then the expression of her eyes seemed the natural one at such an occurrence. Call that anthropomorphism if you like, but it is just such impressions which give the bird painter the key to that "rightness" of expression for which he is always striving.

At work, she was not so much a woodpecker as a barkpeeler. She attacked the bark by rearing back, her head usually off to one side, and striking at an oblique angle. Often the loosened bark was flipped off, after one or two blows, by a quick movement which appeared to combine a slight twist and a lateral flick of the head. Hammering was not rapid or persistent, but the bird's long neck gave tremendous thrust, for when fully applied these glancing stabs knocked free pieces as much as half a foot long and 3 or 4 inches across, though the ground below her was mostly strewn with smaller chips. Now and again she would wedge her bill under the bark immediately following a stroke and rapidly on in, in two or three short pushes, spreading the bark against the broadening bill until that big chisel of hers was pretty well buried, as though rushing after retreating borers. After resting quietly for a time she suddenly flew off in straight ducklike flight in which there seemed to be very little movement of the "inner wing"–the secondaries–most of the action being beyond the wrist.

So the days slipped away. Gradually I got my sketches and notes. Liza and I became increasingly good friends to the point where I could help her with the churning without her standing behind me in that ridiculous paper-bag hat and the skimpy print dress over her bony frame, clucking and worrying about what Mr. Henry would say, and to the point where she could warn me about being in the woods after dark. The woods, she said, were full of "hants." But the only spirit I could hear was the voice of doom for this entire natural community, epitomized by that poor lone ivorybill (which should have been feeding well-grown young these days, had she a mate) and vocalized by the shrill squeals of the donkey engine which worked all night bringing out the logs.

Before leaving, I rode a gasoline car back into the cutting. It *put-putted* along uneven narrow-gauge rails like a launch in choppy water and teetered precariously over the bayous. In the worst spots, two Negroes sitting in front, poured sand on the rails to increase traction. German prisoners of war were employed for much of the work, supervised by a lumberman and with one army guard for every four men. The guards had no eye for the beauty of primeval forest, and they didn't like the mosquitoes, the ticks, or the mud. They called it "Little Guadalcanal." But the prisoners were enjoying themselves, except that to a man they hated their Prussian sergeant, who still maintained discipline over them. They were, as any European would be, incredulous at the waste—only the best wood taken, the rest left in wreckage to rot. I watched one tree come screaming down and cared to see no more. Most of the wood was used for packing crates and tea chests, I understand.

Possibly there are still, at this writing, ivorybills in the South, though the Louisiana birds are gone. If you consider the Cuban ivorybill to be a small race of the same species, there may remain a few of these also. But it would take an optimist indeed to foresee any hope for the species.

We tend to place value on rarity at all levels of experience. Perhaps that is why these few days live so vividly in my mind. But I think not. I have seen other birds rarer in museum collections and about which much less is known. My experiences were in no way unique; others have seen ivorybills, and some have known them far more intimately. I have had higher adventures in more exotic places. No, it was the stamp of Fate which impressed this experience upon me. Nature is little concerned with the fate of the individual, but there is no greater tragedy in the scheme of things than the extinction of a species.

DURWARD L. ALLEN

Of Skunks, Facts, and Time

Dr. Durward L. Allen, Professor of Wildlife Management, Purdue University, was born October 11, 1910, at Uniondale, Indiana. He was graduated from the University of Michigan in 1932 and received his Doctor of Philosophy degree for work in vertebrate ecology at Michigan State University. He has been a research biologist for the state of Michigan and a research biologist for the U.S. Fish and Wildlife Service at Laurel, Maryland, where he became Assistant Chief, Branch of Wildlife Research, before leaving in 1954 to accept a professorship at Purdue. Dr. Allen's major books are Our Wildlife Legacy *(Funk & Wagnalls Company, 1954),* Pheasants Afield *(The Stackpole Company, 1954),* Pheasants of North America, *Editor (published by Wildlife Management Institute, 1956), and* Fox Squirrel Management. *His principal wildlife research has been with pheasants, cottontail rabbits, skunks, and fox squirrels.*

OF SKUNKS, FACTS, AND TIME

REFERRING to wildlife management, Aldo Leopold, acknowledged "father" of the science, once said, "Perhaps the day will come when many states will learn that research cannot be turned on and off like a spigot."

While there are many aspects of this truism—and Leopold was aware of them all—one that particularly impresses me concerns the cumulative experience of the research man. Day by day, and year by year, the student of environmental biology draws facts from many disciplines that, in the fullness of time, may qualify him for original interpretation in his chosen technical microcosm.

I suppose this learning usually is a slow, unrealized process, but at times the pieces fall into place in a manner that is arresting—almost startling. Such a sequence of events began in the winter of 1939–1940, when Warren W. Shapton and I were studying the relationships of animals in their winter underground dens at the Rose Lake Wildlife Experiment Station, near Lansing, Michigan. That fall, on our 1,200-acre area, we located more than one hundred dens and staked them for easy location under snow. Later, we used the labor of a crew of Civilian Conservation Corps (CCC) boys to excavate thirty-six of the burrows which showed signs of winter use.

In an earlier study, I had dug out three ground dens which contained male and female skunks in the ratios 1 to 10, 1 to 10, and 1 to 7. It suggested that the large aggregations of winter-sleeping skunks one hears about are mostly females, and that when a male moves into such a burrow he may repel other male invaders. This was something on which Shapton and I wanted more information. During the summer and fall previous to the winter study, we operated box traps baited with smoked herring, and we ear-tagged as many skunks as possible for later recognition.

In the course of the winter it became evident that skunks were unusually active—they were tracking about in cold weather when they should have been (we thought) packed away in snug nests below ground. Also, they were seen abroad in the full light of day, which is contrary to their usual behavior. We received reports of dead skunks being found by a WPA labor crew. Several of these animals, too far gone for usefulness, were examined, and we managed to retrieve a fairly fresh carcass from which the hide had been removed. This specimen was sent to the Game Division pathology laboratory in East Lansing for autopsy.

A woman called our office and told of a skunk in her basement. Would the "skunk man" please come and get him out of there? Most certainly he would. We studied this animal carefully as it crouched before us on the laboratory table. It stood with head down and eyes closed, occasionally trembling, alive but in a deep coma. It was a beautiful, fat, glossy specimen. In the pathology laboratory it, too, was autopsied, and its tissue cultures were injected into captive skunks in our pens. Nothing came of it.

Six feet underground (in the deepest burrow of all), we found a live male skunk abiding with the remains of a second animal which was almost completely eaten. This was different, since it was my first observation of apparent cannibalism in skunks. There were more reports, of dazed skunks wandering around bumping into things. Then, one day, Shapton and the crew encountered a wild-acting, vigorous animal which they overpowered and tagged. It tried to bite repeatedly. It was bleeding at the nose and cut about the head as if from fighting

—it was the second individual we found with such signs of combat.

After some hours, Shapton tracked this skunk from the spot where it was liberated. It had entered one of the marked dens. We watched the snow at this burrow for two days, and there were no tracks leading out. So our crew went to digging. The tagged animal was found dead in a grass nest. We brought the fresh carcass in for examination before it went off to the pathologists. It was in a peculiar condition:

There was a solid rope of grass wound tightly around its middle. Had our lives depended on it, we could not possibly have tied that dry grass into such a solid, confining belt. Evidently the animal had turned over and over in the burrow, entwining the grass a wisp at a time. How many hundreds of times had it turned in one direction to bring this about? And, above all, why?

"I suppose," said Shapton, "that if we knew the story of this one, we might have the answer to a lot of things." How right he was.

That winter we accounted for ten mortalities among skunks on our study area, and it became obvious that the animals had declined in numbers. Fur dealers' reports for the southern half of the state showed the same trend. Reports from farther south indicated a "die-off" of skunks in Illinois and Indiana the winter before. It appeared that some contagion had moved north into Michigan.

We turned in three specimens that were in good condition for pathology studies, but there was no gross evidence of disease other than the usual parasites. Tissue cultures produced nothing, and results were negative for slides made from the various organs—with one exception. Cells of the cerebral cortex in all three of these animals showed "inclusion bodies" which probably were significant. S. C. Whitlock, Game Division pathologist, sent these slides out for study by specialists. Months later, he told me:

"It probably was some unknown virus that affected the central nervous system. You could call it encephalitis, but that's as specific as anyone could be."

After the war and a change of positions, I sat one evening with the staff of the U.S. Fish and Wildlife Service in the library of the Patuxent Research Refuge, in Maryland. Don R. Coburn, Fish and Wildlife Service pathologist, was showing moving pictures of waterfowl mortality from botulism at the Bear River marshes in Utah. In one of the scenes, a redhead duck sat on the water and spun round and round.

"Don," I asked, "what on earth is the matter with that duck?"

He stopped the film and ran the section over again. There was the redhead, whirling like a dervish.

"That is what happens," he said, "when the motor centers on just one side of the brain are damaged. It's caused by some kind of encephalitis."

Later I thought about this and realized that, over the years, some pieces were falling into place. I decided that now I knew the story of a skunk that turned over and over in its grave back in Michigan in February, 1940.

ROGER TORY PETERSON

Roger Tory Peterson is the originator of the illustrated Peterson Field Guides so well-known to amateur and professional naturalists in America. Born in Jamestown, New York, August 28, 1908, he attended the Art Students' League and the National Academy of Design in New York City. He began his career as a decorative artist in 1926; was an instructor in science and art, Rivers School, Brookline, Massachusetts, from 1931 to 1934; and from 1934 has been engaged in painting birds and as an illustrator of bird books. He was on the staff of the National Audubon Society from 1934 to 1937 and since 1946 has been Editor of his Field Guide Series for Houghton Mifflin Company. In 1944 he was awarded the Brewster Medal of the American Ornithologists' Union for his Field Guide to the Birds; *the John Burroughs Medal in 1950 for his* Birds over America. *He received an honorary de-*

gree of Doctor of Science two years later from Franklin and Marshall College and in 1958 was awarded the Geoffroy St. Hilliare Gold Medal from the French Natural History Society in Paris. He is a Fellow of the American Ornithologists' Union and the author or coauthor of some ten books.

THE LOST FLAMINGOS

My first view of Laguna Colorada, the "Red Lake," was a fit setting for some dread nightmare. Flashes of lightning, heralding the daily afternoon storm, played about the 19,000-foot peaks that loomed above a lake of deepest red. A waterspout twisted in a sinuous column, binding the sanguine waters to the murky clouds. But who had ever seen a waterspout in the mountains? We were on the roof of the world, nearly 3 vertical miles above the Pacific which lay 200 miles to the west. To reach this unbelievable place we had goaded our Dodge power wagon, geared for high altitudes, over 16,000-foot passes in the Chilean Andes until we crossed the unattended border into Bolivia. My mission was to find the James' flamingo and, if possible, to take pictures of this almost mythical bird.

Most people are unaware that more than one species of flamingo exists in the world. In fact, there are six. The rarest, *jamesi*, has been known to science since 1850. It dropped from sight about 1909, and for a period of nearly fifty years no one, apparently, recorded it. In 1956 when Robert Porter Allen of the National Audubon Society published his classic monograph, *The Flamingos, Their Life History and Survival,* he could say little about the James' flamingo.

"The mystery that surrounds that strange three-toed little highland flamingo today," he wrote, "is matched by an equally obscure history that goes back more than a century. . . . The most astonishing fact concerning *Phoenicoparrus jamesi* is that its habits and nidification have never been described. No actual breeding sites, past or present, are known. . . . Although the fact that *jamesi* has not been observed for many years may be a result of its isolated range . . . we cannot but wonder if James' flamingo still survives. At the moment this would seem to be one of the outstanding mysteries of the avian world."

An enterprising Chilean ornithologist, A. W. Johnson, reading these words, was moved to action. Twenty-five years earlier, he had made two expeditions to the salt lakes of the altiplano in search of this *rara avis*, but his efforts had drawn a blank. Now past sixty, but still of good wind and stout heart when traversing the high *puna*, he determined to have another try at it. With two of his countrymen, Behn and Millie, he piloted his jeep through the high passes for six weeks, examining each *salar* and lake, finding only the widespread Chilean flamingo and sometimes the less frequent Andean flamingo. Late in January of 1957 the disheartened party crossed the border into Bolivia and reaching Laguna Colorada, they spotted, among the thousands of ordinary flamingos, a small minority of the lost *jamesi*—about twenty-five or thirty pairs.

In December of that same year Luis Peña, who perhaps knows the high Andes more intimately than any other field naturalist has ever known the cordillera, guided me to this virtually unknown lake. But we found, instead of "a small minority" of *jamesi*, conservatively 8,000 and possibly as many as 10,000 individuals! On the entire lake, nearly round and 4 miles from shore to shore, we saw but 300 Chilean flamingos, which we easily identified by their pinker color and gray legs with red joints. There were also about 100 Andean flamingos, unique among flamingos in possessing bright yellow legs. This disparity in numbers in two successive years precipitated a controversy that later was to rage from New York to Santiago.

Peña and I agreed that the little *jamesi* is certainly the loveliest and most petite of the flamingos, lacking some of the grotesquery of its relatives. Its much shorter, more gooselike neck gives it more pleasing proportions, and its stubby chrome-yellow bill and deep red legs add distinction. Long red plumes on the lower back and a scattering of red feathers on the breast accent the whiteness of its body. This is the *chururo* of the Quechuas, those descendants of the Incas who still scrape out a marginal subsistence in the barren mountains. Since Inca times they have probably egged the almost inaccessible colonies of Laguna Colorada, and yet no white man had ever seen a nest or an egg of *jamesi* until 1957.

I shall not go into detail here about our trepidations when we crossed the empty Bolivian border where we half expected a brush with bandits who were known to be ranging the neighborhood, nor shall I tell of the rather serious trouble we had later with a band of seventeen nomadic Quechuas who resented our invasion of their lake. Fellow man can be coped with in some fashion, but nature is uncompromising. My main doubts, before I left home, had been centered around the problem of high altitudes. Earlier in 1957 I had done rather poorly on a climb to Carl Akeley's grave on the saddle ridge between Mt. Mikeno and Mt. Karisimbi in the Congo, where the altitude was a mere 12,000 feet. How would I function at 15,000 or 16,000? A series of tests at New York City's Medical Center had indicated that my heart and lungs would be equal to the extra strain. Shots and vitamins were prescribed to build up my red-corpuscle count. Thus I came to the Andes somewhat prepared, but when the altimeter of our power wagon registered 12,000 feet, where the coarse yellow stipa grass of the *puna* begins to clothe the eroded slopes, I fell heir to the usual splitting headaches and "*puna* throat," the dry sore throat and hacking cough that comes from breathing the rarified air with open mouth. At least I was spared nausea and nosebleed. Without two weeks or so to acclimatize, it is an effort simply to lift one's feet—unless one is a highland Indian endowed with massive chest expansion and an extra pint or two of blood in his veins.

From a lookout on the black volcanic slopes above our camp we could spot the main nesting colony of the flamingos, a long pink line almost lost in a mirage in the dead center of the lake, fully 2 miles from any point on the shore. But how to get there? Great shallow bays, extensive mud flats, and long ridges of white salt intervened. Luis Peña sent his assistant, Gerardo, out onto the lake to make a reconnaissance. With him went two Indian boys who had accompanied us from Chile. Returning just as the afternoon storm broke full upon our camp, they reported that flamingos were indeed attending eggs and that there was a way to get to them.

Morning, as is the invariable rule in December, dawned sparkling and cloudless on a chill landscape. Fresh snow had fallen on the mountains, and a quarter-inch sheath of new ice had formed on the placid red waters of the lake, for the temperature, a comfortable 70 degrees at noon, drops to 5 degrees above zero at night. We reminded ourselves that this was summer in the Andes; at home this very day people were trimming Christmas trees. Crunching through the glassy ice and wading in the shallow water, scarcely deep enough to float our rubber boat, I found that the bottom was quite hard and crusty for the first quarter of a mile. Gradually it gave way to softer mud and deeper water. The boys had no waders such as mine with which to protect their bare legs against the cutting edges of the numbing ice. We were therefore forced to wait until about 9 A.M., after the rapidly rising sun had melted the last micalike slivers of ice. The main purpose of the collapsible boat was to transport our equipment, particularly the heavy movie cameras, long lenses, and tripods. Only in places was the water deep enough to float the added weight of a passenger.

As we progressed, first pulling the boat in tandem, then pushing it, the mud grew deeper. Eight inches of water, red with algae, covered 18 inches of soft white mud. We dared not separate ourselves from the buoyant boat; there was too much danger of slipping into some bottomless pit where a subterranean geyser bubbled into the lake. The lake was in fact a catch basin for the surrounding volcanic peaks, a great saline sump without an outlet. The water level was lower than it would be a month later; the rainy season had scarcely started. Our folding boat, which had seemed such a good idea, could be used for scarcely half the distance that we must negotiate. Dragging it with exhausting effort over the mire, we abandoned it when we reached a great flat where the salty crust seemed firm enough to walk on. But the added weight of our gear, now strapped to our backs, was just heavy enough to cause us to break through at every second or third step. Deeper and more treacherous mud lay ahead. This was no ordinary silt, but rubbery muck that gripped our tired legs like plasticine. The flamingos had chosen their site well. No Andean wolf or fox would venture out there. No one but a Quechua, naked and dragging a llama hide bladder in which to stow the eggs—or a mad *norteamericano*.

We soon learned the varying qualities of the mud, which was encrusted with cubic salt crystals and decorated with the tracks and defecation of flamingos. Yellowish mud we could trust and also the red mud; it would not be too deep. But a round patch of grayish white muck could be bottomless. The aluminum poles with which we probed before taking each step went down and down to the hilt. Slipping into one of these pockets meant a mud bath. Half lying, half crawling, we assisted one another, and long before we approached the apprehensive flamingos we were caked, head to foot, with white slime that dried to a baking-soda consistency.

That night Luis Peña had a nightmare so vivid that he remembered every detail. "I looked for you, Doctor," he related, "but I could not find you. I called and called. No answer. I went far out onto the lake where I had last seen you. There I found your red cap. It was lying on the mud. I went over to the cap. I lifted it from the mud—but no Doctor!"

My waders, purchased at Abercrombie and Fitch in New York, were of the sort that salmon fishermen use; I wore woolen socks inside and heavy shoes outside the long waterproof legs. Great balls of muck clung to the oversized shoes, so to avoid complete exhaustion I discarded them and hoped that the sharp salt crystals would not cut through the rubberized fabric that protected my feet.

Close to the limit of endurance and with my pulse throbbing like a tom-tom I had scarcely noticed how close to the flamingos we now were. Lifting my head from my preoccupation with each exhausting step I saw through sweat-blurred eyes that the colony, every last bird a James', was in agitation. Slowly unbending their collapsible red legs they rose from their mud mounds, each revealing a single goose-sized white egg. Sedately they walked a few feet, and then with a short run and a flapping of wings the mass of birds took to the air. What a stirring sight were the long skeins of white, red, and black birds against snow-capped peaks; how unlike the popular image of the flamingo as a bird of tropical, palm-studded shores.

There were about eight hundred occupied nests in this colony. Including the birds not nesting, there must have been two thousand flamingos present on this part of the lake.

Signaling my companions to stay behind, I dropped to my knees and set up the camera. The tripod was a problem, for it would not remain level on the unstable mud. Some of the birds had not flown, and I judged this to be the closest approach that they would tolerate. Incessant egging by the Quechuas had made them much more shy than flamingos I had photographed in Africa and elsewhere. Aiming my Weston meter at the eye-hurting panorama of glaring mud and salt, I recorded a light reading of between fourteen hundred and sixteen hundred, four times the brilliance of an ordinary sunny scene in Connecticut. Soon the air-born birds returned and walked slowly back to their nests. For an hour I feasted on a sight never before witnessed by a North American, and as fast as I could shoot, I exposed film.

What a remarkable adaptation to a hostile environment! Living on diatoms and algae that they strain from the mud with their extraordinary bills, flamingos exist in an environment that scarcely any other vertebrate creature wants. Probably for this reason alone these conspicuous, gregarious, gentle birds of ancient lineage survive. The James' flamingo, with about fifty-four lamellae per inch of bill edge, three times as many as in the Chilean flamingo, can presumably strain smaller organisms from the thick mud soup. It is unquestionably the most specialized member of a highly specialized family.

Scarcely an hour had passed when Peña signaled me that we had better leave. Storm clouds were beginning to form over the peaks. We must return to the boat and get back to camp, if possible, before the storm broke. It was only then that I faced up to the fact that getting to the birds was but half the battle. My parched throat and cracked lips reminded me that

I had foolishly left my canteen in the boat. Dehydrated and played out, I dropped to my knees every 50 yards or so to restore my energy. At one point I began to doubt whether I could make it back, but I did. It was ghastly. Two years later, when William Conway of the Bronx Zoological Park, struggled through the same morass with Luis Peña and Gerardo, they came to a large salt island that gave promise of a place to sit and rest. Apparently our old trails were still visible, for Gerardo remarked, "Here Doctor [Peterson] crawl on knees." Conway told me later that it was like being shown the tracks of a dinosaur.

While we pulled our boat across the open water, the clouds began to drop their burden. A few cold drops pelted us, followed by icy hail. This was routine weather for the flamingos in their exposed colony; at times they may even incubate their eggs with snow on their backs. Of such hardy fiber is the James' flamingo.

After the rain and hail, fortunately of short duration this day, came the inevitable wind. It always blows in the afternoon, an unrelenting wind that piles up the waters on the far side of the lake, a sort of wind tide that recedes at sunset when the gale dies away.

With severe cramps in my legs and a painful burn from the unfiltered sunlight, it was good to be in camp by the sweet spring that gushed from the mountain. There must be an easier way to reach the colony I thought, but we never found it. After two abortive tries we made our second successful assault over precisely the same route we had taken the first time. By that time I was beginning to toughen.

J. DEWEY SOPER

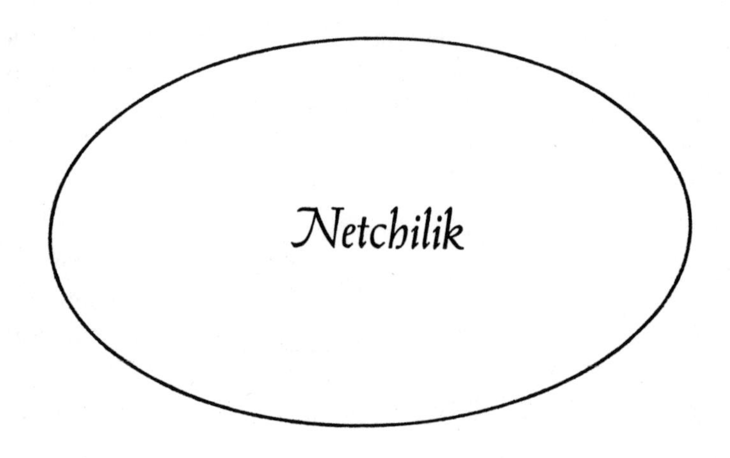

J. Dewey Soper, in retirement at Edmonton, Alberta, Canada, has completed a book, The Mammals of Alberta. *Born on a farm near Guelph, Ontario, May 5, 1893, Mr. Soper was educated at Alberta College and the University of Alberta, where he did work in zoology and later specialized in ornithology and mammalogy. As a naturalist for the Canadian government he has visited Labrador; Baffin, Bylot, Devon, and Ellesmere Islands; and northern Greenland. He was in charge of Canadian government expeditions from 1928 to 1931, making wildlife investigations and geographical surveys of unknown and unmapped parts of the Canadian wilderness. In his two-year survey of Wood Buffalo Park in Alberta and Northwest Territories, he made special investigations of the northern bison. He has been Chief Wildlife Officer of the Canadian Wildlife Service in the prairie provinces, Alberta, Northwest Territories, and the Yukon. He is a member of the*

Ottawa Field-Naturalist Club; Charter Member of the American Society of Mammalogists; and a Fellow of the American Ornithologists' Union and Arctic Institute of America.

NETCHILIK

WHO can fully fathom the singular fascinations of the polestar and the aurora borealis? How they symbolize the remoteness and mysteriousness of the polar lands! Almost as far back as I can recall these cast a curious spell over my mind; what reveries and vague imaginings! As a farm boy in Ontario I well remember making a secret vow that some day, if at all possible, I would visit the far-off lands of the Eskimo and the polar bear. This deeply rooted yearning was never completely stilled. I read every available book on arctic exploration with absorbing interest, but there was growing up to do. There were long years of schooling ahead; specialization in zoology; and groundwork periods of roughing it in the wilds of northern Ontario and the foothills and mountains of western Alberta. Through it all the siren voice of the arctic persisted.

Finally, my opportunity came. In the early spring of 1923, I was appointed naturalist, by the National Museum of Canada, to the Canadian Government Arctic Expedition of the following summer. In mid-July we sailed from Quebec City in the government schooner *Arctic*—a staunch, thick-hulled wooden ship of current vintage that had successfully bucked the pack ice of polar latitudes on several previous expeditions. The thousands of miles of voyaging that summer to Labrador; Baffin, Devon, and Ellesmere Islands; and Greenland only served to whet my appetite for more familiarity with "the lands forlorn." One could sense great opportunities; vast areas were totally unknown to the white man. What lay hidden beyond this veil of exciting inscrutability?

At this time, among other things, ornithologists were keenly interested in discovering the then unknown nesting grounds of the blue goose. Our 1923 expedition unfortunately revealed nothing new about it; however, certain vague information from the Eskimos suggested possible success in the southwestern interior of Baffin Island. Was it worth the gamble? My heart was set on this venture, but the truth could not be known unless a naturalist penetrated to Nettilling Lake—"Netchilik," or the Eskimo's "Lake of Seals"—and the vast, reported tundra lowlands beyond it to the east coast of Foxe Basin.

Happily, the National Museum of Canada had full confidence in the possibilities of further investigations and scientific collecting and backed my proposed expedition to southern Baffin Island for the years 1924 to 1926. In due course I was landed from the schooner *Arctic* at Pangnirtung, Cumberland Sound, in late July, 1924. There, by prior arrangements, I was officially quartered with the Royal Canadian Mounted Police until the spring of 1926. Eager as I was to push inland, it was much too late in the summer of 1924 for a serious expedition in that direction. I must wait until the following spring, for the earliest migrations of nesting waterfowl. I spent the autumn and winter in zoological collecting and explorations in and about Pangnirtung Fiord and the upper reaches of Cumberland Sound.

The winter seemed interminable. I could solve the mystery of the nesting grounds of the blue goose only by penetrating the unknown interior of the country. With Eskimo helpers I spent most of March and early April, 1925, making reconnaissance trips by sledge to Nettilling Fiord. I hunted ringed seals for dog food, set up forward caches of seal meat and equipment, and generally got organized for the expedition to the "Lake of Seals." All my plans and preparations were based on an estimated absence of five months.

The basic purpose of the venture, of course, was to locate the then unknown breeding haunts of the blue goose; second, to make in this virtually unexplored region as comprehensive a collection of mammals, birds, and other animals and plants as time and opportunity permitted. In the beginning, my party consisted of eight Eskimos and my old friend Constable Thomas Tredgold of the Royal Canadian Mounted Police. Much to my pleasure, he elected to officially join the expedition not only to provide me with companionship, but to study conditions in the interior and possible sledge routes for future police patrols.

Five large sledges (*komatiks*) were needed, to be hauled by a total of sixty-eight dogs. One of the sledges was specially constructed with a 3-foot beam and a length of 18 feet to carry a large sail-rigged surfboat for exploration and surveying on Nettilling Lake; to pull it required twenty of the finest huskies obtainable.

At last the time of departure arrived—April 22, 1925. The day dawned clear and cold with a temperature of 8 degrees below zero. Local snow conditions were excellent with a firm, wind-packed surface and slick draught that goes with moderate temperatures. Any later departure was risky in relation to skirting the slowly crumbling ice around the great tide rips in Nettilling Fiord—the only feasible route—with heavily loaded *komatiks*, for the long trek of about 145 miles to Nettilling Lake. Following the lengthy preparations, the impatient waiting, and the pandemonium of the last hour, it was a great relief to get started. There were the last bandied salutes of farewell to friends being left behind, the crack of whips, the swelling tide of primitive clamor from the dog teams, and we were off for many months of unpredictable adventure.

We set a direct course for Imigen, about 35 miles westward across Cumberland Sound. Then, in following days, past the Pooutoon Islands, Kangerlukdjuak Bay, and northward into Nettilling Fiord. There we were to meet the treacheries and difficulties of bypassing the mighty tide rips (*shukbuks*) of Sarbukjualik and Sarbukjuak, caused by rotting, undercut, and crumbling ice in the rock-walled gorge. In some areas, long delays resulted from inseeping sea water under the snow, involving doubling-up of dog teams and exhausting efforts to extricate our heavily laden sledges.

Sometimes our progress was reduced to a mile an hour, or less. What with relaying half-loads, killing seals for dog food at the *shukbuks*, and handicaps created by deep, loose snow, frost fog, ice pressure ridges, and blizzards, we did not reach the head of Nettilling Fiord, at Kangia, until May 3. Up to this time we used snow igloos for night camps, with temperatures ranging between 15 degrees above to 20 below zero. However, with night temperatures approaching 32 degrees above zero, snow houses slowly melt and drip, and we abandoned them in favor of canvas tents.

We were now only some 20 miles from the eastern end of Nettilling Lake. Our route lay up and over the height of land via a series of five fresh-water lakes and short connecting streams. After supper that evening, from the camp at Attitukdjuan Lake, I snowshoed for several miles over the rolling hills to the north. From a 500-foot elevation, I had a magnificent view that unfolded over the wintry leagues of rugged domes and ridges that stretched away in every direction. Far to the west, I could see the shaggy hills bordering the great Lake Nettilling, which we had struggled so hard to reach and on which all my hopes had been centered for over a year. All around lay the vast unknown; under the enchanting spell of its silence and blue distances there seemed to be nothing but a sense of peace and coming fulfillment.

May 5 was a glorious day, calm, and with brilliant sunshine tempered by the most springlike temperature we had yet experienced. Snow melted slightly in sheltered nooks facing the sun. After passing over the height of land and sledging the lengths of Amittok and Takuirbing Lakes, we reached the eastern extremity of Nettilling Lake at eight in the evening. This locality is known to the Eskimos as Isoa. It is situated at the mouth of Takuirbing River in latitude 66° 22′ N. Judging by old camping signs, the place has been an age-old favorite with the Cumberland Sound Eskimos from which they had hunted the barren ground caribou for food and clothing. Most of the *tupik* stone "rings" were very old and now encrusted with lichens and mosses.

Our party was in a happy mood that evening as we pitched our tents for the first time that season. The evening sun still swung relatively high in the northwestern sky, and a few male snow buntings managed to impart a vernal touch to the otherwise bleak landscape. We had seen little game on the way in, although we sighted a few small bands of caribou in the distance and had occasionally seen tracks of arctic foxes, weasels, and lemmings in the snow.

The following morning our party broke up. Four of the Eskimos and all of the dogs but seven were scheduled to make the return trip to Pangnirtung. It was rather hard to part with these cheerful comrades of the trail. I tried to persuade the men to tarry at Isoa for one day of rest, but they were all anxious to make an immediate start for home. They were shrewd in their knowledge that the fiord ice was daily getting thinner and more treacherous, with rapid expansion of the ice-bounded tide rips that would presently extend from wall to wall of the canyons. When this occurs, difficulties are compounded in making necessary detours over neighboring hills and valleys of rugged bedrock.

Our interior party was now reduced to six for the summer and autumn—my four Eskimo assistants, Constable Tredgold, and myself. We had retained seven dogs and a sledge for local exploratory and survey work as long as snow and ice lasted; they were also to be used for hunting and transporting game, of which most of the skins and skulls would become scientific specimens for the National Museum of Canada.

Our first care was to put the camp into the best possible shape to withstand the belated spring storms that we knew were sure to come. To start with, we built thick, head-high snow walls around the tents as a protection from cold, high winds. This was well-advised, as between spells of early spring-like weather, we were raked with a succession of gales, fresh snow, and blizzards until early June, with temperatures vacillating between 20 and 40 degrees.

Now and again came a clear day and some warmth from the sun. May 22 was superb; in a sense it was the first genuine day of spring. The air was soft and scented with a lazy southern breeze. In early morning the temperature was 39 degrees and by noon, it had risen to 48. In the polar regions even this degree of warmth seems exquisitely comforting after enduring freezing temperatures for eight or nine months.

Day after day of the finest weather followed. Snow began to disappear from the slopes and ridges; hourly, the dark, rounded backs of the hills protruded more and more from the great snow fields, and myriads of little rills and brooks babbled melodiously on their journeys to the lake. From the newly exposed patches of tundra rose the sweet, pungent odors of soil and moldering plant life. Barring a few minor setbacks, this was arctic spring!

While we had seen straggling snow buntings previously, the first real migrational wave of them swept into the Nettilling country on May 23. It was not long before the males burst into full song. Not content with the long days, they even sang throughout the midnight hours, which were now quite light. Two males that had staked out their territories near camp came up with endless repetitions of *Swee-e-a-we-a-swee-e-swurt* that might be phrased, *Now look here, sir, now look here, sir, quit.* The range of melody of the snow bunting's song is slight and delivered in a rather high register with relatively little modulation. The intervals, however, are notably pure and sweet. One's first impression is that of a hurrying melody, fraught with passion and sadness as though tempered by the melancholic backdrop of the forbidding granites. For me, it was love at first hearing—the first songbird harbinger of spring and one of the most enchanting singers of the polar land.

I was naturally very curious concerning the Eskimo reports of ringed seals (*Netchik*) in Nettilling Lake, after which they had named this body of water. It was some weeks after our arrival at Isoa before it was possible to verify that they were there, but the animals were far from common. One day Akatuga, one of my Eskimo companions, and I were traveling by dog team among the numerous islands to the west when the dogs suddenly detected a seal breathing hole under the snow. After a considerable display of patience, Akatuga finally succeeded in harpooning the animal and hauling it to the surface. In later weeks, with open water, we shot several more near the mouths of the Takuirbing and Amadjuak Rivers and at other points in Nettilling Lake. Getting these specimens proved to be one of the highlights of our inland investigation. Later, at the National Museum, Dr. R. M. Anderson found that they represented a new subspecies that he named the Nettilling ringed seal, *Phoca hispida soperi.*

With the gradual unfolding of spring in late May and into June (bringing the first stirrings of plant and insect life, and the return of birds), our scientific collecting of animals and plants became our chief concern. The remoteness of the region, combined with the pioneering nature of the work, made our researches of great interest and value. For several months, we spent the forenoons collecting, near and far, and the afternoons in camp preserving our specimens. Now, to keep abreast of the advance of spring and its golden opportunities, I seldom worked less than sixteen hours a day. During the three weeks of the midnight sun in June, it was not often that I retired before midnight, and I snapped back into action at seven in the morning.

In those enchanting, aspiring days, working in one part of the twenty-four hours was as good as any other. Despite fatigue, it somehow seemed a sacrilege to go to bed at midnight with the sun shining brightly and the birds rapturous with song, for it seemed tantamount to sleeping away the glories of a spring forenoon.

At this period happenings fairly tumbled over each other. Caribou appeared in increasing numbers as they trekked into the western lowlands from wintering areas about the fiords and in the high mountains of the east. We now saw wolves and arctic foxes with greater frequency. New bird arrivals were daily events. Horned larks were among the earliest migrants; they were soon followed by large numbers of pipits, plovers, red phalaropes, purple sandpipers, and other shore birds, gulls, loons, and old squaw ducks.

Between May 29 and June 8 considerable numbers of Canada geese, lesser snow geese, and blue geese arrived. They wheeled in restless flocks over the still frozen lake, rested, and fed in bordering snow-free patches of tundra, and swam in narrow lanes of open water along shore. Our expectations were high that these blue geese would nest nearby, or in meadowlands about 35 miles to the west-southwest. Our hopes were rudely dashed, for presently, all the blue geese and lesser snow geese disappeared from our district for the duration of the breeding season. This was a great disappointment to me in relation to one of the major aims of our expedition; but more of that later.

It seems appropriate here to make special mention of the Lapland longspur. Previously this bird was a stranger to me except for occasional brief meetings with it during its migration on the western prairies. Now it became an immediate favorite of mine as, for the first time, I thrilled to its sweet aerial singing over the tundra at Lake Nettilling. Numbers of them first appeared on the opening day of June, but without song or enthusiasm. Their peculiar call note, a lazy *yeep-er*, or *yer-up*, with a nasal intonation, was easily distinguishable from the medley of calls and songs of the snow buntings.

The following day, several males invaded our camp area in full song. In the days that followed I was to appraise them as the finest singers of the land, the arctic's most beautiful expression. To my ear its song was distinctly reminiscent of the bubbling tintinnabulum of the bobolink—the same wild, passionate copiousness which seems to overflow with ungovernable gladness; it is neither so loud nor so well sustained as the bobolink's, although it is full, rich, and tinkling, with a wealth of sprightly sweetness, a veritable cascade of sparkling notes. Like that of the snow bunting, the song comes more often from the bird during its flight performance, which may be repeated twenty or thirty times an hour.

Plants were also responding rapidly to the enticements of spring. The earliest blooms were the round, velvety catkins of the dwarf arctic willow, but the first real flowers of the season were those of the diminutive purple saxifrage, first noted on June 9. This plant is very attractive, grows in small mats over rocky slopes, and bears a riotous profusion of reddish-purple blossoms. By the middle of the month they were legion and often painted restricted areas with an unbroken mass of color.

In the weeks that followed there were eye-arresting displays of flowering lousewort, white heather, mountain avens, arctic poppy, arctic Labrador tea, dwarf blueberry, crowberry, bearberry, and many others. The Lapland rosebay is outstanding because of its delicately scented bloom, for fragrance is rare in arctic flowers.

Lateness of the 1925 summer season turned out to be a keen disappointment. I had anticipated that Nettilling Lake would become ice-free by the third week of July. Had this happened, it would thus have enabled us to proceed immediately, at about midsummer, for wildlife and topographic exploration and mapping of southern Nettilling Lake and the powerful river draining the lake to Foxe Basin, known to the Eskimos as the Koukdjuak (great river). However, the deeply candled * ice did not finally break up and disappear under pressure of a southeasterly gale until the night of August 9.

On the following morning the tents and gear were rapidly packed and taken to the beach. With the supreme efforts of all hands we eventually launched our surfboat into the open water at Isoa, and our voyage of exploration commenced along the shore to the west and south. Our immediate objective was the mouth of the big river reputed by the Eskimos to flow north from Amadjuak Lake and to empty into the southern extremity of Lake Nettilling. Our sailing was fast and buoyant with a spanking wind from the north; in tow we had an 18-

* *Candled* is a term for a vertical fracture in ice immediately prior to final spring breakup.—The Author.

foot freighter canoe for exploring streams where the heavy surfboat would be useless.

The high spirits of the Eskimos and ourselves alike is well remembered. We were all imbued with the exultation of going farther into the unknown after being held up at Isoa for more than three months. The country was new to everyone; not one Eskimo of the party had ever seen the southern part of "Netchilik" or any of the vast area lying westward to the coast of Foxe Basin. These people are wonderful companions in the arctic wilderness. What I particularly like about them is their toughness, their courage and efficiency, their carefree laughter and merry joking. Their good humor was further stimulated when we killed a seal or caribou for the scientific collection, which also assured plenty of meat in camp. How characteristic were the evening fires of *keookta* (white heather) with the meat pots simmering and the black smoke trailing away to leeward!

An amazing aptitude of these natives was their memory for the principal geographic features about the lake. Although they had never actually seen these places themselves, they nevertheless had unerringly memorized the place names from the tales and descriptions of Eskimos who had. Thus when we arrived off a prominent headland 32 miles west of Isoa, Akatuga and Kungasenil instantly recognized it as Tikerakdjuak, signifying "the big point"; likewise, a deep indentation in the shore line 10 miles south they recalled as Nunachava, the bay bordered by a wide sweep of wet meadowland grown to sedges and arctic cotton grass.

At Tikerakdjuak we left behind us the maze of islands typifying the eastern arm of Nettilling Lake. Here for the first time the mainland was clear of islands and well-defined. Now to the west and southwest we saw a vast expanse of open water to the limit of visibility; no land was detectable along the distant horizon. This was partly explained by the fact that nothing but low tundra lands existed in that direction all the way west of Nettilling Lake for nearly 100 miles to the sea.

How regrettable is the fleetness of the arctic summer! For a few brief weeks it dispenses a haunting beauty and fascination difficult to describe. Already the first signs of autumn were at hand. Berries were ripe, or ripening, and diminutive leaves became painted with red and gold. Again capricious gales roared across the interior. On two occasions the polar silk tent occupied by Tredgold and myself collapsed before the onslaught of wind and rain, forcing us to flee to the crowded security of the heavier native shelter. Slowly we moved south against adverse winds and seas, through a boiling Padli Narrows and into the island-dotted Kangidlirn Bay.

It was now August 24. Another gale howled in from the north, mantling the whole country with 3 inches of wet snow. Most of it melted the next day. We searched now for the Amadjuak River, the mouth of which was finally discovered behind a screen of overlapping islands and points. Navigation of this stream was impossible owing to miles of furious rapids; the best that we could do was to investigate it for several miles on foot and then hasten to explore the west shore of Nettilling Lake to the Koukdjuak River.

Bird life became increasingly scarce as the season waned. Still common were snow buntings and Lapland longspurs; others that we saw in varying numbers were Baird's and white-rumped sandpipers, herring and glaucous gulls, rock ptarmigan, long-tailed jaegers, and red-throated, common, and arctic loons. Many of the earlier migrants were already leaving for the south. We frequently sighted numerous caribou, singly or in small groups, on both mainland and islands; the majority were cows, and calves of the year.

Far to the southwest a conspicuous, lone hill towered high,

with flanking ridges, above the seemingly boundless flat tundra. The Eskimos called it Pingualuik. They recalled that in olden times one of the very finest caribou grounds lay on the lowlands between that eminence and Nettilling Lake. Cows and calves predominated there. As the summer skins of these are greatly prized by the Eskimos as clothing for their women and children, hunting parties gravitated annually to Kangidlirn Bay, and southwest, where large numbers of caribou were killed. The hides were staked out to dry in sun and wind, tied into bundles, and in late summer or early fall transported to Cumberland Sound.

The west shore of Nettilling is everywhere low and swampy, or marked by low ridges of broken limestone containing many fossils. For many days we followed the beach to the north-northwest in fair weather or foul, sometimes under sail, or again becalmed, when it was necessary to make laborious use of the oars. Snow squalls now became almost as frequent as cold rains; night temperatures occasionally dropped below freezing, crusting the coves and shallows with thin ice.

For a pleasant change, August 30 was bright and warm. That afternoon we reached the lake outlet and proceeded down the wide, swift Koukdjuak for about 15 miles. This turned out to be an unfortunate decision. My original intention had been to descend the river to the sea to determine its length and character, and to explore for goose populations and other bird life. That night we camped on the sodden tundra; another gale blew up with sleet, snow, and freezing weather. Here we were trapped by bad weather into the fourth day, and it began to appear likely that the beginning of winter might not be far off. It was now obvious that too much risk would be taken in going all the way to Foxe Basin and fighting our way back against a strong current. The season was getting on, our supplies and gasoline fuel were running low, and we still had to retreat to Nettilling Fiord, well over 100 miles to the east.

Many caribou of all ages and both sexes were still resorting to the western plains, but already some were moving toward the higher terrain to the north and east. The most interesting spectacle in the locality at this time was the hundreds of snow geese that continued to feed and fly over the tundra; we watched flocks through our eight-power binoculars as far as they could be seen toward the western horizon. Most of them migrate south by the middle of September.

Many years ago, in this district, the Eskimos killed large numbers of these geese during their molting period in July. In their kayaks, the Eskimos rounded up the flightless birds on the water, drove them ashore, and then directed them into previously prepared stone-walled pens where they were easily killed. We found such corrals in various places along the western shore of Nettilling Lake and on islands in Koukdjuak River. Most appeared very old, darkened with lichens, and with a plentiful scattering of moldering goosebones in the debris of the peaty floors.

This whole western plain appeared highly favorable for the breeding and nesting of both snow geese and blue geese. While I saw no blues at the Koukdjuak, the over-all situation was certainly suggestive of possible blue goose nesting, but perhaps nearer to the coast to the west and southwest. The bountiful numbers of snow geese also had some significance, as that species and blue geese commonly associate, not only during migration, but also on the breeding and wintering grounds. It was my opinion at the time that if blue geese nested on Baffin Island at all, the breeding ground would likely be located somewhere between the Koukdjuak and the northern coast of Foxe Peninsula.

At last, on September 2, the weather gods contrived a more

genial mood with blue sky and milder atmosphere. It was only a pleasant pause before the coming storms and cold of early winter. No urging was needed for our party to feverishly break camp, load the surfboat, and start upstream.

Unluckily, no favoring wind blew from the west. For the lack of it we were into the third day fighting the river current by poling and track-lining before the calm waters of Nettilling Lake, at Nikosiving, were reached again. After a time, a wind blew from the west-southwest, and our boat sped along rapidly. Traveling via Kingakjuakdjung and Tikerakdjuak Points, we arrived safely at Isoa on September 9.

Now began the strenuous journey to the sea through the chain of five lakes and six portages. The surfboat had to be beached for the winter at the southeastern end of Amittok Lake, as it could be taken no farther without dogs and sledges. Now, relaying loads with the freighter canoe, we reached the head of Nettilling Fiord on September 13. By previous arrangements, our Mountie friends arrived a few days later with the powerful, seagoing patrol boat *Lady Borden*, and we were all back home again at Pangnirtung on September 21 after an absence of five months, less a day.

By this time early winter had settled upon the land; all migratory birds had disappeared; the long purple shadows of noontime and the vastly lengthened polar nights were close at hand.

The "Lake of Seals" was now but a memory, withal a pleasant memory—with its varied experiences, stimulating discoveries, and our acquisition of rich and new collections of natural history specimens. There was plenty for me to think about and to write about during many ensuing weeks of winter when fresh explorations were wholly impracticable. The "Netchilik" venture left many deep impressions on me that time cannot erase; some of them remain with me almost as clearly as though they had happened yesterday. As I look back on those adventures of almost forty years ago, they seem, in some ways, to stand out more vividly, and to have been more rewarding, than any of my succeeding arctic expeditions.

It is not easy to explain this. However, it occurs to me that perhaps it arises from the fact that this journey was my first experience practically alone and independent with the Eskimos in the interior of an arctic island and intimately associated for the first time with all arctic seasons from late winter until late autumn.

EPILOGUE

In 1925, Arthur Cleveland Bent, in his *Life Histories of North American Wild Fowl*, U.S. National Museum Bulletin 130, wrote:

"The blue goose is one of the few North American birds which we know only as a migrant and a winter resident in the United States. It has generally been regarded as a rare species, but it is really astonishingly abundant within the narrow confines of its winter home on the coast of Louisiana. . . . To find the breeding resorts of the blue goose is one of the most alluring of the unsolved problems in American ornithology."

On June 26, 1929, J. Dewey Soper, on his expedition of 1928–1929 to southwestern Baffin Island, came upon a small colony of nesting geese on the tundra near Foxe Basin in latitude 65° 30′ N. There were ten nests of which eight were of the long-sought blue goose, two of the lesser snow goose. The area was near Bowman Bay, about 65 to 85 miles south of Koukdjuak River. In Mr. Soper's report, "Discovery of the Breeding Grounds of the Blue Goose," published by the Canadian Department of the Interior in 1929, he gives all the details of his long search. His concluding sentence, by its quiet understatement, is a dramatic ending to one of the most thrilling searches in natural history.

"By varied means of progression since 1923, I had traveled a total distance of 30,300 miles. Thus ended the long line of adventures in the quest of the blue goose."

Twenty-eight years later, the originally discovered nesting territory of the blue goose on southwestern Baffin Island was set aside by the Canadian government as the Dewey Soper Bird Sanctuary by Order-in-Council 862, Parliament of Canada, 1957. —The Editor.

F. FRASER DARLING

On Becoming a Naturalist

Dr. F. Fraser Darling, Vice-President and Director of Research, The Conservation Foundation, New York City, was born in Scotland in 1903. He received his Doctor of Philosophy degree at the University of Edinburgh, where he later became senior lecturer in ecology and conservation. From 1944 to 1950 he directed the West Highland Survey, a study of the influences of land use and environmental change on the ways of life in the Scottish Highlands. Darling's work has taken him to Alaska and other parts of North America, to Northern Rhodesia and the Mara region of Africa, and to remote islets in the North Atlantic, where he lived for several years while studying the life history of Atlantic gray seal. He first came to the United States as a representative of UNESCO and served for a number of years as a member of the scientific advisory council for the Conservation Foundation be-

fore being appointed to his present post in 1959. He has written seven books about his various studies, of which one of his latest, Wildlife in an African Territory, *appeared in 1960.*

ON BECOMING A NATURALIST

I can well believe that a sudden revealing experience may influence a child or a young man to become a naturalist, and when it does happen, that he may be stirred so deeply that he remembers it as a turning point in his life. Frank Kendon in that classic of childhood, *The Small Years*, recounts throwing a stone at a wren, quite thoughtlessly, and merely because it was an almost impossible target; but the stone killed the bird, and the shocked boy gazed upon the glistening still-contracting entrails of the tiny and exquisite creature. Life, sound, and action were so recent, death at his hand so sudden; his imagination called up the bird's life and environment and what it might at this moment have been doing were it not lying there with its guts trailing. Knowing Frank Kendon well, and having talked over the incident with him, I have felt the little bird was not a fruitless sacrifice, for Kendon was a poet and one of the most humane of men. His delicate sensitiveness to the small, silent phenomena of nature suffused all his work.

But nothing like that happened to me. I cannot remember not being drawn to animals with an intense, uncritical love. My mother found me supporting myself against the legs of the work horses in the paddock about as soon as I could walk, and again, after being lost, I was discovered sitting under a haycock nursing a dead rabbit and weeping, though I could not have known the nature of death. This preoccupation with fur, feather, and down was probably little more than a physiological tropism, for the form, movement, and scales of a snake repelled me—as they almost do now. Life for me has been a consistent journey of laying aside the intense, uncritical love of fur and down, and also the uncritical repugnance to snakes, and the unfolding of an early sense of wonder.

Wonder is itself uncritical at first, but in its development it loses nothing by attaining to such comprehension as we reach. Indeed, with growing understanding, wonder wells up into a convecting imagination which may yield insight, that strange experience that sends the reason forth to the analytical investigation called research. If the wonder of childhood survives the many hazards to which it is subject in the course of bringing up, it is the reciprocative source for such imaginative research into the processes of nature as was displayed by Darwin, Rutherford, and Gowland Hopkins. Each of these naturalists had the capacity for insight, and each kept his sense of wonder. Some may question the inclusion of Rutherford as a naturalist, but who was looking deeper into the nature of nature? Eddington had the power of wonder, so had the physiologists Sherington and Haldane, and Einstein was perhaps the supreme example of the humility which wonder maintains in the moment of insight and comprehension. Many of us who are lesser men still feel that it is the continuing sense of wonder which has carried us forward to be practicing naturalists in adult life, rather than the sudden revealing experience.

How far are wonder and mystical revelation one and the same thing; or is the moment of light a distillate or quintessence of wonder? The journals of the young Wordsworth were published a few years ago and contained passages of the intensity of perception which are near to suffering. Such experiences make boy and man lonelier; he is driven back to the world of form and light, of the intricacy of life and process, which as yet he cannot accommodate into a satisfying philosophy of God in All.

These incidents of intense perception with their disturbing leaven of the spirit are fresh in my own memory, but they were not turning points so much as milestones on a long journey. I can remember waking at dawn on a May morning when I was seven years old; perhaps the dawn chorus of singing birds itself had woken me, but it was a complete wakefulness in which I felt an independence of action, untroubled by thoughts of whether I should or should not. Perhaps I was the only conscious mind in the whole house, or at least all was silence within as I dressed, stole down the stair, and went into the open air. The very air itself seemed to carry the spores of an unfolding day. The early morning air was significant to the sense of touch, and, above all, the sense of smell made it evocative of the fullness of nature. I walked in the growing light along the hedges of two or three fields till I reached the Great Wood which held for me already something of sanctuary though it was in later years to be so much more a retreat for body and spirit. Forest still has that quality for me, the capacity to suffuse, absorb, and spread the personality.

When the sunlight came, it threw long shadows from the base of each oak tree and hazel bush, and the bracken stems now about to throw wide their fronds scintillated from the dewdrops held in their curl. How polished was the bark of the hazels, showing that mixture of brown and green that has thrilled me ever since when I have seen it in a woman's eyes, for what makes a woman lovelier than that she should mirror a beauty one has found earlier in nature, that she should become nature personified!

I saw no furred animals that morning, and I do not remember seeing the birds particularly; the enduring experience is of the breaking forth of light and color in the wood and the sound of bird song, the crowning brilliance of the wild scyllas which are English bluebells, and the cascades of willow warblers' songs which seemed to join with the shining dewdrops to give them life and movement. As I left the wood, I saw a wren fly from beneath a tree root at the bank of a stream. The secreted nest was there, exquisitely woven, and the eggs were visible, many of them, so delicate that the pink yolk showed through the shell. This was the first nest I had found alone, and it remained unforgettable; I could have gone on gazing, but the wren was calling sharply, and I knew enough that eggs must be kept warm and that nests were sometimes deserted by disturbance. Another thing I remember about that morning is that the expected remonstrance from my mother did not come. It was she who had first shown me the lark soaring and told me to look for the bird's startling fall to earth; she had first identified the red grouse for me and its call "go-back, go-back," so perhaps she divined something of that morning's necessity.

The stream which ran below the wren's nest gave me other things, such as the vision of a family of water shrews playing on a tiny shore of sand 2 feet below my face watching over the bank: a joyful experience, but not in the way of that May morning or of another day when, farther up the stream's course in the Great Wood, I sat on a fallen log in its bed, the fern fronds almost meeting above my head. Again there was the disturbing intensity of perception, not of light and sound this time, but of the tiny silences of living things and the dimness of their homeplace, moss, mossy saxifrage, a spider, and some springtails, those dark little primitive insects, in the rotting wood on which I sat. I must have seen them all before, and many a time since, but not as on that hot afternoon in the coolness of the stream bed.

The world of books on natural history was a tremendous and heartening discovery for me. They did not make me a naturalist, but they confirmed me and schooled in me an eager inquisitiveness. They brought order and classification; I succumbed to "Lepidoptera" but not to "Aves"; primal inquisitiveness saved me from being a nice little snob of a budding Scientist with a capital *S*. All the same, having linked up with other boys also interested in nature, I must admit to being one of the founders of the United Natural Sciences Association. We had not then heard of the Royal Society, and its headquarters were in London anyway. We were fairly civilized as I remember, having a little hut where we set out our several collections and shared our books. Fellowship was exclusive, based on whether a chap was a decent sort and whether he could pass an examination set by the rest of us. Each desiring to show his own virtuosity, each tended to think the other Fellows' papers a trifle on the stiff side: "Explain the meaning of the following terms: frenulum, auxiliary palp, instar, ovipositor"; "Describe the courtship behavior of the male wood warbler, *Phylloscopus sibilatrix*." By the time we were fourteen years old, our United Natural Sciences Association deferred to the Royal Society, and we agreed to disband. Also, a school natural history had been formed.

This period of life was a dangerous one, in that "shades of the prison house gather round the growing boy." There was the constant pressure from elders: "Yes, but what are you going to do seriously in life?" And the growing boy had lengthened his legs to the extent that he could get farther afield. Northern moors and mounting weather disturbed the spirit again and drew him on. A cliff of sea birds on a northern island was almost a shattering experience in its utter reality of light, smell, and a composite sound as of praise. ("But what are you going to do seriously in life?" had so little to do with reality.)

Schoolwork went downhill badly and did not improve after one of the greatest discoveries of my life. At fourteen years of age I bought a copy of *The Origin of Species*: possibly I understood rather less than half of what I was reading, but at that first reading of many, it was enough. The book took me three months to read, during which time one of my despairing schoolmasters had caught me at it. He almost spluttered; his subject was mathematics, and mine wasn't.

One of the biggest impacts of *The Origin* was religious: why had the elders fooled me all this time with a religious upbringing little different from the Father Christmas stuff one had dropped by five years old? I was angry, but somehow, I never lost faith in God. Had not Darwin mentioned the Creator reverently in the last paragraph of his book? God thereafter went into a resting state, rather like the apparent disorganization of the caterpillar after it becomes a pupa. The puzzle of His nature and expression did not begin to be resolved for another twenty years or so, though the moments of light so moving in childhood began to fit into a world of organic evolution so much easier than into the conception of the jealous Lord thy God of whom my grandmother had made a private policeman to help keep me out of mischief.

"But what are you going to do seriously in life?" It was here again, the constant, haunting specter.

"I should like to be a gamekeeper," I told my mother.

She fetched me a resounding clout over the head.

The funny thing is that finally that is exactly what I have become, a gamekeeper, one who is interested in the conservation of animals in their natural habitats. But I had to do other things first; become a farmer (that last resource for the parent of a boy who is apparently no good); take a scientific agricultural education which let me carry on from where I left off; and it also taught me how unscientific so-called scientific agriculture is; do postgraduate work in genetics and animal breeding which brought me into a great field of literature nearer my own heart; and though Charles Elton is only three years my senior, I came on his newly published *Animal Ecology*, which he wrote when he was twenty-seven; and I had already read some of his earlier papers. This book was another milestone because it brought order and direction again into my mind. I had been wandering free in an intellectual wilderness, an excellent thing to do, but one has eventually to come out of the wilderness and take one's place, doubts to some extent resolved, and with positive ideas of one's own.

Gradually, the uncritical love of animals, different from the childhood moments of light which were enduring phenomena of life, became orientated through several studies of animal behavior and grew into a critical ethic of conservation. This ethic is founded on the experience of the immanence of God in nature, in the inorganic world as well as the organic, in lowly life as in higher, and that man is part of nature. I had scarcely been willing to give men that dignity until those studies of deer in Highland forests and gray seals on lone Atlantic islands had shown me the elementals of human behavior, making me understand my own kind, accepting the notion that man as the only animal capable of reflection and true free will must take on the immense responsibility of his evolution for the care of the rest of creation.

The respect for life that the ethic of conservation fosters is not uncritical or sentimental. It is rather a stern discipline of realizing that the maintenance of habitat is the basis of conserving animals, and that to allow a population of animals to develop beyond the power of the habitat to sustain it is against the ethic. One must be prepared to kill when necessary and to continue killing, for few areas are such untouched sanctuary and large enough that populations of all animals can be left to take their own course. One comes to realize that respect for the stock is absolute, but the individual must not be loved so sentimentally that one falters at removing it from the population. The same ethic of conservation should guide mankind to curb the conception rate in his own species to prevent degradation of the human habitat for posterity.

But conservation is not all ethic: it is science as well, an acceptance of ecological principles such as that the more complex biological communities are the most stable and that wanton simplification such as forest clearance and the destruction of wild animals without clear understanding is wasteful of that which is not ours. Biological communities of plants and animals are wholes greater than the sum of their parts and worthy of respect as expressions of God in All.

The boy who looked upon living and seeing, feeling, hearing, and smelling as more important than "doing something seriously in life" has grown into the same shiftless sort of man. He does not specialize in animal behavior, for example, and become an authority on the subject. His ecological studies do not show detailed application; his interest in the large view can be interpreted as lack of profundity. But the wonder remains and sometimes an experience, employment of the senses rather than the exercise of cerebration, brings forth an idea which makes for the joy within. To have spent several months with the great seals on an otherwise uninhabited Atlantic rock was not wasted time; it was living and preparation for living. To jump from genetics to animal behavior and then into ecology of land use and of the larger grazing animals seems erratic to some people, but to me it is a continuance of a biological education. The mounting of the years is pleasurable rather than an inevitability to be borne, for as one grows older a wide intricate web of experience does give some small comprehension of nature. And this in itself stimulates the imagination when one faces new environments: the time for travel is not necessarily when one is young because not enough has been seen and apprehended and thought through. Travel has been much more rewarding to me in later years, and to stand on the arctic slope of the Brooks Range of Alaska watching caribou and Dall sheep, or in the midst of an African wilderness with a fauna moving round you that has survived from the Pleistocene: all this has the smack of the continuing wonder which is the breath of life to a naturalist.

HERBERT L. STODDARD, SR.

The Hunting of the Cooper's Hawk

Herbert Lee Stoddard, Sr., ornithologist and wildlife management expert on game and songbirds has done much of his field work on his 1,000-acre plantation near Thomasville, Georgia. He was born in Wisconsin in 1889 and early in his career became a field biologist for the U.S. Biological Survey. For nearly twenty years his main studies were of the life history and management of the bobwhite quail, first with the federal government from 1924 to 1929, and later, from 1931 to 1943 as the Director of the Co-operative Quail Study Association of Georgia, under private auspices. For his book, The Bobwhite Quail: Its Preservation and Increase, *the first American monograph on a single species of bird, he was the recipient of the Brewster Medal, awarded periodically by the American Ornithologists' Union for the most distinguished work published about birds of the Western Hemisphere. Mr. Stoddard is a Fellow of the American Ornithologists' Union and of the American Association for the Advancement of Science, an honorary member of the Wildlife Society, and a member of many other scientific societies.*

THE HUNTING OF THE COOPER'S HAWK

I had long suspected that on heavily stocked quail preserves in the southern United States, Cooper's hawks hunted quail by ear as well as by eye. Cock quail whistling from exposed perches were noted to attract these "blue darter" hawks from considerable distances, and sometimes lost their lives in consequence. A note I made on July 25, 1945, on a heavily stocked preserve in Jefferson County, Florida, clinched this belief, and reveals, I believe, some hitherto unrecorded hunting behavior of the Cooper's hawk. This note is quoted just as I jotted it down in the field:

"Eating my lunch, sitting quietly in my auto parked in an open pine grove. Noted a juvenile Cooper's hawk alight in a pine . . . some fifty yards distant. After watching him awhile, I decided to test his reactions to a whistled imitation of the quail's 'scatter call.' Hence I whistled a series of seven or eight of these notes, then a couple of 'Bob Whites.' To my surprise, the hawk sailed to the ground just a few yards away. Paying no attention to my motionless auto, or to me in the car, he walked about in the short grass cover, jumping up and flying a few feet, buffeting the tops of the broom sedge and low bushes with his wings. He repeated this several times, and pretty well worked the concealing cover nearby. Then he again alighted in a pine and sat quietly, only to go again into the ground cover and beat about at my repetition of the quail call notes. Then up into the pine for another quiet wait.

"I resumed calling and a second juvenile Cooper's hawk sailed into the tree with the other, then both took to the ground cover and flew very low and close together through and around the woods in the vicinity, working just above the sedge and buffeting it with their wings; the sound much resembling that made by a dog handler trying to flush quail by beating the cover with his whip. After several moments of this, both alighted in a pine some seventy-five yards away.

"After a short wait, I resumed my call notes, using mainly the 'scatter call' of the bobwhite, and this time it was immediately answered by a bachelor cock quail, which flew in and alighted in scant ground cover some twenty-five yards to my left. There he gave the excited 'caterwauling' note several times as he scurried about in plain sight searching for the expected hen bird, all caution discarded in his eagerness for a mate. The hawks remained motionless on their perches, probably not seeing the quail and apparently tired of the deception. I gave another call and the cock quail answered instantly, and started to run across an open space toward my car.

"When not over fifteen feet away, a hitherto unseen Cooper's hawk, a large adult female, came down in a lightening-like dive straight for the quail. This bird pounced upon the unfortunate cock quail and drove her talons into his vitals—not a sound from the quail except its spasmodic death flutter. While 'spread-eagled' over her prey, waiting for the spasmodic jerking to cease, the 'blue darter,' aware of my presence for the first time, looked up and into my eyes. Holding my gaze for a second, she flushed with the quail clutched in both feet and flew off toward Kelly Pond, both juvenile Cooper's hawks close behind her."

As these young hawks were apparently not long from the nest and not yet entirely on their own in getting food, their behavior in quail hunting was either instinctive or acquired very early in life. Certainly they were attracted by the quail call note and used the best possible method for locating and flushing concealed quail. And the young hawks and the cock quail both showed the usual uncanny sense of direction in coming to my imitation of the quail call notes.

The Cooper's hawk is a fairly common resident species in suitable woodlands of southwestern Georgia and adjacent parts of Florida, in the vicinity of my home, the headquarters of the Cooperative Quail Investigation in the Thomasville, Georgia–Tallahassee, Florida, region, where my studies of the life history of the bobwhite quail started in the spring of 1924. There are large blocks of mature pinelands here, and creek, river, and "branch" valleys which are grown up to very large pines and hardwoods mixed. Such country is very much to the Cooper's hawk's liking, especially for its nesting.

Because of limited and careful selective cutting of these woodlands in the past twenty-five years, and following a period of forty or more years of no lumbering at all, the game and forest preserves of the southwest Georgia region are in great contrast to the heavily lumbered Coastal Plain Pine Region to the east, which has been heavily exploited from southeast Virginia to east Texas. On the east coast of Georgia, there are similar but more scattered hunting properties varying in size from 1,000 to 50,000 acres, also in the Carolinas, and in Alabama and Mississippi, but very few of the age of the southwest Georgia and Tallahassee group, which is unusually well consolidated.

On these hunting lands, the bobwhite is King, and the quail

are maintained in abundance by various management measures of which controlled burning of the land at frequent intervals and the building up and maintaining of small spots of bushy cover are the most important to building populations of bob-white quail in the pineland areas, which compose most of the acreage. With the controlled use of fire, the pinelands are open and parklike with a prairielike flora predominating, very much as they were when the first Spanish explorers saw them. The forested parts of these hunting lands, especially, are more nearly in biotic balance than the more heavily and recently farmed uplands, most of which have been subjected to many applications of poisonous insecticides and artificial fertilizers during the past three-quarters of a century.

The Cooper's hawk, extremely shy and wary where persecuted by man, has not suffered as greatly from the hostility of the sportsman and farmer as have the other hawks, and as a result maintains a high population level in comparison with the less wary and more conspicuous red-tailed and red-shouldered hawks. Few except the most expert woodsmen have any idea of the numbers of Cooper's hawks in well-timbered sections. I have long felt sure that this big blue darter was the leak that causes a considerable drop in the quail population level in spring. Cooper's hawks probably kill more mature quail at this season than all other natural enemies combined. In densely populated quail territory, they seem to acquire a taste for the quail above any other prey. However, it is the migratory Cooper's hawks on their northward journey to northern breeding grounds that so drastically reduce the spring quail population, *unless* the game manager has put in the recommended "refuge coverts" well distributed over the terrain. If he has, the hunting Cooper's hawks are frustrated and the quail survive for the breeding period just ahead. In my opinion, no creature has a better right to the quail they can catch than the

Cooper's hawk, even though their killing and eating of poultry has given all other birds of prey a bad name.

The comparatively few Cooper's hawks that remain to breed in the Coastal Plain region of the deep Southeast do, of course, keep considerable pressure on the quail while rearing their own rather large families. Their rather compact nests of sticks, with finer material for lining, may be built from 30 to nearly 100 feet above the ground in either pines or hardwood trees. Three or four bluish-white eggs are laid, and not infrequently two to four young are reared to maturity. The hawks may be very wary and secretive in and around their nesting woods, and the landowners are seldom aware of their presence. If they are not persecuted, their *cac-cac-cac* call notes may be heard as one enters their woodlands, especially during the mating time.

We have accumulated notes on Cooper's hawk–bobwhite relationships during the past thirty-six years and find the provision of the previously mentioned well-distributed bits of bushy refuges not more than 100 yards apart over both open woodlands and fields are by far the best protection one can provide for the quail; then the Cooper's hawks go hungry in a land of plenty, for the quail can easily elude them. Shooting or pole-trapping the migrating Cooper's hawks is a waste of time, is illegal in many states, and the pole-trap often catches other birds than hawks. It is about as effective in reducing the population of Cooper's hawks as attempting to dry the oceans with a tin dipper.

While the bobwhite quail seems a happy-go-lucky fellow in most respects, and shows no lasting fear even of the quail hunter and his dogs, the quail's reactions to a Cooper's hawk on the hunt shows that this hawk is nature's traditional controller of the bobwhite's kind. After a narrow escape from a Cooper's hawk, the lone quail or the covey hug the ground motionless for as much as a half-hour, as the hawk walks about on the ground trying to find and flush them. Any bird that loses its nerve and flies is generally doomed.

For a long time after the hawk has given up the quest and left, the hidden quail usually take no chances on the killer being hidden in a nearby dense bush or tree. When they do relax and start to move about, it is very quietly and cautiously at first, and they stick closely to the best of cover after a few members of the covey have paid the penalty of carelessness. As time goes on, it is becoming increasingly clear that this age-old battle of wits is largely responsible for the outstanding qualities of the quail as a game bird. Without the Cooper's hawk to keep its reactions perfect and its body well exercised, Bob-White would probably become in many respects a softie like "civilized man."

GEORGE MIKSCH SUTTON

Caught in a Dust Storm

George Miksch Sutton, ornithologist and bird artist, currently Research Professor of Zoology, University of Oklahoma, was born in Bethany, West Virginia, May 16, 1898. He was a student at Texas Christian University, attended Bethany College, the University of Pittsburgh, and Cornell University, where he received his Doctor of Philosophy degree in 1932. From 1919 to 1925 he was a member of the staff of Carnegie Museum, Pittsburgh; and Curator of Birds at Cornell University, 1931 to 1945. He has made numerous expeditions to arctic Canada and on Southampton Island, Hudson Bay, 1929 to 1930, he discovered a nesting place of the blue goose at almost the same time that J. Dewey Soper discovered the hitherto unknown nesting grounds of this bird on Baffin Island. He has painted birds to illustrate many American books and while at Cornell University got instruction in bird art from the great painter of birds Louis Agassiz Fuertes.

He is a Fellow of the American Ornithologists' Union, a past president of the Wilson Ornithological Society, and an honorary trustee, Oglebay Institute, Wheeling, West Virginia. He is the author and illustrator of Eskimo Year, Birds in the Wilderness, Mexican Birds, *and other books; also editor of ornithology for* The American College Dictionary *and Encyclopedia Arctica.*

CAUGHT IN A DUST STORM

THE Dust Bowl, as I experienced it while studying the birds of the Oklahoma Panhandle in 1936 and 1937, was an appalling place. It was not a desert in any ordinary sense, though desert it certainly was. Even in midsummer it had a bleak, wintry appearance. The glare of its smooth dust drifts was like the glare of snow. The telegraph poles that lined its highways, the small, colorless houses, the half-buried farm machinery and toppling fences, the blasted cottonwood and hackberry trees—these seemed utterly unreal on a warm, bright morning in June. Seen through the dust that blew nine days out of every ten, they called to mind a setting for some gruesome crime. They loomed against the dun void like sandstone grotesqueries carved by the wind.

Dust was everywhere. It was on every twig, every blade of grass, every strand of wire. It was in the plumage of the horned larks that flitted along the roads. It was in the hair of the half-starved jack rabbits and prairie dogs. It was the unfamiliar bloom on the tiger beetle's emerald wings. It softened even the bull snake's bold color pattern, clinging tenaciously to the skin between the velvety scales.

Dust was part of every dawn and every sunset. Especially

was it part of every noon, for especially at noon did the wind blow. It settled reluctantly when the blast subsided; but the instant a zephyr stirred, it was up again. With every step a man took through the dead weeds a pungent cloud ascended. Let him touch a twig, and there was a puff of gray. Rains occasionally drenched the parched waste, and pools formed; but with the passing of the clouds the sun appeared, the wind rose, and lo! a thick veil of dust shut the new-formed pools from sight.

I drove across the Dust Bowl eight times between 1932 and 1937. I experienced what was called "bad local dust" in the stretch from Guymon to Boise City, Oklahoma, six times of the eight. The inhabitants of Cimarron and Texas counties—the westernmost counties of the Oklahoma Panhandle—had become so accustomed to this local dust that they paid little attention to it as a rule. Nobody talked about it. It was taken for granted, along with sunlight and air.

Occasionally, however, there swept down from the north a vast cloud of dust that was not local. It may have been Kansas dust, or Colorado dust, or dust from one of the Prairie Provinces of Canada. Such clouds moved slowly. Not often were they accompanied by a gale. But they were inexorable. They turned day to night. Death was in them. These storms were called "black dust storms" by the cattlemen who lived in the valley of the Cimarron. It was such a black storm that caught me at about six o'clock on the evening of May 21, 1937, while I was watching a bird among the mesas near Kenton, Oklahoma, a few miles east of the New Mexico state line.

That had been a pleasant day, calm, bright, not unusually warm. Our party of four—John B. Semple, Karl Haller, Leo Luttringer, Jr., and I—had been out all morning, studying, photographing, and collecting birds for scientific study. At noon we had returned to the little hotel at Kenton.

Since my catch was not large, I had finished my drawing and preparation of bird specimens by five o'clock in the afternoon, somewhat earlier than usual. Realizing that I had a few hours of daylight at my disposal, I decided to go after a canyon wren, a species that had thus far eluded us. Taking my shotgun and specimen basket, I started for my automobile.

"How about giving me a lift to that mesa just east of town, Doc?" called Luttringer, our photographer. "I want to get some good shots of this country before we leave. The light's perfect this evening."

"Sure!" I replied.

I deposited Leo and his big Graflex at the foot of his mesa and drove slowly on. It was a windless evening, a trifle warmer than it had been, I thought, but not disagreeably so. I enjoyed the prospect of a leisurely walk. I loved this mesa country. The fragrance of the piñons and junipers always did me good, and the mysteriousness of the arid canyons fascinated me.

Within twenty minutes I reached an eminence from which I frequently had surveyed the broad flood plain of the Cimarron. Pulling the car to the right of the road, I stopped to listen. Sure enough, on the rise just to the north, and not very far away, a canyon wren was singing. The very bird I was after! How clear and bold was that cascade of notes! With my mind's eye I could see the small performer perched on the top of a boulder, the feathers of his white throat lifting and quivering.

I locked the car; then, glancing at it as I usually did before leaving it, I noted that the right rear tire had lost most of its air. It was not flat, but it was down. It would have to be changed.

Unlocking the car, I started to drag out the jack and wrench. Then, impulsively, I shoved them back and relocked the door. I'll not change it now, I thought. I'd better go after the wren while I know where it is. That tire's been having slow leaks anyway. If I get the wren right off, I'll be back long before dark.

I swung away, crossed the fence, and within a quarter of an hour had reached the base of the vast, tablelike slab of rock which crowned the hill. From the side of the slab gigantic boulders had broken away. Back of these opened low caverns, some of them large enough to furnish the cattle a shelter in winter.

In this rough and shadowy world lived the wren I had heard. In and out of the crevices, under and behind the boulders, through the darkest, most remote parts of the caverns, now at the brow of the rock rim above me, now in a fissure at my very feet, the little bird flitted and ran. Part of the time he scolded me, using his harshest voice. Then, after a period of complete silence, during which I had no notion of his whereabouts, he emerged, mouselike, from his hiding place, looked at me with glittering eyes, lifted his head, opened his slender bill, and sang as if he rated me, of all possible enemies, the least considerable. I with my great blunderbuss of a gun! I with my clumsy feet, picking my way about *his* rocks! I could have shot at him several times, but I didn't. His temerity, the ripple of echoes that his song roused, the way he scuttled about–up and down, this way and that, as if he never in his life had tripped on anything–all this must have cast some kind of spell over me.

I watched the little bird as he lifted his head to sing. I saw him clearly, for he was perched at the very edge of the rock above me. All was blue-bright back of him, the blue brightness of the sky. He sang two notes of his descending scale, two bold, ringing notes, then stopped. Stopped as if he had been stricken. Stopped, faced about, crouched, turned his head to one side as if following with his eyes the towering of a prairie falcon, and darted into a crevice.

No falcon appeared. So far as I could see there was nothing for the wren to fear. Then why this strange behavior, this abrupt breaking off of song? Had the little bird seen a speck in the upper air, some point of black too far away for me to descry? At once it dawned on me that the evening chorus of the mockingbirds and lark sparrows too had ceased, that the world had grown unaccountably silent.

I looked once more for the wren. He had disappeared. Above the spot at which he had sung, and sharp against the sky, was the bright edge of a thick cloud. That this was an unusual cloud I sensed immediately. It looked solid, like a grayish yellow wall hung with smoke. That it was slowly rising I perceived in an instant, for more and more of it showed above the rock.

To see more clearly I ran back a little and clambered up out of the cavern. Before me was such a scene as I had never beheld before: a vast brown cloud, the only cloud in the sky, stretching as far to the east and as far to the west as the eye could see, so dense and so low-hanging that it had completely obliterated the northern horizon. Its uppermost borders, which were eerily bright, were the grayish yellow wall I had first seen.

Slowly and gracefully the cloud bank moved, upward with the rolling effect of smoke from a great conflagration, and forward. I watched it spellbound. The beauty, the ineffable serenity, the horrible majesty of the thing! No wonder all the birds had ceased from their singing. As the wall advanced, it shut out more of the world to the north. Now even the purple dome of the Black Mesa was going. The last glimpse I had of the mighty mountain made me think of Napoleon and his final look at the Kremlin as it stood there unscathed in the midst of burning Moscow.

Suddenly, with a feeling of impotence that fairly buckled my knees under me, I realized that this opaque mass bearing down upon me had nothing to do with rain. That it was dust! That shelter in the caverns along the side of the hill would be no shelter at all from this! I looked once more at the advancing cloud, then back toward the highway. The storm would catch me long before I could reach the car.

I ran across the rock-strewn slope, memorizing certain details of what I saw before me. I perceived that if I made a certain low ridge, I could crawl along that ridge back to the highway no matter how thick the storm. Out of breath, I turned to face my pursuer, noting that it no longer seemed brown, but was white instead. Its edges were feather-soft. Behind and below the fluffiness of these nearest wisps was a darkness sullen and menacing.

I reached the little ridge. The highway was not far off. Terrified though I was, I now felt that I could not lose my way. I glanced at the car, remembering . . . the tire.

When I turned once more to look at the dust, it was upon me. No sky was visible now anywhere to the north. The vague blueness above me was plumed with gray and white. A mass of dust with the fluid appearance of muddy water slipped along the ground a little in advance of the high cloud, running between the trees and boulders like a wave about to break. There was no breaking of this queer wave. No ripple, no splash, no foam. Forward it slipped, always keeping just a little ahead of the cloud itself.

I saw the wave of dust flow about my shoes. I saw it grow deeper, shutting my knees from sight. Its thickness and its unexpected coldness struck new terror. Running headlong, I reached the fence along the north side of the highway. The wave was winning. Running again, I crossed the highway, grasped a strand of barbed wire, and sank to my knees.

By this time the light was going, for the wave was engulfing me. The wind was not as fierce as I had expected it to be. It was strong, but not fierce. And it was cold. With it rose a hissing moan. I looked toward the south, toward the only light that remained. That light was weird, unearthly, reddish in cast. In an instant it was gone—as if a huge curtain had dropped; as if a vast lid had suddenly been clapped on the world. "Awful! Awful!" I seemed to be saying, almost aloud. "Being buried alive must be like this. Drowning must be like this—drowning at the bottom of the sea!"

Just as the light had gone, a bird had fluttered past me. It had flown close enough for me to identify it as a mockingbird. It had careened off downwind as if in a wild dream. That bird was the last thing I clearly saw for a long time. Its image, black against the lurid light in the south, was to linger in my mind for years. It, too, drowning! It, too, at the bottom of the sea!

With my hand upon the friendly fence I breathed hard, thankful that I knew exactly where I was. For a moment I wondered if I could possibly survive. It was so dark that I could not see my hand or handkerchief no matter how close I held them to my face. My eyes did not pain me. I knew I had not been blinded. No, the light had simply gone. There was no light anywhere. The evening that had been so serenely bright had turned to utter darkness—the darkness of the tomb.

I realized that the dust was not choking me. I could feel dust on my lips and against my tongue and teeth, but I was not suffocating. I was surprised that breathing was as easy as it was. I kept my eyes shut and my face turned away from the blast.

With the passing of the first thick wave, the wind grew stronger and a trifle cooler. The complete darkness must have lasted twenty minutes. Then I thought I saw a dull red glow off to the north. Looking at my handkerchief again I could barely see it when I held it a few inches from my eyes. The worst was probably over.

I followed the fence to the car, holding my eyes shut most of the time. Fitting the key into the lock at last, I opened the door, turned on the lights, found a flashlight. The tire was down, flat.

Fearing that my companions might have started in search of me, wondering what fate had befallen Leo Luttringer, and feeling that it would be much better in every way to be at Kenton for the duration of the storm, I changed tires. It was a laborious, anything but pleasant job.

The headlights of the car penetrated the dust only a few feet, but I managed to turn around, to keep to the highway, to get back to the small bridge where I had let Leo out. There I stopped, blew the horn, and shouted as loudly as I could, shouted and blew the horn again. No response.

I drove on. So thick was the dust that I might have missed Kenton had it not been for a light at the very edge of the street near the one and only filling station. That light made me think of a photographer's darkroom.

Friends at the hotel laughed when they saw me. Though alarmed they had sensed full well the futility of starting after me, for no one knew where I had gone. "Where were you when it struck?" they asked, almost in a chorus. "What did you do, get under something? Did you notice the way the cattle stood, looking up at the cloud? Did you notice the way the birds all stopped singing?"

I told them of the wren, of the race back to the highway, of changing the tire. Everybody in the place had some observation to make, some tale to tell. It was all so absorbing that I actually forgot about Leo.

Then all at once I remembered. "Say, where's Leo? Isn't he back yet?"

They, too, had momentarily forgotten. My question brought a look of concern to every face. Somebody went to the front door for a glance at the storm. It had abated, but the dust was still so thick that it was impossible to see across the street.

I thought of the way the storm had caught me. Of the awful darkness that had shut down. Of Leo trying to make his way down a steep slope, along an unfamiliar ridge, among the pathless junipers. "We ought to go after him," I said. "A fellow might get lost in this and wander around all night. He's on that first mesa to the east. Leo doesn't know this country anything like as well as I do."

I started for the car. Pard Collins stepped forward. "Guess you don't mind if I go with you," he said. Collins was an old-timer in the Black Mesa country, one of that country's real pioneers. He had seen many a dust storm and knew a bad one when he saw it.

We had turned the car and started eastward when the form of a man loomed directly ahead of us in the middle of the street. In the form's hand was a squarish object, a box with a handle. It was Leo and the Graflex.

Leo was almost in tears. Not because there was dust in his eyes. Not because he might have lost his life or broken his leg. Not because he had got his hands and knees full of sandburrs and cactus spines—but because he had not taken his movie camera with him to the mesa.

"Doc," he almost shouted at me. "Think of it, Doc! There I was with that terrible thing coming right at me. Why, it would have been a world-beater! It would have been worth real money! There I sat on that mesa looking at it for twenty minutes before I realized what it was. I thought it was just a low cloud. Honest, Doc, just a cloud! I could have come back and got my movie outfit and got a record of the thing from start to finish! I'm just sick about it!" He held his hand to his stomach. "Honest, Doc, it gives me an empty feeling right here to think of missing a chance like that. I'll never have it again, never as long as I live. Never!"

Leo had got down from the mesa before the storm struck. Running for Kenton he had stumbled into a deserted house at the east edge of town just as the darkness shut down. Inside the hotel once more, where we could really see him, he looked like a mummy with glittering glass eyes. His hair reminded me of the ruff of a great anthropoid ape that had wallowed in dust. His whole person was gray—his face, his hands, his clothes. His mustache was a trifle muddy. He laughed hilariously, saying that he had never seen me looking so funny. I laughed at Leo. We all laughed. We were a very happy party now that we were reunited.

Some of the darkness was now the darkness of night, for it must have been well past nine o'clock. After Leo and I had taken off our shirts and given ourselves a thorough washing, we all went to the kitchen. Supper had been ready at six o'clock, but with the coming of the storm, plates had been put over all the food and the meal forgotten.

We turned out the light so as to watch the electricity playing about the base of the big iron stove. Pard Collins told us he had seen such sparks shooting out from the horns of cattle and the ears of horses. "It's a bad storm, this storm is," he declared. "It's like the black storm we had in April a few years back. I don't know but maybe it's even some worse."

It was good to see my friends, all safe about me. We were hungry as bears. There was an unwonted sparkle in the eyes that turned my way now and then during supper.

The wind continued most of the night, but when morning came all was calm. A thick gray haze shut out the horizon, gave the Black Mesa a ghostly dimness, softened the outline of the nearer hills and ridges. The sun did not appear at its accustomed hour. Finally we saw it, halfway on its climb to the zenith. It was not the golden sun we had been seeing. Nor was it red, as we had thought it might be. It was white, silvery white, and about it shone a faintly opalescent halo.

The above account was written in 1937. On February 16, 1955, in the little cemetery in Kenton, they buried Pard Collins. The afternoon of the funeral I stood in the kitchen of the Collins home, the building that had once been the town's only hostelry, looking with a feeling of indescribable affection and loneliness at the stove about which we had seen the sparks playing on that memorable evening so long before. Pard Collins's widow, Pearl Collins, a fragile, beautiful woman, smiled as I spoke of the way we had all watched that stove, wondering what would happen next. Wesley Collins, Pard's fine man of a son, was there, smiling too. Pard's little grandson was there, his hand in Wesley's. Of the four of us, only the lad was not smiling. He did not have the black storm and the sparks to remember. I realized as I stood there near the old stove that I would never forget Pard Collins and the way he had offered to help me find my friend Leo in the storm.

PART FIVE

DAVID LACK

Migration in a Pyrenean Pass

Dr. David Lack, Director of the Edward Grey Institute of Field Ornithology at Oxford, England, was born in London in 1910. His father, a surgeon, gave young Lack a traditional English education—preparatory school, public school, and Cambridge University, where he read zoology and was a choral scholar of his college. At school he wrote his first scientific paper on the habits of nightjars, which he discovered had two broods a season instead of one, as formerly believed. While at Cambridge, he went on expeditions to St. Kilda, Bear Island near Spitsbergen, East Greenland, Tanganyika, and the state of California. At Dartington Hall School in Devon, where he was a biology master in the 1930's, he watched and studied European robins—research that culminated in his book The Life of the Robin. *An expedition to the Galapagos Islands re-*

sulted in his internationally known book on bird evolution, Darwin's Finches. *During Army service in World War II, he helped to show that birds in flight could be detected by radar and is currently engaged in radar studies of birds in migration. Dr. Lack's recent books are* Swifts in a Tower *and* The Natural Regulation of Animal Numbers.

MIGRATION IN A PYRENEAN PASS

THE most memorable days for a naturalist combine grandeur with novelty, the beautiful with the rare or unexpected. As a boy, such experiences came to me through seeing for the first time a new kind of bird. Then, as a student, I happened on the courtship of the European nightjar, which was not only a lovely sight, and partly undescribed, but opened to me a whole new world—that of bird behavior. As I grew older, such memorable days became much rarer, for though the beauty was still there, the unexpected had gone, and most of the big rewards came gradually through persistent observation. But there was one much later occasion, just after my fortieth birthday, when in lovely autumn weather amid superb scenery, a deeply impressive spectacle was combined not merely with the knowledge that no one had written of it before, but that one of the puzzles of migration was solved. This happened on October 13, 1950.

There had been much dispute in the past as to whether migrating songbirds cross or avoid high mountains, and recent Dutch research had suggested that even low hills were avoided by migrant chaffinches in autumn. This gave my wife and me the idea that the Pyrenees might provide a barrier which no small migrants would cross. For these mountains, rising to 10,-000 feet, extend continuously from east to west across southern France, from the Mediterranean on one side to the Atlantic on the other, with only one small gap about 3 miles wide between their western edge and the sea. We predicted that through this gap we might see funneled a huge stream of southward-moving migrants. To test this idea, we visited the area in October, since in western Europe most of the visible migration of finches and other birds occurs in this month. Now October is outside the holiday season, particularly in France, where nearly all the hotels close on September 30, and this is undoubtedly one reason why what we saw was previously unknown.

First, we felt that we ought to make quite sure that there was indeed no migration through the high mountains, so we arranged a short visit to Gavarnie in the High Pyrenees. The village of Gavarnie is near the head of a long steep-sided valley running from the plains southward into the heart of the mountains for some 20 miles, and it ends in a huge cirque, a semicircle of vertical precipices between 4,000 and 5,000 feet high. On October 13, we left the village of Gavarnie at first light, when it was very cold, and climbed the western side of the valley by a steep winding path. Two hours later, we had climbed into the sunlight and could look down on the valley of the cirque, which made a magnificent scene, the giant gray precipices still in shadow, and a thin waterfall tumbling over their full height to start the little river Gave, which ran through alpine meadows and stunted beechwoods, the leaves of which had turned a rich brown. No one was in sight, nor, so late in the year, were any domestic animals in the meadows.

We now continued southwest along a narrow path up a subsidiary valley towards the Port de Gavarnie, a pass about 7,500 feet above sea level and only some 50 yards wide, at the divide forming the boundary between France and Spain. The climb, chiefly through bare meadows and at the end over scree, took another two hours, and in this time we saw hardly any birds, though when the sun had warmed the rocks, a few griffon vultures and a lammergeier soared off from their roosts on the cliffs above us. Nor did we see any people until, just before we reached the head of the pass, a man in priest's clothing, his cassock tucked into his trousers, appeared from the Spanish side at a rapid run, cut the hairpin bends of the track by sliding down the steep scree slopes with his stick between his legs, gave us the curtest of nods as he passed, and rushed on toward France.

We reached the bare top of the pass at 11 A.M., and as we did so, a party of goldfinches fluttered past us and dropped down on the other side into Spain. We had so convinced ourselves that there would be no migration that this came as a great surprise. But it was soon clear that a moderate migration of small birds was in progress. We had not seen it on the way up because the birds kept much higher up the slope until they were funneled into the narrow pass at the top. It was now a bright sunny day, with a chill wind from the west-southwest in the face of the migrants, which made them fly low. We settled in the shelter of a tall rock at the top of the pass, looking back down the valley, toward France, with field glasses, notebook and pencil, to observe and record what passed. In the next three hours we counted, in all, some 200 goldfinches, 400 chaffinches, 100 linnets, and 30 serins. These small finches were known to leave northern for southern Europe at this time of the year, but it was not previously known that they cross the high mountains on their way. There were also a few meadow pipits, white wagtails, and skylarks, making in all nearly 800 small birds in three hours, a modest movement compared with what one might see in the plains, but impressive for so high and bleak a spot.

We probably counted almost all the birds that came through, for the pass was extremely narrow and the migrants flew low, many of the finches skimming only a few inches above the ground. Indeed, because our silhouettes were hidden by the rock at our backs, the birds were often just above our heads, and we felt that we could have stretched out an arm to catch them. A few individuals seemed to lose heart on the steep final ascent, settling on the boulders a few feet below the top, then calling anxiously, until with more excited calls they rose to join another party coming over. Chaffinches were particularly prone to alight, and gave repeated alarm calls, the rocky slopes evidently being too unlike their native woods. In the same connection, we were interested to see that the pipits, wagtails, and larks, which are birds of open country, flew decidedly higher than the finches, usually from 6 to 20 feet above us; they were evidently more at home there. Nearly all the birds came in small flocks of five to twenty individuals, and very few flew singly, such single birds being particularly inclined to alight near the summit. It should perhaps be added that all the birds really were migrating. None of these species are resident at the Port le Gavarnie, all flew in the same direction, southwestward from France into Spain, and their steady progression looked very different from the usual daytime flight of the species concerned.

Flocks of wood pigeons started passing at noon, and in all we saw five hundred of them, together with a few stock doves. Hence they were nearly as common as the finches, but we saw much less of them because they came through in a few large flocks. Also most traveled high, crossing the pass several hundred feet above our heads, but one flock of about three hundred came through extremely fast and low, some even hitting the rocks with breast and wings, in panic from a pursuing peregrine falcon. The falcon was resident in the valley and doubtless subsisted on migrants at this season. Two sparrow hawks, presumably migrants, also came through. So did a few griffon vultures, all flying southwest, but as they are resident there, we do not know whether these were migrants.

The steady passage of small birds at so high and bleak a spot was, it may be supposed, sufficient treat for one day, for not only was the sight impressive, but we had established beyond doubt that small songbirds migrate through the High Pyrenees. Yet as it happened, birds were the least spectacular migrants that day, and just this once in our lives, we were more excited by the insects. Butterflies of several kinds were traveling steadily over the pass in the same direction as the birds, their number gradually increasing during the hours that we were there. The commonest were clouded yellows, their sulphur-yellow wings with broad black tips contrasting with the gray rocks. Even brighter were the red admirals, with nearly black wings set off by a red band and white flecks. This second species was at first scarce but later became as common as the clouded yellow. There were also a few pale clouded yellows, and a very few bath whites, a small delicately colored white species. The butterflies flew steadily up to the top of the pass, across and over it, and then down into Spain, keeping head to wind like the birds, but flying even lower, most of them only a few inches above the ground, which made them hard to see more than a few yards away. Ornithology being our business, we did not have time to count the insects, but at a guess, butterflies were passing at a rate of at least one hundred, and possibly five hundred, an hour. By butterfly standards this is evidently a small movement, but at the place in question it was exhilarating to see. We also saw one hummingbird hawk moth, which was presumably on migration, though we did not actually see it across the pass.

When we arrived, dragonflies were passing in numbers about double those of the butterflies, but an hour later they were much more abundant, and in the second half of our visit there were probably about ten dragonflies to every butterfly. Whenever we looked at right angles to the stream of insects, we could see at least six and sometimes twenty dragonflies in the air at once. They may well have been passing at a rate of several thousand an hour, but as they flew closer to the ground than did the butterflies, and were much less brightly colored, this may have been an underestimate. We had not expected them, and anyway were mere bird watchers, so we had no collecting apparatus. But we realized that entomologists would surely want to know the species involved. So eventually I took off my shirt and found that I could drop it onto a few of the most tired dragonflies at the top of the pass, after which we packed them in our sandwich wrappings, so as to bring them home for identification. There were two forms, both of the same size and appearance, much the commoner having a red body and the other a gray one, and they turned out to be the male and female respectively of *Sympetrum striolatum*. Previously, this species had occasionally been seen migrating in the plains, but not through mountains, and the fact that we could catch such normally rapid and wary insects with a shirt may help to show how exceptional the scene was.

Even this was not the end, but it was not until we had been at the pass for over an hour that we realized that another insect was migrating in larger numbers than all the other insects and birds put together. This was a little hover fly with a black and yellow striped body, and it was immensely common, there being at a rough guess at least twenty times as many as there were dragonflies, and perhaps a hundred times as many. The hover flies, like the dragonflies, flew steadily up to and over the pass, keeping their heads to the wind, but they flew even closer to the ground, and that was why, together with their small size, we at first did not even notice them. Shortly before we left at 3 P.M., the whole surface of the pass, at about ankle-height above the rocks, was a shimmer of iridescent light, due to the reflections of the autumn sun on myriad tiny wings. Once more, it seemed essential to collect some specimens. But everyone who is familiar with the rapid flight and changes of direction of a hover fly will realize how impossible that seems with only the aid of a shirt. Like the dragonflies, however, the hover flies were flying slowly and steadily forward, without their customary rapid darts, so it was not, after all, difficult to add a few to our collection in the sandwich papers. They turned out to be of one species, *Episyrphus balteatus*.

In order to reach the village again before dark, we had to leave the pass in midafternoon, and it was striking how, as soon as we were about 100 feet below it, all traces of the migration of insects and small birds had gone. Only the high-flying pigeons could still be seen, and several more large flocks came over us as we descended.

In conclusion, I add some general comments on our observations. We saw finches and other small birds crossing the Pyrenees in various other places that autumn. Clearly, high mountains are regularly crossed by small birds, and unknown to us then, further observations were being made at this time in Switzerland to the same effect. The Dutch observations concerning the avoidance of hills have turned out to have a different and complex explanation, which need not concern us here.

With the butterflies, those that we saw belonged to species that were already well known to migrate northward in Europe in the summer, but up to that time it had been widely believed that their movements were due to overpopulation in the south, and that though the individuals concerned might live for a short time, some even breeding, all were destined to extinction, and that there was no return. Yet it might on general grounds have been suspected that natural selection would not allow so self-destructive a habit, and shortly before our visit, Dr. C. B. Williams had argued on these lines, and had collected scattered records of southward flights in autumn, especially of red admirals in England. Our visit put the existence of regular return flights beyond reasonable doubt, especially as on other days we saw more such southward flights in various parts of the mountains. Since bird migrants regularly fly north in spring and south in autumn, the idea of a return passage in butterflies did not surprise us so much as it did most entomologists. But there is this important difference, that whereas in birds the flights at both seasons are performed by the same individual, in nearly all butterflies each is undertaken by a different generation. Thus the red admirals and clouded yellows that fly north in spring die after breeding, and it is their offspring that return south in autumn, and their grandchildren that fly north once more in the following spring. Only in the American monarch butterfly is the same individual known to make both journeys.

That dragonflies might also make regular seasonal migrations, north in spring and south in autumn, had not previously been suggested, and our visit made it evident that they behave like butterflies in this respect. But how rarely does one see anything really new in nature. Soon after our return to Oxford, we read how the Oxford classical don, Warde Fowler, saw dragonflies traveling through the Swiss Alps in September, and a Swiss observer had also seen hover flies, but the significance of their short reports was not appreciated. Hence while hover flies were occasionally known to appear in masses, migration in the sense of a directed movement was not merely unknown but unsuspected in this group of insects; yet at Gavarnie they were the most impressive migrants of all.

So the chief discoveries that day concerned the insects, and my most memorable day as an ornithologist was the only occasion in my life when these lesser creatures took precedence over birds. But I was bird-watching at the time, and the chief discovery was, after all, that insects migrate like birds, so birds played a key part in the story; anyway, no entomologist would have been so stupid as to climb the high mountains in October. Finally, of course, it was the picture as a whole that was so impressive, for, omitting the priest, the procession through the pass included creatures ranging in size from griffon vultures to hover flies, all moving steadily in the same direction.

LESLIE H. BROWN

Leslie H. Brown, now Acting Director of Agriculture, Kenya, East Africa, was born in Conoor, South India, August 25, 1917. He spent much of his boyhood in the Nilgiri hills and there acquired his interest in birds and other wildlife. He was educated in India and in Britain and attended St. Andrews University, Scotland, where he got a degree in science with honors in zoology. On his first appointment with the Colonial Agricultural Service, he spent five years in Nigeria before being sent to Kenya. He is a recognized authority in agriculture, particularly in land use planning in East Africa, where he is in charge of a staff of four hundred and the agricultural development of a country the size of Colorado and New Mexico combined. He has specialized in studies of birds of prey and flamingos, and lives in a house he built himself on a 15-acre plot at Karen, outside of Nairobi. The magnificent crowned eagle that Mr. Brown writes of is known to

scientists as Stephanoaëtus coronatus. *According to* The Birds of the Belgian Congo *(Part I) by James P. Chapin, it lives in "West and central African forests from Portuguese Guinea to Cameroun, Angola, most of the Belgian Congo, and thence to Mt. Kenia and Usambara, and southward in the more wooded districts as far as Natal and eastern Cape Colony."*

THE CROWNED EAGLE

IT is now many, many years since I saw my first crowned eagle. To be precise it was on December 26, 1942, at a place called Igbete in Nigeria, West Africa, where I had gone to spend the Christmas holiday exploring a group of rocky hills. At that time Igbete lay on the edge of the thinly populated savannas of the upper Ogun valley, and as far as I was concerned it was the gateway to wild Africa. Once beyond Igbete you left the human race behind and entered a realm where game, if not abundant, was then common. Among the rocky hills there were many interesting birds. That day I walked along the top of the biggest hill, reveling in the cool dry harmattan breeze that blows from the Sahara Desert at that time of the year, and thinking how much better I was enjoying myself than I should have been if I had been at a party the night before.

I spent a happy morning exploring the top of the big rocky hill. From there I enjoyed the spectacle of kites and harriers soaring effortlessly on the updraught from the northern face, and I watched a hyrax sunning itself on top of an inaccessible pinnacle. When I felt the heat of the day increasing, I thought to explore the forest that lay at the foot of the sheer rocky slopes. It was choked with a mass of creepers festooning huge boulders, and I fought through it, sometimes passing through dark caverns where any moment I could have come on a leopard or been blinded by the spittle of a cobra. I had a certain feeling of relief when I came out into a small clearing in which grew a silk-cotton tree of massive girth.

My gaze ran upward over the huge gray bole. At about 70 feet above the ground, fair in the middle of the tree, its trunk was arrested by a huge nest. Hardly had I time to think, with a sudden rush of excitement, that it looked like an eagle's nest, before its owner left it. I had a fleeting view of rich chestnut underwing coverts and strikingly barred flight feathers before she disappeared behind a tree. Anxious not to lose a chance to see this great bird at close range, I hurried after her, to find her settled on a bare branch in full sunlight about 20 yards away.

Never had I seen so splendid a bird. The regal crested head, outlined against the sky, was perfectly poised between the hunched wing joints, and the plumage of the folded wings was black and silky, with a bloom as of grapes upon it. The richly patterned breast, warm buff, barred with black, merged into a pair of great legs, placed well apart, slightly bowed, each seemingly as strong as a man's arm, and beautifully trousered with narrow black and white bars. Her long barred tail hung vertically beneath the branch, and she seemed as big as a baboon as she gazed down at me with an expression of faint curiosity. Being even then a lover of eagles above all other birds, I had already pored over the illustrations of West African species and knew the text almost by heart. Thus I knew instantly that this was a crowned eagle, perhaps the finest of all African birds of prey, and hitherto unrecorded in Nigeria.

Nothing brings a keener thrill than the discovery of a new bird in your area, and when that bird is an eagle, and the finest eagle you have ever seen, the day is unforgettable. I determined to savor it to the full and climbed a little way up the hill to a huge boulder with a notch in its top that served admirably as an observation post. The eagle was already back in the great tree. As I watched, she hopped down from a branch and landed with an audible thud on the nest, wherein I saw a small but very active white eaglet. There she stood, sheltering her offspring from the sun with her partly tented wings, the wind from time to time raising her black-tipped double crest till she wore an expression of implacable savagery however mild her emotions may have been.

The day was hot, and the eaglet, in the shade of his mother's wings, grew quiet while his parent dozed. Many hundred feet above, a pair of lanner falcons were playing together, screeching as they tore across the sky. Suddenly they tipped and shot downward in a glorious hurtling stoop. When just above the eagle's tree, they separated. Coming in from each side, in two perfect graceful curves, they whizzed through the branches of the tree, passing each other only a scant foot above the eagle's head. For sheer speed, timing, and accuracy I had only once seen anything to equal that splendid stoop. Today, however, my eyes were on the eagle, and she quickly put the falcons, fine as they were, out of mind.

In sudden rage her feathers rose. She swelled to twice her real bulk and closed her wings in a protective tent over the chick. Gone was the sleepy look, and she glared about her with crest erect, looking verily as if she would tear and rend any mortal thing that had the temerity to approach. She held that attitude of pure savagery for half a minute; then her crest slowly sank, her wings relaxed, and she looked down between them with mild gaze at the little chick. The contrast between her sudden savagery and her quick relapse into gentleness was, as I wrote in my diary at the time, "quite the prettiest and most impressive piece of behavior I have ever seen."

This experience, besides providing one of those great days in my life's memory of birds, gave me plenty of other food for thought. Here was a crowned eagle, supposedly an inhabitant of pure forest country, living on a rocky hill at least 40 miles from any extensive area of forest. Moreover it had not, up to that day, been seen by anyone in Nigeria, or, if seen, had not been recognized and recorded. Up till then I had, rather humbly, accepted what the authoritative bird books said as gospel, and had assumed that I would be unlikely to see any species new to the country. But the eagle, and the circumstances of our meeting, plainly said that you never could be sure, and that it was up to an ornithologist to keep a lookout for the very unlikely as well as the birds that ought to be there. And once this principle has been grasped, the ornithologist quickly becomes one of those who on days he is listing birds is one ahead of his fellow enthusiasts and can indulge himself with an irritating display of birdmanship when he recounts the day's doings.

It was seven years later before I renewed acquaintance with the crowned eagle, this time in Kenya, East Africa. Then it was probably that remembered clue–that one must not bind oneself only to the birds that ought to be there–that made me almost certain that a crowned eagle must be the owner of the huge nest I was looking into from the swaying upper branches of an adjacent fig tree. The nest was built in the main fork of a big croton tree. It was larger and more massive than any other eagle's nest I had seen in Kenya, and the African who was up the tree with me said it belonged to a *Koi*. Not far away I had seen a pair of martial eagles, and I should have been justified in supposing that this great nest belonged to them, but somehow I felt that it did not. My African friend explained that a *Koi* was as big as a *Ndiu*, as he called the martial eagle, but much more handsome. In Africa this could mean only one thing, and even though the spot was an even more unlikely haunt than that hill in Nigeria, it was really no surprise to me when a male crowned eagle swept past my face and alighted on a dead bough 20 feet away. As he glared fiercely at me, I felt the same rush of admiration and pleasure at his magnificent stature and plumage as I felt when that other crowned eagle slipped off her nest seven years previously.

This pair, living on the mountain I call Eagle Hill, have now taught me most of the crowned eagle's secrets and have afforded me continual pleasure through a decade. Each of the three big eagles of Africa—the crowned, the martial, and the black or Verreaux's eagle—has given me unforgettable moments. But it is always to the crowned eagle that I return in allegiance. As day after day I sat under their nest tree and watched the great birds going about the business of hatching and feeding their young, I grew to realize that the conventional idea of an eagle—a scarce, shy creature hiding in mountain fastnesses to escape the persecution of mankind—did not apply to them. They may have felt slightly uneasy when my heavy body crashed about in the branches of the big fig, but I like to think that it was because I was a large and possibly dangerous animal rather than because I was a man. In the shady gloom of the forest I often saw the female, which was a huge bird of exceptional presence and power, staring down from only 20 or 30 feet above me. Until you are accustomed to it, it is a little daunting to find a great eagle looking at you as though you were a piece of possible prey. Yet, if she had any thoughts about me at all, they probably were only mild curiosity.

For ten years I have watched them now, and besides the secrets of their species they have taught me most of what I know about the more obscure facts of the lives of big eagles. After four years I knew the limits of their foraging range, their favorite hunting areas, the details of the shared duties of male and female in hatching and tending the eaglet, what they ate, where they slept—indeed far more than is known about many lesser birds. Now after ten years I begin to understand a little about such things as the longevity of the species, and the life span of an individual in the wild. In the ten years I have known the nest there has been one new female and one new male, and in that time they have reared five eaglets in six attempts. Assuming that the missing mates had died and not simply been unfaithful, and again that half the eaglets reared die before they reach breeding age, I can calculate for them an average life in the wild of twelve years.

It means, from what I know of the young crowned eagle after it leaves the nest, that nearly all of them survive their first six months, for they usually appear, hanging around the nest, at the onset of the breeding season following that in which they were reared. Thereafter they seem to disappear, perhaps driven away by their parents, and may have to undergo a period of solitary wandering in conditions that may not be ideal. In all my time I have seen only a few subadult * crowned eagles, and it seems to me there may be a high death rate before the adult plumage is assumed. But this is about the only aspect of their lives on which I must conjecture—the rest is based on observed fact. In a few years, the female that came to this nest in 1952 will doubtless disappear. She is still there with her second husband. When and if she disappears, I shall then know at least something definite about the life span of one wild crowned eagle.

I now see crowned eagles less often than I used to, but I keep in regular touch with them, and I know them so well that they have few surprises in store for me. When I am going about my business in other parts of East Africa, something is always added to the landscape for me by the presence of a crowned eagle. It is usually a male that I hear high in the sky in

* Term of ornithologists for a young bird of a species that requires more than one year to mature. Most small birds acquire their adult plumage and breed in the spring following the summer they were born. Eagles, gulls, and other large birds are exceptions, and some may require three years or more to gain their adult plumage and sexual maturity.—The Editor.

a flight display. Then it seems as if I have made a connection on the telephone with a friend, and that I am joined by some kind of thread, tenuous if you like, to the great bird in his ecstatic flight far above. He may only be a speck against the blue, but I know that he is throwing himself about up there in a series of dives and upward swoops, and that as, with a few flicks of his mighty wings he maintains momentum at the top of his curve, his head is thrown back as he pours out his melodious whistling *kewee-kewee-kewee* for minutes on end. And it is not difficult for me to imagine the sensation he enjoys, as of an airy roller coaster, and almost to wish that I were he. My companions see me halt and gaze into the sky, and are mystified, and I feel apart from them at that moment.

Imagine, then, my satisfaction when, sitting for the first time in the study of my new house at Karen, near Nairobi, East Africa, to write on a Sunday morning, I saw a pair of crowned eagles building a nest in a huge tree only 600 yards away. All through 1958 I had watched a pair about the Ololua Forest reserve, but I had been unable to locate their home, for the reason, as I now saw, that they had none. And now here they were, in 1959, building a new one just as I had done. I watched it progress for a month and then had the pleasure of seeing the old eagle lay her egg—also on a Sunday—as if especially for my convenience. Thereafter I thought I would see little that was new till after the young bird flew, but the eagles have firmly taught me the lesson of "don't be too sure you know it all."

For one thing, the female alone incubated, whereas with all others of her species I have watched, the male shared in incubation. She underlined, if that was necessary, the lesson that one or two records, which is all that most people have the time or energy to amass with eagles, are insufficient evidence on which to base generalizations about breeding patterns. This is especially true in birds like eagles, where every individual is a distinct personality. This female kept on underlining her differences from others of her kind as time went on.

She hatched her egg on the day I thought she should, from past records, and thereafter continued to play the dominant part at the nest, feeding and tending the eaglet while her mate, a small, dark, unusually shy bird scarcely appeared except when he brought food. Many a time I watched her collect the green branches with which, like other eagles, she was wont to line the nest cavity. She tore them off bushy trees within 100 yards of the nest tree, flopping about with her wings spread for balance like some gigantic moth. And she seemed to like to do this when she had nothing better to do, as for instance when the chick was large enough not to need brooding; however, she was still tied to the vicinity of her nest as a guard.

I was relieved that she did not seem to take her guard duties too seriously, for at other nests I have watched there was a very real danger of the attending eagle attacking and striking a human intruder. This one seemed a placid bird that paid even less attention to me than most of her species, and when I climbed into an adjacent croton tree to admire her, she would scarcely leave the nest. One day, after I had cast the danger from her aside, I climbed the tree and clung spread-eagled to the thin topmost branches of the croton, one hand round a weak bough and the other occupied with field glasses as I sought to identify the prey the pair had brought to the nest.

Suddenly the female attacked me from 100 yards away. The first I knew of it was the swish of her great wings a foot above my head. I started, and clung, trembling, to my insecure perch. I put away my glasses, took a better grip of the tree, and let her circle and settle again behind me. I did not turn my head to look at her, but watched her out of the corners of my eyes, so that she might have another go at me if she felt like it.

She did, and I watched her take off and come low over the treetops. She was silent and charged with grim purpose, and when she was only a few feet away I whipped around and faced her. I was looking clearly into her yellow eyes as the great barred wings and spread tail put her into a steep bank to avoid me. Thereafter she seemed to know she could not take me by surprise, and all my efforts to induce another attack, to be filmed by a hidden accomplice, failed. She simply sat on a bough and glared, and was not to be deceived.

She has now reared her eaglet safely, and I have been watching this great booby of a young bird for more than three months since it took its first flight. It is very adequately equipped, one would think, with strong talons and beak, yet it is being fed on the nest platform to which it returns, squealing, whenever a parent appears with food and calls to it. It seems that the young crowned eagle is dependent on its parents for food more than three months after it has first flown, and how much longer this will go on I do not know. Certainly I have learned something new every few days about the life of this young bird now that it has learned to fly and has left the nest. It is not fed every day, and the parents have been bringing substantial kills once every three or four days. For years I had known that Kenya crowned eagles breed on the average in alternate years, and I realized now that this protracted postfledging feeding of the young one may be the reason for it.

We all have our favorite bird, and the crowned eagle is mine. Not only is it bold and handsome—to my mind the finest bird of prey in Africa—but the study I have been able to make of it has been a thread running through nearly twenty years of my life. Yet these crowned eagles seem always to be saying to me, "However well you think you know us, we can always show you something new."

OLIN SEWALL PETTINGILL, JR.

Honeymoon on Cobb Island

Dr. Olin Sewall Pettingill, Jr., of Wayne, Maine, is Director of Development, Cornell Laboratory of Ornithology, Ithaca, New York, and President of the Maine Audubon Society. From 1936 to 1953 he was a member of the faculty of Carleton College, Minnesota, where he taught ornithology and other courses in zoology. For more than twenty-two summers he taught ornithology at the University of Michigan Biological Station in northern Michigan. Dr. Pettingill was born in Maine and was graduated from Bowdoin College. He received his Doctor of Philosophy degree from Cornell University. As a zoologist and photographer, he has made expeditions to Mexico, Iceland, Hudson Bay, and the Falkland Islands. Some of his nature films have been used by Walt

Disney productions and shown and narrated by Dr. Pettingill on his Audubon Screen Tour lectures for the National Audubon Society. He is the author of A Laboratory and Field Manual of Ornithology *and a two-volume work,* A Guide to Bird Finding [*in the United States*]. *He has also been President of the Wilson Ornithological Society, and Secretary, American Ornithologists' Union.*

HONEYMOON ON COBB ISLAND

LATE in the afternoon of June 22, 1933, my bride and I boarded a dilapidated fishing smack at Oyster, Virginia, and headed east across the shallow Broadwater toward Cobb Island, a long, low barrier of dunes on the oceanside of Cape Charles. The one-lunger pounded strenuously, rattling the craft from stem to stern and making conversation virtually impossible. Camping equipment and cameras shimmied underfoot. In the distance a thin yellow line appeared on the horizon.

From gestures and bellowed phrases, my wife, Eleanor, and I learned that the line was "Cobb Island . . . 8 miles away . . . Coast Guard Station on it . . . couldn't land there without permission . . . would pull in at Captain Cobb's . . . queer old duck . . . owned the island . . . lived alone."

Instead of relaxing in the soft, warm Virginia evening, I was plagued by the question: Would we be allowed to land, camp, and study birds as we had planned? In the rush of events before starting on our honeymoon, I had neglected to communicate with anyone about Cobb Island. I simply knew that it was an exceedingly attractive spot for marine and coastal birds.

My growing concern was momentarily diverted by eight long-winged birds flying parallel to starboard. Striking creatures they were, jet black above and immaculate white below. As they maneuvered liltingly just above the waves, their bodies jerked up and down by strong wing strokes, I could make out their vermilion beaks with the knifelike lower mandibles protruding grotesquely. My first black skimmers! Of all the birds nesting on Cobb Island, they were the ones I wanted most to photograph.

Slowly the island assumed definite character. Near the southern extremity loomed some buildings. Built high on piles so as to escape the tide, they seemed lifted above the island like a mirage. Golden sunlight reflected from their windows. We soon passed the United States Coast Guard Station and approached a frame house flanked by two small bungalows.

It was then that I caught sight of a man standing squarely on both feet, hands on his hips, and motionless. He wore a blue shirt, khaki trousers, and hip boots; his head, though bald, was dignified by a corona of white hair.

As the boatman eased his craft toward the landing and killed the motor, I called, "Are you Captain Cobb?" No reply. We jumped out. The man still did not move or speak. Somewhat unnerved by now, I extended my hand, "My name is Pettingill."

"I'm George Cobb, glad to meet you," was the response in a low, pleasant voice. We shook hands, and he nodded graciously to Eleanor. Captain Cobb was the warden posted here by the National Audubon Society, or National Association of Audubon Societies as it was called then.

I was impressed with Captain Cobb's massive build and erect, noticeably stiff posture. Though his tanned face had the deep furrows of a man of sixty, his physique possessed the vigor of one many years younger. His expression, not unkindly, remained immobile and serious.

"We'd like to stay awhile," I began cautiously, "to camp and study birds."

At this his face brightened, and I sensed a sudden unbending.

"Do as you wish," he said warmly. "Anyone who likes birds is welcome. Lots of people come to see them."

Much relieved, we unloaded our duffel. The boatman poled his craft from the shore. He and Captain Cobb, I realized, had not exchanged a word or glance.

Still not having taken a step, Captain Cobb said, "You'd better not camp tonight, it's nearly dark."

His words were persuasive, for night was settling down, but the yellow glow in the west still gave some light.

"The upstairs rooms in my house are empty," he continued.

Uneasy lest I hurt his feelings, I tried to explain. "We want to camp—something we've never done together." Had we not wished to appear seasoned to the rigors of the outdoors, I might have told him that my wife had never camped in her life.

"Do as you like," he said. "There's a flat place over there between two dunes where you can pitch your tent. Come with me."

From our campsite on the southern tip of the island, we could see the eastern beach rising to the dunes and the marsh stretching westward. Captain Cobb's house was just north of us on piles overlooking the marsh. A wooden ramp extended from his porch to the dunes. The Coast Guard Station was a quarter of a mile away.

In the semidarkness we set up our tent. Meanwhile Captain Cobb disappeared and returned shortly with a pail and some pieces of iron pipe.

"Drinking water," he said. "My well filled with salt water during the last storm. Caught this from the roof. It's good."

Just as I thanked him, a breeze rushed by, collapsing the tent.

"Try these for staples," Captain Cobb said, handing me the pipes. "Yours never'll hold in the sand." In no time the tent was up for keeps.

"Sorry we can't offer you a chair," I said, "but how about a cigarette?"

"Never smoke or drink," he replied.

After our uneasy silence, he said, "You want to see birds?"

We learned that we were just in time. The eggs in the skimmer colony on the beach were hatching; there were many nests of gulls and terns in the marsh.

It was dark when Captain Cobb left. The island was soothingly quiet. Above the light rush of surf on the beach, we heard a few skimmers passing close to shore, their calls suggesting the yelps of beagles in pursuit of unseen prey.

Next morning, as we approached the skimmer colony on the beach, the birds sat peacefully on their nests, all facing into the wind like weather vanes. Even when we were within a few yards of them, they failed to move. But suddenly we passed their limit of tolerance, because into the air they went with a rush of wings and discordant cries. The next moment one resentful bird left the throng and flew toward Eleanor. She screamed, folded her hands over her head, and crumpled in the sand.

"They won't hit you," I assured her; "they're bluffing." Just then another skimmer shot toward me at eye level. Not believing my own words, I ducked. The bird veered sharply upward.

Many birds were soon doing the same thing–shooting downward, veering upward, but never striking. Still confident, but not sure that they would not strike, I walked boldly into the colony, followed by my reluctant bride, whereupon some of the skimmers dropped to the ground in seemingly helpless prostration. One rested on its belly with wings limply outstretched; another lay on its side with one wing waving in the air; still another flopped along using its wings as paddles. They were "injury feigning," I explained. Frankly I was surprised to see it in colony-nesting birds.

Nests—mere cups scratched in the sand—were everywhere, often within 2 or 3 feet of one another. Many contained white eggs boldly splotched with black and brown. In a few nests there were chicks, the color of sand, squatting tightly, their eyes closed.

The sun bore down on us; the sand was painful to touch. Realizing that the eggs and chicks could not long endure exposure to such intense heat, we quickly departed, letting the panic-stricken skimmers return to shade their eggs or young ones from the burning sun.

That evening Captain Cobb invited us to dinner. When we strolled up the ramp to his house, there were lights in the Coast Guard Station. The air was calm, and from the still unexplored marsh came a medley of bird sounds.

Captain Cobb, fork in one hand and holder in the other, greeted us at the door and motioned us into a large unfinished room—kitchen, dining room, and living room in one—plainly furnished but tidy. After being assured that we had come with appetites, he returned to his oil stove, where oysters sizzled in a pan. In the nearby sink, silvery hogfishes and huge blue crabs still waited his attention. This was to be a very special meal, of the best the sea could provide—and it was.

After dinner Captain Cobb became voluble, revealing his attitudes and philosophies and, withal, an unexpected sense of humor. Time meant nothing to him. His only timepiece lay somewhere in the marsh where he had flung it in disgust three weeks before. The sun was his clock, he said. Companionship meant little either. He was contemptuous of his only neighbors, the crew at the Coast Guard Station, whom he considered lazy and careless. He hated to think of a ship in distress calling on them for help and pointed to a bullet hole in his wall made during their "target practice." He liked most of the people who came to see the birds, though the women in "trousers" were comical. Of the social life enjoyed by his wife on the mainland, a few days a year was all he could bear. What he wanted, he told us, was to stay on his island every day for the rest of his life.

Cobb Island was his home, settled by his grandfather, Nathan Cobb, when it was longer and wider with rich topsoil and many trees and shrubs. It teemed with birds. The family farm grew "cabbages as big as bushel baskets" and turnips "the size of watermelons." Artesian wells supplied water. A hotel accommodated pothunters and sportsmen.

Toward the end of the last century disaster struck: The pothunters all but exterminated the birds and a great storm, accompanied by high tides, destroyed the buildings, filled the wells, uprooted the trees, and washed away the life-giving soil and a third of the island. The family moved to the mainland.

Captain Cobb, a stubborn man, returned and built the present house. Now he was renovating the two bungalows for people coming to see birds. As for the birds, most of the breeding species had recovered from the pothunters. His present struggle was against the mainlanders who came to steal the beach birds' eggs for food. They hated him, even shot at him, but the National Association of Audubon Societies had appointed him Deputy Warden with authority to enforce bird protection on his and a neighboring island, and that he was determined to do even if he had to shoot in return.

The next day Eleanor and I explored the marsh. She turned up her nose at the musky odors, became tangled in the waist-high grass, jumped out of the way of the scurrying fiddler crabs and into a pool of black, sticky mud which smeared her new slacks and sneakers. Although she expressed doubts that any bird could nest in such a place, she followed me gamely.

Overhead a few laughing gulls circled placidly, and from the grass came the sharp cackles of clapper rails. Moving gingerly lest we step into some unseen hole, we finally reached a place where a gull cried out in alarm. Immediately dozens of gulls, together with several Forster's terns, flushed from the vegetation and milled over our heads. Occasionally one dived at us, but its attack was so halfhearted that we ignored it.

The nests of the gulls and terns were clustered here and there on clumps of debris—dead sedge stalks, seaweeds, and driftwood washed in by excessively high tides. In each nest on the top of the debris were eggs, usually three. Several were pipped; there would soon be chicks.

The clapper rails we did not see, for they cleverly managed to keep behind a wall of vegetation. Their nests, however, we found easily, for the grasses over them were pulled together and entwined at their tips in a telltale knot. Some of these nests contained as many as fifteen eggs.

In the ensuing eight days I divided my time between the beach and the marsh, using blinds so that I might observe the birds without their showing fear. Many of the eggs hatched. The weather was perfect, nearly always sunny with a slight breeze. Nights were balmy, moonlit, and delightful. Using information and ideas gathered on these days, I was able, later, to write and publish my observations in two scientific papers in an ornithological journal.

Early on the morning of July 3, I awoke with the tent slapping against my face. Struggling through the opening, I discovered a guy rope loose. After tightening it, I looked about.

Overhead from the northeast sped low, thick clouds, blotting out the rising sun already dimmed by an upper stratum of haze. Dark chasms furrowed the ocean's gray surface. The marsh bore a weird olive color, the beach an intense yellow. My deeply tanned hands and arms were sickly amber.

As I stood, pajama-clad, in the wind, I called sharply to Eleanor. At that moment, with a fresh burst of wind, another guy rope gave way, and Eleanor's sleepy, bewildered face peered out of the tent.

"Get dressed and get out," I shouted, struggling with the ropes. Her head snapped back into the tent like a turtle's.

No doubt Captain Cobb had been watching since dawn, had seen me emerge, and later had watched Eleanor, fully dressed, assume the role of detached guy rope while I had my turn inside. We were glad to see him coming down the ramp, his pace slow, reassuring.

"Better take down your tent and move your gear to my porch," he advised. "There'll be a high tide out of this. Have breakfast with me."

Minute by minute the wind increased; each gust seemed stronger than the one before. The tent blew down. There was no argument. With the wind tearing at us, we rolled up the tent and carried our duffel up the narrow ramp to the house. More than once we were thrown off balance and against the railing, which saved us from a tumble into the marsh.

The tide, which, according to Captain Cobb's battered almanac, was due to be high at eleven, reached its normal high soon after we were safely in the house. But what time was that? No one knew. Our watches had run down, and there was no sun. Captain Cobb "guessed" eight o'clock. There would be three more hours of rising tide!

As the tide exceeded its normal mark, the ocean seemed to lift up. Great walls of surf rose above the beach, hesitated menacingly, then collapsed in thunderous roars, sending avalanches of white water against the protecting dunes. The swelling tide rushed and swirled into the Broadwater. Small ponds appeared in the marsh; the ponds became lakes; the lakes fused into one vast expanse continuous with the Broadwater. Soon the Broadwater crept up to the dunes and under the house. Waves, whipped by the wind, licked at the piles, higher and steadily higher. The ocean sent long tongues of water between the dunes. Our once cozy campsite became a channel. The ramp drifted away. The Coast Guard Station, its piles invisible, seemed afloat. From the boat at the Station dock came exhaust fumes indicating that the crew was ready for any emergency.

The plight of the beach-nesting birds was all too apparent. Above the beach a cloud of skimmers hovered momentarily, settled on the sand, hovered again, settled again. Each time they rose, we knew that a wave had swept over their nests, destroying both eggs and young. Above the marsh, now totally flooded, families of clapper rails drifted on the water at the mercy of the gale. Weak swimmers, they floundered helplessly. Parent birds attempted to round up scattered broods by cutting wide circles and giving frantic calls that we could hear above the roar of the storm. One by one the chicks, exhausted, heavily soaked, and already submerged to their heads, were swallowed up by the waves and tidal whirls.

The heaps of debris on which the laughing gulls nested now floated like small rafts, often with nests intact and still holding eggs or chicks. While adult gulls fluttered anxiously over them, sometimes attempting to alight, the wind forced the rafts steadily southward away from the island and into the open Broadwater. There mounting waves tore them apart, spilling their living cargo into the sea.

Our dismay over the fate of the birds was distracted by a muffled crash. A bungalow dropped on its side; water entered the other. Moments later the waves began slapping the floor of our house. Captain Cobb still showed neither emotion nor alarm. The collapse of the bungalow, the destruction of the colonies, even the floor boards darkened by rising water, evoked no comment from him.

I was, I remember, looking through a window on the ocean-side and watching the spindrift whipped from the towering waves, when I realized that the surf was breaking over the grass-tufted tops of the highest dunes—our one remaining barrier against the fury of the sea. Suddenly an enormous wave, its force fortunately eased by the dunes, struck the side of the house at floor level, jarring the structure and spraying the windows.

Eleanor gasped. We turned toward Captain Cobb. Instead of the expected evidence of disturbance, I saw one of his rare smiles.

"Tide's turned," he said, pointing to the water flowing eastward out of the Broadwater.

The following morning Cobb Island sparkled under a sunny sky. Gone, however, were the bird colonies. Nature in one great sweep had rubbed out that which she so generously fostered. The beach where the skimmer colony had been was as smooth and hard as a floor, without sign of eggs or chicks. Beyond the site of the colony several hundred skimmers huddled close together. When we approached, they rose in a body and silently alighted farther away. Nowhere in the marsh was there a gull. We heard a few clapper rails and marveled that they had survived.

"Sorry you must go," Captain Cobb said, as we packed that night. "Come back next year. There'll be more birds than ever."

In August of that year, when another devastating storm battered the Atlantic Coast, we thought of Captain Cobb and wondered how he had fared. Weeks later in *Bird-Lore*, the journal of the National Association of Audubon Societies, we were shocked and saddened to read:

> George W. Cobb, this Association's warden on Cobb's Island Virginia, lost his life, on August 23, in the severe storm that lashed the middle Atlantic coast. The meager information received may be all that we will ever learn concerning the fate of this sturdy Virginian of well-known pioneer stock, who thus ended his lonely vigils on the wind-swept, wave-battered stretch of dune and marsh which was his ancestral home. Search by airplane and boat has failed, as yet, to reveal his body which, no doubt, rests somewhere among the extensive marshes of the Virginian shores. The storm which took Mr. Cobb's life, we are informed, completely demolished the few buildings on the island, leaving nothing but the drill pole of the United States Coast Guard Station.

HARRISON F. LEWIS

The Eider and Her Helpers

Dr. Harrison Flint Lewis, of a Nova Scotian family, was born December 15, 1893, in Sag Harbor, Long Island, New York. In 1911, he and his family moved to Yarmouth, Nova Scotia, where young Lewis attended Yarmouth County Academy and Nova Scotia Provincial Normal College. He taught school for a while, had military service in World War 1, and after the War became Chief Federal Migratory Bird Officer for Quebec, during which time (1920–1943) he organized the bird sanctuary systems on the north shore of the Gulf of St. Lawrence and on James Bay. In 1944 he was appointed to the Canadian Wildlife Service, from which he retired, as Chief, in 1952. Since 1952 he has lived in a rural area on the southwest coast of Nova Scotia. Dr. Lewis earned his Master's degree at the University of Toronto, his Doctor of Philosophy degree at Cornell University, with a major in ornithology. He has been the editor of Canadian Field Naturalist, *and* Sportsman's Province. *He is Chairman of the Nova Scotia Resources Council and President of the Nova Scotia Bird Society.*

THE EIDER AND HER HELPERS

SHELTERED between two outstretched arms of solid rock, the waters of the little cove were pleasantly rippled by a light northerly breeze. From cloudy June skies an occasional morning shower descended.

Near the head of this indentation in a small island off the coast of Nova Scotia, a flock of common eiders moved slowly about, while its members dived repeatedly to obtain mussels or other food from the rocky bottom. Included in the group were nine downy young and their two mothers; two adult drakes, in magnificent panoply of black and white; several one-year-old drakes, identifiable by their brown plumage, with white patches on the fore part of the body; and more than twenty broodless females, presumably maidens that had hatched a year earlier and would not mate until two years old. On the summit of the north point dozed an adult great black-backed gull. As viewed from my blind, pitched on the crest of the beach terminating the cove, the scene was one of nature undisturbed.

Suddenly I became aware of low notes issuing from a dense thicket of small firs in the woods behind my blind. They were the guttural *wahk-wahk-wahk-wahk* of a mother eider coaxing her ducklings to follow her. Young of this species are commonly led to water by the mother within a few hours after hatching. Could it be that a brood from one of the many eider nests concealed among the trees was coming to the cove on that first journey, so short, yet so toilsome and fraught with dangers?

I had not long to wait. Out of the woods, past my blind, down the sloping sandy beach walked or waddled triumphantly a sturdy eider mother. She was followed closely by four downy, grayish-brown ducklings, which were putting all their infant strength into the struggle to keep pace with her. They were complying well with the first rule of life for eiders of that tender age—"Keep close to mother and do what she does!" If maternal pride was evident in the mother's glance and bearing, she had good reason for it. No finer ducklings had ever been seen anywhere.

As they approached the water's edge, the ducklings began to utter a shrill *peep, peep, peep,* the characteristic note of their kind. Then mother and brood halted close to the water and squatted on the sand. A momentous event, the first launching on salt water, their true home, faced the youngsters. There seemed to be need for a brief rest before going ahead with it.

Evidently the notes of mother and ducklings had attracted the attention of the eiders feeding in the cove, for at that moment a group of the full-grown maiden ducks began to swim toward the new arrivals. No less than eleven of them, uttering guttural croaks like those of eider mothers, hastened toward the recently hatched little fellows.

The mother duck and her four offspring entered the quiet water as easily and unconcernedly as though all were old hands at it. Close to shore the broodless females crowded eagerly about and completely surrounded the little family. Like teenage girls admiring a baby, they examined the new little eiders with intense interest. In a moment they were joined by additional yearling eiders, including two males.

For a few seconds the mother of the ducklings permitted without remonstrance the enthusiastic attention that the jostling crowd of year-old ducks was giving to her children. It may at first have pleased her, but soon she seemed to find the curiosity and the crowding excessive. Neither she nor the ducklings had room to move.

With a few vigorous jabs of her bill, mother eider forced some of the assembled birds to move back a few inches. A slight commotion developed in the group. It so startled the ducklings that, without waiting for mother to set the example, they made their first brief dives!

For several minutes the mixed group of ducks swam slowly back and forth at a short distance from the beach. The downy young were alert to follow close to their mother and no other. When she stepped ashore for a moment, they came ashore too. When she re-entered the water, they went with her. She continued to strike at other females that she considered too familiar.

Soon the ducklings seemed to be looking for food. They swam with their heads under water and occasionally one dived. One bright-eyed mite "stood up" in the water, as an adult duck does, and flapped its downy, ineffective winglets. *Ridiculous! But a chip off the old block!* The ducklings had become members of eider society and were launched on the sea of life.

Ducklings of the common eider, averaging four to a brood, are frequently sought by hungry predators, the most prominent of which in Nova Scotia are great black-backed gulls. The low ratio of success that these gulls achieve in their attempts to seize eider ducklings may be attributed to the effectiveness of the protective precautions and cooperation that the eiders have developed.

The chief reliance of the eiders in defending their young seems to be placed in what may be called the convoy system. From two to half-a-dozen eider mothers commonly pool their broods and share the responsibility of protecting the group of ducklings thus formed. As the eider is a heavy, powerful duck, a match for a great black-backed gull in open combat, several cooperating eider mothers can protect very effectively their closely grouped offspring. A few individualistic mother ducks fail to participate in this system. Drake eiders take no part in caring for their progeny and are seldom associated with them.

There is every reason to believe that female common eiders do not breed until they are two years old. Most of the numerous females without young of this species that are to be found in small companies near the nesting islands in early summer are apparently nonbreeding one-year-old birds. They have little to do except to find good feeding grounds and to profit by them.

As is shown by the incident already described, these eider subdebs take a keen interest in the young that are hatched by older females. They try to associate with them and to take part in caring for them. Most of the time the mother eiders reject the proffered assistance. They prefer to attend to their ducklings themselves or in cooperation with other matrons and want no voluntary young helpers.

In an emergency, however, this attitude of aloofness is dropped. Any help is then welcome. The following incident, which was observed a fortnight later in the season than the first one described, is revealing.

On a calm June morning, two mother eiders were convoying a group of ducklings near my blind while they fed quietly along the boulder-bordered shore of a large cove. In some manner unknown, these mother ducks had become the guardians of sixteen young, an unusually large number for two broods. Probably their original little flock had been joined by several waifs.

Near the south point of the cove two adult drake eiders and five full-grown females without young were peacefully feeding. They seemed to be strictly minding their own business. Several adult great black-backed gulls perched on the rocky ridge of the point or circled over the cove, seeking their breakfast.

One of the gulls suddenly hovered low above the two eider mothers and accompanying young, which were then feeding near a large boulder standing in shallow water, a few feet from shore. The side of the boulder nearest to the eiders was flat and vertical, a small cliff, 2 or 3 feet high.

The mother eiders were alert to the gull's threat and responded to it instantly and well, though they were handicapped by the excessive number of young that they had to protect. Pointing their rounded bills upward and warning the gull away by voice and gesture, they swiftly herded their charges close against the flat face of the boulder. In this way the arc to be protected was reduced to half a circle and the long-winged gull was denied the space that he required to maneuver.

Checked for the moment, the gull alighted on the boulder's top. Sixteen lively eider ducklings, little impressed by their dire peril, could not long be kept crowded in a small space. The gull could afford to bide its time.

But in their time of need, help for the hard-pressed eiders was at hand. From the group of ducks that were feeding off the point, 100 feet away, three full-grown females detached themselves and swam straight to the threatened group of young. Their prompt action changed the balance of power, and the gull's opportunity vanished. Two more gulls appeared, and two more female eiders joined the group of their kind, but the outcome had already been decided. The gulls flew away to seek food elsewhere.

It appears that the numerous one-year-old female common eiders present in the regions where this species nests and rears its young are endowed with a strong instinct to protect duck-lings produced by older females of their kind. This instinct may, in time of urgent need, lead to useful defensive action. It may be a significant factor favoring a satisfactory survival of eider ducklings.

IRA N. GABRIELSON

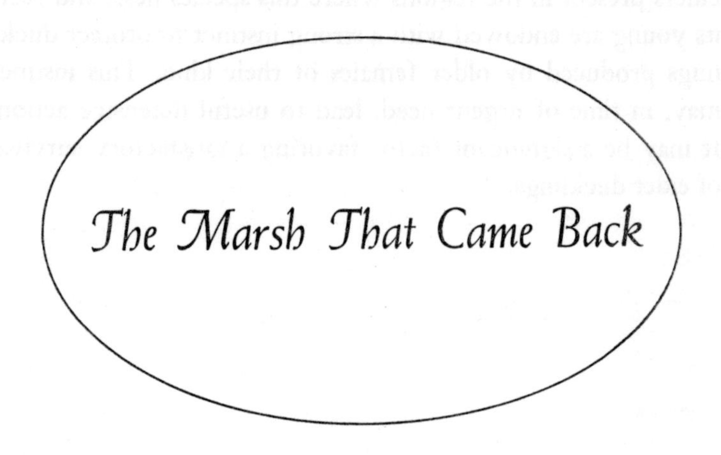

The Marsh That Came Back

Dr. Ira N. Gabrielson, President of the Wildlife Management Institute, Washington, D.C., was born in Sioux Rapids, Iowa, September 27, 1889. He was graduated from Morningside College in 1912, and after teaching high school biology for three years, he entered the federal service with the U.S. Biological Survey, now called the Fish and Wildlife Service. In his work as a government field biologist he became recognized as an authority on birds, mammals, and plants, particularly of the western United States. In 1935 he was appointed Assistant Chief of the Division of Wildlife Research and became Chief of the Bureau in the same year. In 1940 he was named Director of the newly created Fish and Wildlife Service, from which he retired in 1946 to accept his present post. He has traveled extensively in North America and is noted as a keen field naturalist and capable administrator of wildlife resources. In 1936 Oregon State College conferred on him an honorary degree of Doctor of Science; in 1941, Morningside College honored him with an LL.D. He is the author or coauthor of six books of which one of his latest is The Birds of Alaska.

THE MARSH THAT CAME BACK

IT is a terrible thing to see a great marsh die. It is one of the most heartening experiences to see such a marsh, once dead, restored to life. Two of the unforgettable experiences of my life were watching both happen to one of the great natural marshes of North America—Malheur Lake in eastern Oregon.

It was late summer in 1919 when I first saw Malheur in all its glory. The marsh was not completely full of water, but there was enough so that I could see great expanses of open water from Cole Island, a point which I reached almost dry-shod by carefully picking my way around the wettest spots in the shallow channels between the island and the shore. It is impossible to forget the impression when, looking through my binoculars, I swept the great expanse of water ahead of me.

It was dotted, and in many places almost covered with birds. Great fleets of white pelicans outnumbered all other birds, including scattered family flocks of Canada geese and the snaky black cormorants sliding along through the water, sometimes with only their heads and necks showing above the surface. Herons of many kinds stood in the shallows, some fishing, others just enjoying a siesta. Ducks were there in myriads—mallards, pintails, gadwalls, and cinnamon teal, redheads, and ruddy ducks. These seemed to be the dominant species at the time, although scattered among them I saw canvasbacks, widgeons, and green-winged teal. Coots and Florida gallinules were visible in any direction I turned my glasses. Shore birds were more difficult to see, although the taller, long-legged avocets, stilts, and curlews were conspicuous even among the more numerous ducks. It took real searching to find the smaller fry among the shore birds, but they were there too. One had only to turn his binocular on the nearer mud flats or shallow bars to see western and pectoral sandpipers, Wilson's phalaropes, and many others. This was truly a great bird concentration, the first of such magnitude that I had ever seen. I stood on the island drinking in the great living spectacle before me until it was too dark to see clearly. This was Malheur, the Malheur about which Bill Finley, Oregon's great bird conservationist, had written so vividly years before. But it was a Malheur that was doomed.

It was doomed partly by drought and partly by the increasing diversion of its life-giving water. Malheur Lake is the sump formed from the runoff from two rivers, the Blitzen from the south and the Silvies from the north. The Silvies had long been cut off during the summer, but the spring flood waters from both rivers together with the flow of the Blitzen were enough to maintain the marsh water at some level, except in periods of the driest years.

With the increasing diversion of water from the Blitzen to establish irregular water rights, Malheur began to shrink. It was not a sudden and merciful death; it was slow and agonizing, with occasional years in which the patient showed some improvement. But in the early 1930's when the great drought struck, Malheur became mostly a memory. By midsummer each year, it was little more than an alkali flat; in the wetter years, when a little more water reached the lake, there might be a stinking mudhole, but this was only a remnant of a once great natural resource. The birds were gone, together with all of the other life. As the lake shrank, the crowded fishes and frogs provided a feast for the birds that lived on them, for the birds had a concentrated food supply until the final catastrophe. Then the oxygen content of the lake became so low that the fishes died by thousands and tens of thousands. Now there was no more food, and the birds were forced to go elsewhere. It was a tragedy to watch, the dwindling of the birds as one area of marsh habitat after another died from lack of water. Many of the aquatic plants were tenacious, and only a little water would start them growing again, but the water never lasted long enough to really revive most of them. Gradually the area in which plants disappeared widened and became more and more desolate until those of us who had known and loved Malheur avoided the place almost as one of pestilence.

In those years, every conservationist who lived in Oregon had the restoration of Malheur Lake high on his priority list, although hopes were almost at the vanishing point. When the opportunity came to make recommendations to the President's Committee on Wildlife Restoration, everyone, including Bill Finley and Stanley Jewett, another Oregon conservationist who had long fought to save Malheur Lake, made it the first consideration of any restoration program attempted in Oregon. To do that required buying the "P" Ranch that controlled the flow of the Blitzen River. The great "P" Ranch, however, had also fallen on evil days in the drought years and was not a money-making proposition.

In some almost miraculous way, the U.S. Biological Survey got enough money to buy the entire ranch. I vividly remember the excitement in the Portland office of that agency when a telegram arrived from Jay N. "Ding" Darling, then Chief of the Survey, saying that the ranch had been acquired, and that we were authorized to start the water flowing back into the lake. There were rumors that there would be opposition to it from some of the lake-bed squatters, but Stan Jewett and I started for the "P" Ranch, got the keys, and opened the gate on the main diversion dam above the lake. For both of us it was a moment of tremendous satisfaction to see the water flowing into the channel that led to the thirsty lake bed.

Then came the anticlimax. The water did not take too long to traverse the few miles of channel that lay between this last dam and the lake, but when it got to the lake bed it disappeared. It ran for days, and the days stretched into weeks, before the great mass of thoroughly dried-out peat of the lake bed had soaked up enough so that we could see water in the deepest of its great weathered cracks. Long before spring the water commenced to show in places, and it had spread over a considerable area of the marsh that first summer.

If it had been a heartbreaking thing to see Malheur die, it was an exhilarating experience to see how quickly it could come back. There must have been, in spite of the long years of drought, some plant roots there with life in them. It is difficult otherwise to account for the big bunches of cattails, tules, and other emergent plants that suddenly sprang up. The ground must also have been full of viable seeds of the submerged water plants because by the end of the first summer the lake had become almost as full of sago pondweed and other choice duck foods as it had been in the days before the lake disappeared. The water life which still existed in the Blitzen Valley reappeared in the lake, and soon frogs and fishes became numerous again. Within two or three years all birds that formerly nested at Malheur had returned. The great squadrons of snow and Canada geese and myriads of ducks that had stopped there before it dried up returned, and Malheur again became a great marsh, teeming and throbbing with life as it had been before its destruction. It was a never-to-be-forgotten lesson of the power of man to destroy, and also of the power of man—with the help of nature—to restore.

ALFRED M. BAILEY

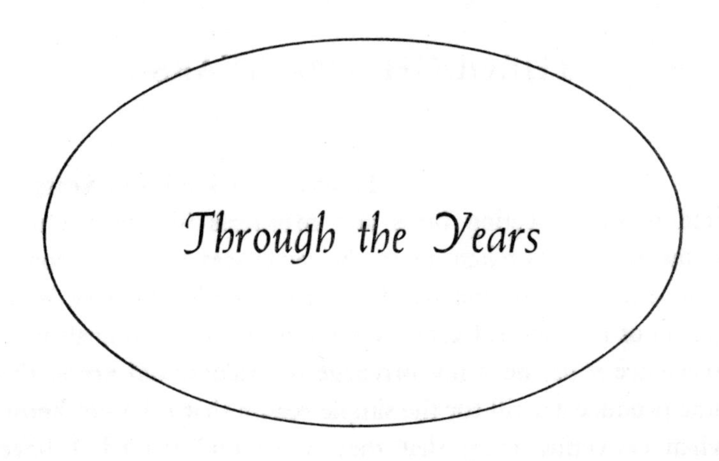

Alfred M. Bailey, Director of the Denver Museum of Natural History, Colorado, was born on February 18, 1894, in Iowa City, Iowa. In his scientific expeditions in search of birds and other animals, he has traveled to the Hawaiian Islands, Siberia, Alaska, Europe, Abyssinia, and the Sudan. More recently he has studied and photographed birds on Wake and Midway Islands in the Pacific, and has led expeditions for the Denver Museum to Canton and Fiji Islands, New Caledonia, New Zealand, and Australia. In the summer of 1960, he traveled to the Galapagos Islands off the coast of Ecuador to collect animal and plant specimens for a new ecological exhibit. He is a fine photographer and has narrated his motion picture color films before large audiences in the United States and Canada for the National Audubon Society's screen tours.

He is the author of two books, Birds of Arctic Alaska *and* Birds of Colorado, *and has written many papers for scientific publications, also articles about natural history for* National Geographic Magazine, Natural History, Frontiers, *and others.*

THROUGH THE YEARS

Looking back on fifty years of field work—collecting birds and mammals for science museums, which has taken me to the seven seas and to all continents except Antarctica—I think my experiences have been devoid of highlights. Certainly the few species of animals new to science it has been my privilege to discover did not at the time produce a thrill for the simple reason that I did not know when collecting them that they were undescribed. I have memories of my first field trip as a youngster in college to, in those days, distant Laysan Island of the Hawaiian group, where for three wonderful months I was associated with thousands of Laysan and black-footed albatrosses and became acquainted with the five species of small birds unique to that island—three of which are now extinct.

My first job after graduation was with the Louisiana State Museum in New Orleans, and thanks to a kindly director, I was privileged to roam the marsh country with Cajun friends—to photograph the great colonies of nesting water birds in summer, and the enormous flocks of blue geese and snow geese in winter. There were many trips to the shell keys and the mud lumps at the mouth of the Mississippi River, where grotesque pelicans and trim terns of many species nested by the thousands.

The work in Louisiana was followed by three years working the islands of southeastern Alaska by gas boat; a winter's journey by dog sled in 57 degrees below zero weather along the Copper River in the interior; and many months of field work along the arctic coast. Especially I recall late fall along the ice-worn shore near our base 300 miles north of the Arctic Circle when Ross' gulls, among the rarest of all northern birds, were flying low over the ice pack. Their rosy breasts and gray backs merged with the overcast skies, and they wheeled directly toward me when I waved a handkerchief to attract their attention. I remember another day of watching the beautiful ivory gulls spotlighted with golden rays as the sun pierced the mantle of clouds, the immaculate white plumage of the birds in brilliant contrast against a black polar sky.

At the same time there were long strings of black brant, and eider, and occasional great yellow-billed loons flying southward, the rustling of wings on this quiet day blending with the gentle grinding of ice moving with the ocean currents.

The sun dropped out of sight to be absent for two months, except for the crimson glow on the horizon to the northeast as a reminder that eventually spring would come. The dark days were wonderful because the majority of our Eskimo friends were in the village and it was a time for getting acquainted. The day that Ned, the mail carrier, with his fourteen dogs appeared out of the storm was a memorable occasion —for he brought me my first word from home in seven months. And with the coming of the sun the weather became more severe; I prepared for a long dog-sled journey by boiling beans and rice and freezing them in pie tins, until we had a flour sack half full. All we needed when camp was made was to crawl into our sleeping bags with a primus stove between us—and thaw out a chip of beans—food for a king.

That 750-mile dog-sled journey from northernmost Alaska to the westernmost point of North America with an Eskimo companion was of special interest to me. Many wonderful skin-clad natives made us welcome as we worked our way southward, sometimes traveling on snow-covered tundra, and again working laboriously through broken ice where onshore winds had caused great pressure ridges to form—but my many pages of field notes fail to mention adventures.

Later, at Cape Prince of Wales I often climbed a spur of Cape Mountain and on clear days could see the cliffs of Siberia looming in the distance across Bering Strait. When on the mountains, I watched for early bird migrants which might pause on ridges swept clean of snow by the seemingly ever-blowing winds. On one rare quiet day flocks of the sand-hill cranes were in great numbers flying northward over open water in Bering Strait until they reached the extremity of Cape Mountain, where fog was massed to the westward. The calling cranes flew into the low-lying belt, and immediately their clarion cries turned to consternation as they became hopelessly lost without land bearings to guide them. Eventually the flocks would circle and emerge again into sunlight.

With the approach of spring there were great waves of eider ducks, murres, loons and other sea birds on their way to distant nesting grounds, and the current in Bering Strait began to run northward carrying the ice of Bering Sea through the narrow Strait into the Arctic Ocean. And with the movement of ice there was a migration of sea mammals. Great whales cruised along the face of the flow—the precipitous edges of grounded shore ice. Seals and walruses in hundreds occasionally were black against the flat pan ice, the bellowing of the walruses often being heard when winds were favorable—far back in the tundra.

The sea mammals on their northward journey were cutting across the path of Ancient Man, who many thousands of years ago migrated from his ancestral home in Asia to new hunting grounds toward the rising sun. At one time there was a land bridge connecting Asia and North America—probably not in the location of present-day Bering Strait. Over this bridge land mammals were able to migrate—over a land mass between the two continents which did not necessarily exist when the primitive hunters made their way to the New World. From the cliffs of present-day Siberia, Cape Mountain would present a challenge to any inquisitive hunter, and it seems probable the journey across Bering Strait by way of the Diomede Island steppingstones would have been a simple matter.

While the Eskimos are supposed to have settled along the shores of Alaska not too many thousands of years ago, it seems not unlikely that the hunters who came long before them to pursue the great mammoths would have preferred to travel along rugged terrain by following the coasts in skin boats—just as the Eskimos have done for centuries—instead of laboriously making their way overland.

In my field work with Eskimo friends at Cape Prince of Wales at the western extremity of the continent, we followed what I visualized as the route of early man. With a crew of twelve natives, we were offshore whenever weather conditions were favorable, and we would stay out on Bering Strait until the oomiaks were loaded with meat—walrus and seal—or until we were forced ashore by bad weather. We crossed the narrow passageway from Alaska to Siberia in our skin boats three times that spring, and could note the passage of the thousands of sea mammals and the great flights of birds of many species as they made their way northward from their wintering grounds in Bering Sea to distant places in the Arctic Ocean.

Alaskan field work was followed by expeditions to other out-of-the-way places—one, a 2,000-mile muleback journey through Abyssinia with the noted bird artist Louis Agassiz

Fuertes—in days when that beautiful country was still a feudal kingdom, with each powerful chieftain a king unto himself. Emperor Haile Selassie was then Ras Tafari, heir apparent to the throne, and we were greatly indebted to him for many courtesies. Our journey took us through much of the rugged country.

We traveled from Addis Ababa southward into the Arrusi Mountains, where we made camp at around 9,500 feet, with the great Rift Valley cutting down Central Africa below us at the right. Great lammergeiers—the bearded vultures—cruised along precipitous cliffs, and many other kinds of birds of prey were numerous. There were five white men in our party, with many native retainers, and one morning I came from my tent at the same time Fuertes appeared from his. High up on the cliff overhead perched a common vulture. Pointing at the bird, I said to Louie, "You want it?"

"Sure," he replied.

Picking up the .22 rifle, I casually aimed 8 or 10 feet above the distant bird, pulled the trigger, and to the amazement of all of us, the bird plummeted downward. When retrieved, it did not have a mark upon it. Fuertes immediately sat down, posed the bird to his liking, and made a rough color sketch of it. Later, when he finished, he showed it to me. At the bottom of the water color he had lettered five *B*'s (B.B.B.B.B.). When I asked, as Louie knew I would, the meaning of the letters, he said, "Oh, that means Bill Bailey's Before Breakfast Buzzard."

Strangely, on an expedition which was of seven months' duration through a fascinating country the thought that comes back to me was a comment by my gunbearer, Alamayu, made in the high country of the Simyen Mountains. It was on the second leg of our seven months' field trip. We had traveled northward from Addis Ababa and had crossed the Blue Nile after three days' strenuous muleback work. The first day we dropped down the sheer river escarpment two thirds of the way; the second day we crossed the Nile and climbed halfway out; the third we emerged into the province of Gojjam, ruled by the second most powerful man of Abyssinia, Ras Hailu. We escaped from the kindly hospitality of that colorful chieftain only after a week of continuous entertainment, and continued northward along the shores of Lake Tsana where Fuertes made his well-known painting of a beautiful small kingfisher. Then on to Gondar with its great ruined castles, and into the land of Dejasmatch Ayalu, where we hoped to hunt *walia*, the Abyssinian ibex, on the sheer cliffs of the northern escarpment.

We proceeded northward, ever climbing, along steep trails into the high Simyen Mountains. Dejasmatch Ayalu had said white men could not successfully hunt the ibex because of the precipitous nature of their haunts, and we had secretly scoffed at such an idea. Our caravan slowly wound its way to 10,000 feet, and finally we came to the northern escarpment, where by a series of drops—as though the land had been cut by a giant knife—the cliffs fell thousands of feet to the rolling hills adjacent to the Red Sea. We came abruptly upon the awesome spectacle, and Alamayu's involuntary exclamation was most descriptive. He stood motionless for a moment and then breathed, "*Mongot yellem!*" ("There is no road!").

And in the following weeks we had occasion to agree with Alamayu, that there was *no road*, as we worked our way along narrow ledges in search of the wary *walia*. Certainly it was a most rugged terrain with precipitous ledges difficult to negotiate. Eventually, we succeeded in our quest—the first Americans to collect the Abyssinian ibex—and we were relieved when the task was accomplished.

All field collectors are happy when their efforts result in the discovery of species new to science, and in the high Simyens

I was fortunate in collecting a new mammal which the leader of our party, Dr. Wilfred Osgood, was kind enough to name for me. Some day I will have to look up the article to find out its generic name.

The finding of species or races of animals or plants new to science is usually accidental, although the majority of fieldmen are watching carefully for animals or plants which differ from those of other habitats. I still remember with pleasure a mule-back trip through the beautiful pine forests of the state of Durango in the high country of Mexico. With me was Boardman Conover, who assembled during his lifetime of study one of the finest collections of game birds of the world—now a valued part of the study series of the Chicago Natural History Museum.

We were not collecting birds, but around the campfire one evening we discussed, as usual, the species of game birds of the area, and Conover expressed the wish that he would like to have a pair of wild turkeys, which abounded in the surrounding forests. Our Mexican guide said the birds could be got easily, for we had an excellent hunter among us. At daybreak the following morning, the man would be sent to the Valley of Turkeys, which was just ahead; he would collect the birds and wait there for our arrival.

Our caravan man, the hunter, started out long before daylight; he saw a flock of birds in an open glade, he stalked them carefully, and lining up two great gobblers, secured both with a single shot. They were unusually fine birds, and our hunter was appreciative of their beauty. He stretched them out in the early morning light, admired their iridescent sheen, and awaited our arrival. Finally, a trifle bored with the inactivity and having nothing to do—he carefully plucked the feathers from each bird—and only naked carcasses of what had been beautiful scientific specimens remained!

A day later, we were camped near a marsh area. I casually remarked we couldn't identify the various birds we were seeing so commonly, and we should do something about it. Borrowing the cook's shotgun and a handful of black powder shells, I shot one each of the birds of the near vicinity. The last was a small sparrow perched on a reed in the marsh. It was inconspicuous and reminded me of a Savannah sparrow. When I retrieved my little specimen, it was so badly damaged I wondered whether it was worth saving—but eventually it was made into a satisfactory skin.

When Outram Bangs, the veteran ornithologist of the Museum of Comparative Zoology at Harvard University received the specimen, he wrote: "Thank heaven for that little finch. I've had one in my collection for forty years and I've always known it was new to science, but hesitated to describe it from one skin." The sparrow proved not only to be a species, but also a new genus, and today is known by the generic name *Xenospiza.*

A pleasant memory is of one of several trips to the great pelican colony on Gunnison Island, Utah, with my lifelong associate Bob Niedrach of the Denver Museum of Natural History. As we set up our tent along the shores, I noticed a tracery of footprints in the fine sand at the base of some dwarfed plants. Pointing to the tracks, I remarked, "I'll bet there have been few new races of small mammals discovered and recognized by footprints." We both realized that animals isolated for any length of time on an island—especially, as in this instance, when surrounded with the brine of Great Salt Lake—probably would differ from those of the mainland. We collected kangaroo rats and white-footed mice, and both were described and named by E. A. Goldman. He gave the kangaroo rat the subspecific name *alfredi* (my first name), with a comment by Goldman that there were "just too doggone many Baileys in the natural history field." I did not know whether to be complimented on having a *rat* named for me or not, until Bob pointed out that my predecessor as Director of the Denver Museum of Natural History had had a *snake* and a *skunk* named in his honor.

We discovered another new race of birds off the Mexican coast. Where we had discovered some of the mammals of Gunnison Island by their tracks in the sands, we recognized a rock wren new to science by its voice! Again Bob Niedrach and I were afield together—this time on San Benito Island off the coast of Lower California, Mexico. Over the rugged landscape were many of the little wrens. Niedrach commented, "Those wrens do not sound like the birds at home." We collected a series and sent them to A. J. Van Rossem, at the University of California, and suggested to him that we believed they differed from the common form in having much longer beaks. Van Rossem named this subspecies *Salpinctes obsoletus tenuirostris.*

Two other experiences remain in memory, one of a day on the summit of St. Col Peak on Campbell Island in the subantarctic of New Zealand. It was toward the end of our two months' stay on that remarkable island with its five species of nesting albatrosses and other interesting sea birds. I was sitting on the lee side of a tussock-clad slope on one of the rare days when blue skies were patched with racing white clouds. Thirty feet in front of me five royal albatrosses—the largest of flying birds (the Campbell Island race averages larger than wandering albatrosses)—were bowing and weaving and thrusting their wings upward to their greatest extent, and standing on tiptoes as they strutted in their courtship performances. Immediately in front of me was my fifteen-year-old grandson, Jack Murphy, on his hands and knees as he carefully worked his hand under an albatross that was sitting on her (or his) nest. Jack pressed upon the breast of the albatross so the great winged bird sat bolt upright, revealing the egg in its brood pouch. And that same evening, in a sheltered inlet of Perseverance Harbour, Jack and I inspected at close range huge old elephant seals. Surely few naturalists have been privileged to have their grandson on such an expedition to such a remote part of the world. Indeed, I would almost be inclined to consider any one of many experiences with Jack on that trip the essence of one fine and unusual moment or hour in my life.

But in the background there has always been one memorable event which could never be duplicated—and that dates back to the early part of this short narrative—my Alaskan journey. I had started the latter part of May and boarded the famous old Coast Guard Cutter *Bear* at Nome and made a summer cruise along the Siberian coast. We traveled around Point Barrow and through the arctic ice to Demarcatum Point, where Alaska and Canada meet. On the return trip I was put ashore at Wainwright, a little Eskimo village 300 miles north of the Arctic Circle, to spend the winter. Then followed the sled journey to the Cape Prince of Wales, the crossing of Bering Strait in a skin oomiak following the path of primitive man from the Old to the New World, and, finally after fifteen months of continuous field work my return journey via a freighter from Nome, Alaska, to Seattle, Washington.

And there on the dock was my wife, and with her was our two-year-old blond daughter Beth, whom I had last seen a year and three months before when she was a babe in arms. I believe the majority of fieldmen who have traveled to the far places will agree that the enjoyment of accomplishment of any task well done can never equal that of the thrill of returning *home*—which to me, on that occasion, was "the unusual moment" that I will never forget.

H. ALBERT HOCHBAUM

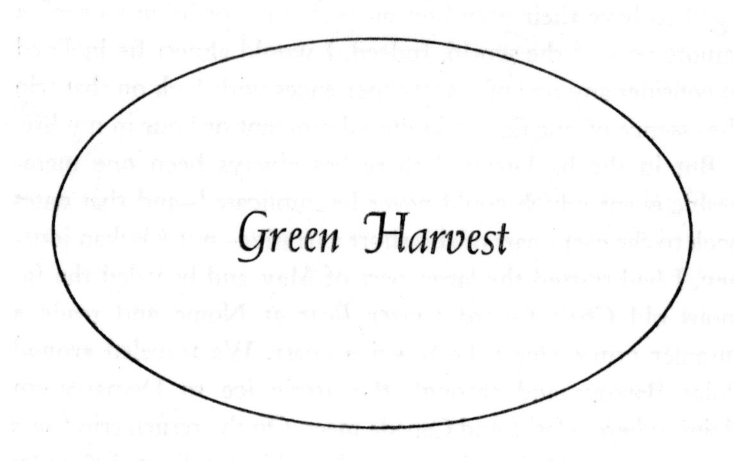

Green Harvest

H. Albert Hochbaum, Director, Delta Waterfowl Research Station, at Delta, Manitoba, Canada, was born in Greeley, Colorado, February 9, 1911. He was graduated with a Bachelor of Science degree from Cornell University and received his Master of Science degree from the University of Wisconsin. From 1934 to 1937 he was employed by the National Park Service; he has been Director of Delta Waterfowl Research Station since 1938. He is a Fellow of the American Ornithologists' Union, from which he received the Brewster Medal, awarded for his book The Canvasback on a Prairie Marsh, *considered the best publication of the year on birds of the Western Hemisphere, and the Second Literary Award of the Wildlife Society for his book* Travels and Traditions of Waterfowl. *Under a grant from the*

Guggenheim Foundation, Mr. Hochbaum is presently studying the aesthetic and material values of marshes and their place in our culture.

GREEN HARVEST

It was a bright October 9, 1938, on Delta Marsh in Manitoba, Canada. Sunup had found ice at the reedy edges, but it melted before noon, and the tall yellow canes reflected warmth. Adult mallard drakes were green-headed and curly-tailed; the plumage of some of the juvenile males nearly as far along. All but the last stragglers of blue-winged teal had departed and had been replaced by green-winged teal. Lesser scaups had arrived, and in those days when the northern birds came down, old Ernie Cook used to say that even with a shoehorn you couldn't get another bird on Cadham Bay. He was pretty nearly right. Canvasbacks and redheads were at their peak. Their morning and evening flights to and from the sago shallows seemed endless, darts of birds seldom out of sight as they crossed the passes. In a few days, however, they'd be gone, all but the strays and cripples.

Despite the duck depression of the middle 1930's, canvasbacks were still common on the Manitoba prairie marshes, and at Delta, my tally of hunters' bags showed them to be second only to mallards in the harvest. Daily, I traveled far and wide over the marsh to look at the product of gunning. Hunters were generous in allowing me to study their gamebags, first to determine the species composition of the kill, then by cloacal examination, to learn the ratio of juveniles to adults.

Just before noon I was going over the bag of a friendly,

open-faced chap from Cedar Rapids, Iowa, a middle-aged gentleman with a three-hundred-dollar Parker double-barreled shotgun and forty-dollar boots. His head was cocked as he watched me, pleasureful pride on his face while he correctly named most of his ducks as I handled them one by one. The bag included four canvasbacks. The first were three young birds—two hens and a drake—the last an adult female, her maturity quickly apparent by the heavier frosting on her greater wing coverts. She seemed a little light as I hefted her, a bit sharp on the keel. "Nice bird, eh?" he said. "The canvasback is the king of the pack, the sportiest and the best eating. Used to get quite a few through Iowa and Illinois, but the flight has pretty well dried up there." I nodded agreement as I made my notes. "Took these four 'Cans' at The-Hole-in-the-Wall, all of them going downwind ninety miles an hour." He chuckled in self-appreciation and pointed his gun in the air, aiming at an imaginary flight, clucking his tongue to indicate trigger pulls. "Sure is a sporty bird."

I thanked Mr. Cedar Rapids for his courtesy as I put his ducks back on the game stringer, returning them to him without calling attention to the old canvasback female's wings. They were better than an inch short of full growth. It would have been at least a week thence before she could have taken her first flight following her month-long flightless period attending the annual wing molt.

Ducks, geese, and swans change the wing feathers but once a year, all of the pinions dropping out together. Then the bird is unable to fly for the three or four weeks required for the growth of the new wing feathers. In the brightly colored males of ducks, for example, as in mallards and canvasbacks, the gaudy nuptial plumage is lost after the breeding season in a postnuptial molt, the drake donning a drab "eclipse" dress which is much like that of the female. This renders him much less conspicuous during the vulnerable flightless period. Once the new wing feathering is complete, the male regains his bright breeding plumage, usually before the fall migration is completed. In the female, already wearing modest dress, the contrast in body plumage is not conspicuous, for there are only minor changes such as the loss of the white face patch in the female lesser scaup.

Until the bag tallies were made at Delta, it was generally considered that the wing molt and flightless period was an event of deep summer. And so it is in most males. Some river ducks are flightless as early as the second week in June, while the peak of the wing molt is in July. The males of the diving ducks have their wing molt later with a peak in August. The molting schedule in all males hinges on the timing of their breeding season; the molt into the eclipse plumage begins after the drake has left his incubating female.

In the female the molt is tied to the brood schedule. Some hens, after one or two unsuccessful nesting attempts, may abandon their reproductive efforts in June, and these few birds molt with the drakes, but the successful females retain their wing feathers throughout the nesting and brood period, not molting until they have left their young. In late-nesting individuals, this break between brood and mother may not take place until late August or early September. Every year a few hens are so delayed, with the diving duck females generally molting later than the river ducks. And in years of a cold, retarded spring, a great many late-nesting mothers may not be ready for their wing molt until September.

In years of late spring, too, the bag tallies showed many young birds still with short flight feathers—again, the diving ducks are later in taking wing than the river ducks. Always, in southern Canada and the northern United States, some young canvasbacks or redheads are not flying until after October 1, and in some years many youngsters are so delayed. While hunters may not often shoot these ducklings "on the sit," still they are especially vulnerable during the first days of their flight. It takes a young duck several weeks to learn the skills of aerial maneuver, although the act of flight itself is instinctive. A great many of these inexperienced youngsters are gunned down before they have had time to learn such fundamentals as the requirements of the take-off and of alighting into the wind.

Many more gamebag tallies at Delta, and elsewhere, have been made during the last twenty years. These have shown again and again the special vulnerability of mother diving ducks and their young during late summer and early autumn. In recent years some kinds have dwindled tragically as hunting pressures increased and the number of breeding marshes declined. Even so, and with all we know about their life histories and their brood and molting times, hunting seasons on the prairie breeding marshes continue to open before the end of summer, sometimes several weeks before all the adult female and young of canvasbacks and redheads are strongly on the wing.

The management of upland game has advanced greatly in recent years. States and provinces husband their native supplies, because once these are gone there is no other source. Thus as biological discoveries arrive, they are quickly applied to game management. Waterfowl, however, depend upon no year-round local responsibilities. The birds come as if by magic from out of the north and carry on beyond into more southern waters. Even if local care is taken, according to current philosophy, something will happen to the birds on down the line. Why should Manitoba, for instance, take any special care if the birds will eventually be shot in Arkansas or Maryland? And, indeed, banding studies do show that local protection cannot save a breeding population under present hunting pressures. Redheads, for example, are safe on the National Wildlife Refuges of North Dakota. But they are driven from them eventually by frost and are not able to maintain strong local nesting populations because of the pressures they suffer once they have departed from local protection.

An important step in the conservation of the diving ducks will be adequate protection on their natal and molting marshes in accordance with the timing of the flight schedules in mother birds and young. Other discoveries regarding behavior and requirements on the waterfowl flyways must still be made so that savings accruing from such breeding-ground management will not be wiped out by ill-planned harvesting during migration and on the wintering grounds.

ALEXANDER B. KLOTS

Thoughts on an Arctic Adventure

Dr. Alexander Barrett Klots, Research Associate in Entomology, American Museum of Natural History, and a life member of the Museum, is Professor of Biology at the City College of New York, New York City. He was born in New York in December, 1903, and was educated at Trinity School, Blair Academy, Dartmouth, Yale, and Cornell University. He taught at Cornell, where he received his Doctor of Philosophy degree; he also taught at the University of Rochester. During World War II, he served four years as Medical Inspector and Malaria Control Officer in the U.S. Army Air Corps. Some of his memberships in scientific societies include the New York Entomological Society, Society of American Naturalists, Explorer's Club, Royal Entomological Society of London, and South London Entomological and Natural

History Society. His field work in natural history has taken him on expeditions to almost all parts of North America, to Mexico, Puerto Rico, Trinidad, British Guiana, Brazil, West Africa, and various parts of Europe. He is the author of many scientific and popular articles in entomology, ecology, and natural history, and of books on insects and desert ecology.

THOUGHTS ON AN ARCTIC ADVENTURE

THE "museum man" is quite accustomed to having a colleague disappear for a considerable period of time, and then suddenly show up again, browner and thinner. He is back from another expedition, perhaps to Arizona, or New Guinea, or Antarctica. If he has been to a sufficiently wild, remote or well-publicized region, he can expect to be interviewed by representatives of the press. And almost inevitably, so eternally doth hope spring in the reportorial breast, one of the first questions will be: "Did you have any adventures?"

That, to paraphrase Dr. Joad, depends on how you define an adventure. But it illustrates a firm conviction held by many people that the life of a field naturalist and museum collector combines the more lurid experiences of Kit Carson, Captain Cook, and Dr. Livingstone. This is perhaps a bit flattering to the museum man, who is, in truth, usually a quite mild (but very determined) person. But the reality is that "adventures" of the popular kind are regarded by him as gross inefficiency. We, in the museums, know that the bloke who has to stand off a horde of onrushing savages with his trusty .410 shotgun, or who staggers across leagues of burning desert sucking the grease from his boots, was probably an incompetent tyro to have gotten himself into such a mess in the first place. Museums do not send out such people; museum directors look dimly upon them. Adventurers do not bring back the series of animal or plant specimens, accompanied by pages of prosaic data, that are the reason for the expeditions. The tribulations of the field collector are mostly caused by unsympathetic or grasping officials, unsanitary natives of the region, and uncontrollable climatic features.

Nevertheless, the life of the field naturalist is by no means lacking in experiences that are, to him, real adventures. Let me tell you of an arctic journey of my own to illustrate this; but first, let me give you a bit of background, so that you may understand why something that was not at all a front-page adventure was still a thrilling and memorable experience.

In the early Eighteenth Century the English were beginning to go "all out" to discover the fabled Northwest Passage. Several expeditions had made a good, although fragmentary, beginning, but the outlines of the northern shore of North America and of the complex archipelago toward the Pole were only beginning to be filled in. Most of what you can see today on any school map was then still represented by only a few dotted lines. The search had already cost lives and ships, and the Norns—the Fate goddesses of the Norsemen—had marked many more.

In 1829 Captain John Ross, Royal Navy, sailed from England in the *Victory*, accompanied by his nephew, Commander James Clark Ross, R.N. The expedition was financed by Felix Booth, Sheriff of London, whose name is now, in consequence, writ large on the map of the Arctic. Great things were expected of this attempt, for the *Victory* was the first steam-driven ship to be tried in the Arctic. Unfortunately the engine proved a miserable failure, and the expedition was forced to rely on sail after all, and was thus underequipped with provisions.

In 1829 the *Victory* disappeared from the civilized world. She sailed up Baffin Bay, westward in Lancaster Sound, and then southward in Prince Regent Inlet between Baffin Land and North Somerset Island. It was a good year in which the waters were unusually clear of pack ice. Finally on the bleak, eastern shore of Boothia Felix (now Boothia Peninsula), she was forced to spend the winter in Felix Harbour, frozen in and constantly endangered by the ice floes. Nor did the ice ever break the next year, so that she was to remain there for two winters; and she was never to leave the vicinity.

During this long period Commander James Clark Ross made extensive overland trips, in all seasons, to the westward in Boothia, and on to King William Land. His most resounding accomplishment was the exact location of one of the great goals of arctic exploration, the North Magnetic Pole. But he also collected representatives of a surprisingly large proportion of the plants and animals of the new lands, and even took detailed notes on their environments and habits.

In 1831 the ice pack finally opened enough to let the *Victory* struggle back northward. She had not gone far before the floes again closed around her, and she was forced to spend a third winter beset in Victory Harbour, where she was abandoned. For the *Victory*, this was the end of the expedition. For the men this was the beginning of food shortages and of the dreadful threat of scurvy. In 1832 the party struggled in small boats across to Fury Beach, where the ship *Fury* belonging to the Parry expedition had been wrecked some years before. There, under conditions of extreme hardship and suffering, they spent the fourth winter. In 1833 they pulled and dragged their tiny boats (three of which were the

Fury's) back to Lancaster Sound. There, by a miraculous chance, they were discovered by the crew of an English whaler, into which they crowded for the return to England.

Anyone must thrill at the courage and determination of such men, but only a naturalist can fully appreciate the purposefulness with which Commander Ross kept intact even the most fragile of the butterflies that he had collected in Boothia in 1830 and 1831. Food was bad and very short; there were not enough of even the tiny, worn-out boats; men were dropping with scurvy—yet Ross took the specimens back to England. Today these very butterflies are in the British Museum, where visiting lepidopterists may study and photograph them, as I have done, when studying arctic animal distribution.

For more than thirty years I had worked on the moths and butterflies of the Arctic without the privilege of seeing alive the sulphurs, *Colias boothii*, *C. chione*, and *C. nastes rossii*, or the satyr, *Erebia rossii*, that were first named from Commander Ross's specimens. I had thought and dreamed about them, and then in 1952, I was sent to their home by the Canadian Northern Insect Survey, to make life history studies and to collect for the Canadian National Museum. By almost any standards it was a very *de luxe* expedition. We were based at Churchill on the west coast of Hudson Bay (where Jens Munk, in the *Unicorn* and the *Lamprey* had wintered in 1619). Owing to the skill of the Royal Canadian Air Force, we not only reached places in the Barren Grounds and High Arctic that would have required six months or a year of travel forty years ago, but got back safely from them, with *living* specimens for life history studies—and no adventures.

I must admit that there were a few "incidents." When a visit to the bleak Cape Churchill region was planned, the Bay was full of ice, and there were no lakes or landing strips. So the pilot landed the rugged little Norseman on the long ridge of an eskar, but only after buzzing off the Barren Grounds caribou that were grazing along it. We dipped and circled over the fleeing animals. Although hardened by some years of wartime flying, I was not at ease.

Whenever our amphibian plane set us down on some lake far out on the tundra, we were well-provided for. We had good sleeping bags, plenty of "iron rations" with lots of vitamins, and (as required by law) a heavy rifle; however, we never saw anything on the Barren Grounds more dangerous than the little arctic fox. Often, when the weather shut in, the planes were days behind schedule in getting back to pick us up, but they always did get back. And since we had plenty of insect repellent (for the blood-sucking insects of the Arctic are literally a hazard of the first magnitude), we did not suffer.

We got our desired specimens. We worked out at least the key stages of many arctic butterflies. To my special joy, we collected *Erebia rossii*, a butterfly named for Commander Ross, and one of the species he had carried, perhaps in a little metal box under his shirt through all his trials in that arctic adventure of more than one hundred years ago! We also got specimens of the more southern arctic population of *Colias nastes*. (Complete life history studies were impossible, since the arctic butterflies hibernate as young caterpillars for at least one, sometimes two winters.) We also studied the paths of the great Barren Grounds caribou migrations, where every plant is eaten or trodden into the tundra, leaving an area which plant and animal life will reoccupy by distinct successional stages.

Finally, toward the end of the work, we flew up along the bleak coast of Boothia Peninsula and North Somerset Island and crossed Lancaster Sound. The day was perfect, and visibility complete, something very rare in the Arctic. Below us, almost clear of ice, were Prince Regent Inlet, Felix Harbour,

Victory Harbour, and Fury Beach; there the men of the Ross expedition had been trapped in the ice, abandoned the *Victory*, spent four winters, pulled along in their small boats and *preserved their specimens.* But above all this, while our Rolls Royce Merlin engines roared in perfect tune, my thoughts were of Commander Ross and of his specimens in the British Museum.

Now *that* was an adventure!